DATE DUE

Rocketry
and Space Exploration

Dr. Theodore von Karman delivering the inaugural lecture at the IXth Annual Congress of the International Astronautical Federation in Amsterdam, August, 1958.

ROCKETRY
and Space Exploration

by

ANDREW G. HALEY

President, International Astronautical Federation

D. VAN NOSTRAND COMPANY, INC.

PRINCETON, NEW JERSEY

TORONTO   LONDON

NEW YORK

D. VAN NOSTRAND COMPANY, INC.
120 Alexander St., Princeton, New Jersey (*Principal office*)
257 Fourth Avenue, New York 10, New York

D. VAN NOSTRAND COMPANY, LTD.
358, Kensington High Street, London, W.14, England

D. VAN NOSTRAND COMPANY (Canada), LTD.
25 Hollinger Road, Toronto 16, Canada

Published simultaneously in Canada by
D. VAN NOSTRAND COMPANY (Canada), LTD.

Library of Congress Catalogue Card No. 58–14413

First Published November 1958
Reprinted January 1959, December 1959

PRINTED IN THE UNITED STATES OF AMERICA

Foreword

In examining the page proofs of his book, I notice that my old friend, Andrew Haley, in his Preface wisely ponders the question as to the reason—the *apologia*— for writing the book. It seems to me he is asking the question at a date which is rather late, as the publishers undoubtedly are already complaining about the tardiness of my Foreword. As I called Andy's attention to a few points which from the scientific point of view were not clear to me, he answered: "A few months after I met you first, you composed a paper *Isaac Newton and Aerodynamics*. You told me at that time that it is remarkable how the greatest of all mathematicians, physicists and astronomers made some trivial mistakes as he wandered over the unfamiliar field of fluid mechanics.

"I claim," said Andy, "that being a lawyer, a radio allocations expert, and an astronaut, I have the good right to be mistaken in some other fields."

On the whole, I must say that I find this book to be a needed contribution to astronautics literature. The author has not concerned himself too much with subjects which have been covered very adequately in other works. Many aspects of modern development of rocketry have been covered for the first time, and neglected aspects have been given adequate treatment. For the first time, under one cover, I find a cohesive treatment of international cooperation and its far-reaching implications. I also find for the first time adequate consideration of extremely important scientific problems, including the use of radio in astronautics. For the first time, also, my eyes are opened to the importance and the serious work of the astronautical societies throughout the world. I am pleased indeed to see the names of old friends and to find in print the recording of some of their contributions and achievements. This alone is a good *apologia* for the writing of the book.

I also note that the author has not undertaken scientific discussions of deep import—he has rather restricted himself to quoting articles on magneto fluid dynamics, and other novel scientific concepts, without becoming involved with the opinions of those claiming *expertise* in complicated fields of theoretical physics and pure and applied mechanics. I recommend this book to the young-ster first seeking information, as well as to the old pioneer who may actually receive some vicarious pleasure in seeing his name inscribed in these pages.

THEODORE VON KARMAN

v

Preface

As a young man studying English composition, I was fascinated by the lucid style of the English essayist and philosopher John Henry Newman, and I was particularly impressed with his *Apologia Pro Vita Sua*. What indeed are the purposeful reasons for man's existence, for the advent of rocket propulsive systems, for flight into outer space and, least of all, for the writing and publication of this book?

There are a great many excellent books on rocket technology, space exploration, history of astronautics, and so on. I believe I have read all these books to date which have been published in the English language and I have mulled through those published in German and French—obtaining an important point here and there because of the basic universality of technical terms. In this volume I have endeavored to add to published information by covering points heretofore not covered or not sufficiently covered.

An example of this effort is the attempt to define the term "astronautics" and describe the relationship thereof to the fields of the social and natural sciences. In this particular quest I find that extensive literature existed with respect to Goddard, Ziolkovsky, Oberth, von Karman, and many other immortals, but that (for example) the literature was comparatively silent with respect to the actual details of the great work in the field of astronautics of Robert Esnault-Pelterie.

In my search for information I was fortunate indeed to be introduced to André Louis-Hirsch, a close friend and colleague of Esnault-Pelterie, and with whom I spent several days in Paris and in Amsterdam. Mr. Hirsch secured for me the monumental essay written in 1912 by Esnault-Pelterie, "Considerations on the Results of Indefinite Decrease in Weight of Engines." This paper was published in Paris in the March 1913 issue of *Journal de Physique*. I have carefully examined the works of such well-known scholars as Heinz Gartmann, Willy Ley, Arthur C. Clarke, Kenneth W. Gatland, and many others, and found no mention of this Esnault-Pelterie epochal and pioneer essay, so I have included an English translation of the essay as an appendix to this book.

Esnault-Pelterie was truly an authentic genius. Louis-Hirsch points out that he was the first to build a single-wing airplane with a traction propeller, the propulsion solution adopted by the modern propeller aircraft industry. He invented the joystick—on which he took a patent in 1907, and the star engine—which he patented the same year, and which are now two basic parts of aircraft.

He was also the first to build an all-steel aircraft and he invented the pneumatic undercarriage.

In the process of this research I found one of the finest statements of international cooperation in astronautics ever written. The REP-Hirsch award was first made to Oberth and in the 1929 edition of his book "Wege Zum Raumschiffahrt," Oberth included the following description:

> The French Astronomic Society has awarded the REP-Hirsch Prize to this book. Besides the important advantage that this reward has brought to me, and will still bring, I must recognize that the moral support cannot be discarded. Quite frankly, I did not imagine that France would award such a prize to a German, all the more that other works were submitted from France, Russia and England. It is comforting to see that Science and Progress are enough to overcome national prejudices. I feel that I cannot thank the French Astronomic Society in a better way than by here taking oath to work at my end for Science and Progress and I undertake not to judge any man than on his personal merits.

I have been assisted by scores of persons in the writing of this book. Indeed, whole passages on rocket systems are the products of teams of collaborators. If I give credit to one person, I would neglect another, so I will simply thank the excellent cadre, one and all, who helped me and they may silently enjoy the criticism I undoubtedly will receive for mistakes and omissions of my own making for failing to follow their texts.

I have endeavored to impart additional information on the development, history and current technical and sociological aspects of astronautics. The science and art move so rapidly that I have been unable to include certain current developments which I know are in the making, such as successor missile systems to those which are briefly described and illustrated herein. No author, however, can do more by way of prediction than simply project the future on the basis of the wisdom and knowledge at his command.

Since I first became active in rocketry and astronautics in 1941 I have participated in this and that endeavor. I have been an officer of this and that company. I have been an officer or committeeman in this or that society, and I have traveled here and there in the interest of astronautics. I found after painful experience that I could not leave myself out of certain recountals because I was a part thereof, but I also found that it was tiresome to refer to myself as the author. Therefore, except in one or two special instances, such as in the case of my relationship with Professor Low, I have referred to myself simply by my surname. I found this technique to be simple and clear, and an aid to narration.

Andrew G. Haley

Contents

The two Delphines, Mary, and the three Andrews dedicate this book to their beloved friend, Theodore von Karman.

List of Illustrations

1

Nado Mechtat!—One Must Dream!

"One must dream," wrote Academician A. N. Nesmeyanov in a Moscow magazine article a few weeks prior to the launching of the first Sputnik. "The thought, will, and labor of people will create and send this artificial cosmic body along its celestial orbit."

Academician Nesmeyanov is the president of the USSR Academy of Science and he is responsible, more than any other one man, for the success of the Russian Sputniks. He is a great scientist in his own right and, like most of the race of man, he has within him dreams of the stars. The scientist and the shepherd, the materialist and the spiritual, all share the dreams. "All creation has been committed and offered to the human spirit," said Pope Pius XII to a group of astronautical scientists in Rome, "for him to penetrate it and, therefore, be able to understand more and more fully the infinite grandeur of his Creator."

Joseph, the son of Israel, dreamed that the sun and the moon and eleven stars worshiped him. He dreamed of the conquest of space. So did his brothers in the vale of Hebron and while feeding the sheep in Sichem. Euripides sang that the soul is immortal because the soul is composed of an imprisoned spark of ether—the substance of stars. From the very beginning of time, all ancient disciplines and cultures related, in some manner, the human psyche to the stars. This kinship we find in the *Brihad-Aranyaka* of Brahmanism; the *Shi-King* of Taoism; *Mo-Tzu* of Confucianism; the *Gathas* of Zoroastrianism; and in the writings of Aristotle and Plato.

The Dieyeris of Australia believed that man and all other beings were created by the moon. North and South American Indians were sun worshipers, as were the Polynesians and Africans. Sun worshiping was an early form of Aryan, Semitic and Egyptian belief. The Chinese astronomers believed that it was the rising of Arcturus which brought springtime, and the early Egyptians believed that the power of Sirius caused the Nile to overflow.

The Greeks projected anthropocentric gods into the stars as Urania,

1

Andromeda, the Hyades, Belinda, Ariadne, Berenice, Callistro, Hesperus, Orion, Cassiopeia, Merope, Phosphor, and so on.

And so we find that the psyche of man from the first generation to the present generation has sought the stars. But, in the nature of man, mere longing is inadequate—man must act to achieve his desires. This inner impulse has slowly but surely urged man on to the first great achievements on the road to the stars. This book is written to portray some of these achievements.

FROM ARCHYTAS TO ASTRONAUTICS

The present generations first became universally aware of rocketry with the wartime bombardment of Great Britain by the German *V-2* missiles. The public did not immediately see the relationship between this totally different scale of warfare and small rocket ordnance devices such as the "bazooka," or the less clear analogy to well-known fireworks. Missiles were understood to be distinct and totally new devices.

The *V-2 was* distinct. An amazing development, it ranks as one of the great scientific achievements of history; but the principles underlying its operation are neither new nor different. The *V-2* has a long ancestry, reaching backward to the shadowy beginnings of science itself. Indeed the principle of propulsion through reaction has been known and used by man for over 2000 years.

Yet, when we think of flight we usually think of a series of power suppliers beginning first with the internal combustion engine, and progressing through air-breathing jets to the rocket engine. Why has it taken rockets so long

NATURE ORIGINATED ROCKET PROPULSION,
BUT MAN WAS NOT FAR BEHIND . . .

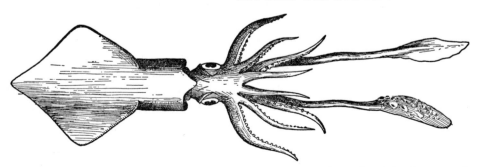

As with most of man's technical achievement, a point of origin for reactive propulsion may be found in nature. Here, the Squid (loligo, a mollusk) propels itself by syphoning and ejecting water, and is capable of startling speeds over short distances.

to come into their own? First of all, while the rocket is a remarkably simple device in theory, it can become exceedingly complex in practice. Add to this the disadvantage of high operating expenses, together with the fact that there was no full understanding of the physical laws governing rocket propulsion, and we have a partial answer to our question. In retrospect, we appreciate more fully the work of the earlier pioneers of rocketry.

We find traces of rocket experimentation as far back as the fourth century B.C., when one Archytas in the Greek city of Tarentum in southern Italy fashioned a wooden pigeon which apparently was propelled by a steam reaction device. Later, in the first century B.C., an Alexandrian philosopher, Heron, manufactured his *aeolipile,* an ingenious forerunner of rocketry. He also used steam power.

For nearly eleven centuries after Heron's work we find no recorded mention of application of the reaction principle, but in the early part of the eleventh century the use of black powder rocket weapons by the Chinese is mentioned. These "fire arrows" were perhaps the inspiration for a later experiment by a Chinese bureaucrat named Wan-Hu. In the year 1500 he is said to have tied himself and 47 war rockets to 2 kites, but upon giving the firing order to a group of coolies, he disappeared in a mighty cloud of smoke.

Writings of the thirteenth century abound with reports of rocketry in

THREE CENTURIES LATER, MAN'S EXPERIMENTS WERE MORE ELABORATE, BUT LESS ESTHETIC . . .

The aeolipile of Heron, an Alexandrian philosopher, made about 53 B.C. Steam rose through the hollow tubes into the sphere, then out of the "L" shaped tubes, imparting rotary motion to the sphere. An experimental curiosity, the device could have been perfected to perform useful work.

Italy, Arabia, China, Germany and England. In the latter country Roger Bacon worked mysteriously in an ancient monastery perfecting the manufacture of gun powder and rockets. His secretive manner, which earned him the nickname of "Doctor Mirabilis" (miracle doctor), led him to set down his recipe for rocket propellants in a Latin cryptogram which defied solution for many years after his death. When his formula was eventually deciphered it proved to be the same as one recorded in a much earlier Arabic manuscript.

Lehan Froissart, of France, suggested in the year 1400 that rockets be fired from tubes to give them direction. Here were all the ingredients for a "bazooka" one hundred years before Columbus. A German military engineer, Konrad Kyeser von Eichstadt, at the same time discussed rockets which would skim across the water surfaces and explode at the vulnerable waterline of an enemy vessel. He also mentioned rockets which would run along a taut string, carrying messages over short distances.

The Italians were also active in military engineering in those days. Joanes de Fontana wrote a book in 1420 full of potentially deadly rocket weapons disguised as rabbits and other creatures which would scamper over rough ground on rollers and explode in the midst of enemy troops.

The German Count Reinhart von Solms wrote in 1530 of rockets equipped with parachutes, which seems to indicate that in rocketry, as in the case of the development of most artifacts, there is little today that hasn't been thought of before.

In 1540, another Italian, Vanoccio Biringusso, described, in terms more picturesque than scientific, rocket combustion processes thus: ". . . and

THE CHINESE DEVELOPED "FIRE ARROWS" . . .

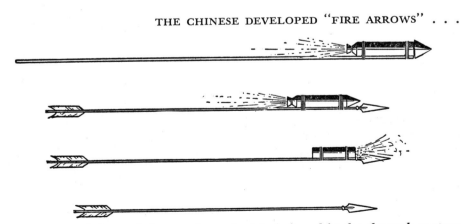

The first recorded use of the reaction principle is found in the eleventh century work of a Chinese, Nu Ching Tsung Tao, who described these "fire arrows." Gradually the arrow head and feathers were discarded.

when the sulfur conducts the fire into the driest part of the powder, fire and air increase—the other elements also gird themselves for battle with each other, and the rage of battle is changed by their heat and moisture into a strong wind."

Seventeen years later, Leonhart Fronsperger of Frankfurt-am-Main produced the word "roget" from which we get rocket. How he derived it remains a puzzle, as no trace of it can be found in any European language. That, incidentally, was the extent of Fronsperger's contribution to the rocket art.

From roughly 1400 until 1600, cannons and guns became highly developed, and little experimentation with rockets is found outside the field of fireworks. Fireworks displays grew to stupendous proportion, however, and even featured step rockets.

The manufacture of fireworks was carried on by a secretive guild that would make a modern labor union appear totally disorganized. Membership in the guild was limited to a select few in order to assure jobs to those persons who had become expert in their trade, which in many instances had been inherited. Those who were not members of the guild could not work

WAR ROCKETS, MORE ELABORATE THAN CHINESE FIRE ARROWS, WERE REPORTEDLY USED IN ARABIA DURING THE SAME PERIOD.

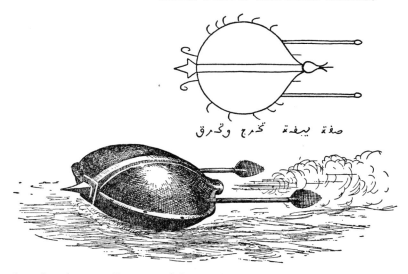

This "combusting egg," reported in an Arab manuscript entitled "The Book on Fighting by Horse and With War Machines," written by Hassan Alrammah in 1230 A.D., slithered across the ground to panic the enemy horses.

in the rocketry field. In 1591, one Johann Schmidlap apparently was thrown out of the guild, and in a fit of anger published all its trade secrets. His discourse revealed that the guild members were learned in the "hows" of rocketry but ignorant in the "whys." The appearance of Schmidlap's book seems to have spurred new efforts in rocketry.

In 1610, the Count of Nassau (England) described a rocket which would dive under water before exploding. Although the Count apparently did not realize it, he was demonstrating that a rocket carried its own oxidizer. No one at that time knew anything about oxygen, but the Count had planted the seed which led to a great deal of study of rocket-propelled marine torpedoes some two centuries later.

In the early 1600's pirates took advantage of the light weight and hard wallop of rockets and employed them in their nefarious naval warfare. Rockets also appeared in ships' signal lockers.

John White of England spoke of highly destructive "incendiary javelins" in 1653 and presented a formula for rocket powder which included about everything but mummy dust. In 1668, Colonel Von Geissler did some practical work with rockets in Germany. His rockets were made of wood, wrapped in glue-soaked sailcloth. One model weighed 55 pounds, and another, weighing in at 132 pounds, carried a 16-pound gunpowder bomb for a warhead.

While men had fumbled with rockets for scores of generations, it was not until the last quarter of the seventeenth century that some of the fundamental operating principles were explained. Sir Isaac Newton, in his famed Third Law of Motion, stated that action is always accompanied by some

THE CHINESE ROCKET-ASSISTED LANCE . . .

This rocket-assisted lance provided the ancient Chinese equivalent of long-range artillery.

equal and opposite reaction. As a noted lecturer explains it, ". . . in jet propulsion, the 'action' is thrown away; it's the reaction that we want." Or, as the famous latter-day rocket scientist G. Edward Pendray explained, ". . . a rocket or jet flies by pulling itself up by its own bootstraps in the process of trying to get out of its own way."

A jet-propelled wagon, ascribed to Newton by some historians, and to the Dutch professor William Jakob s'Gravesande by others, was designed in 1621. It resembled a chemical retort with the neck pointing aft. Provisions were made for a fire to be built over a flat car on wheels, with the spherical boiler suspended directly above. It is known that Professor s'Gravesande demonstrated a working model of this rocket car to his college physics class in Leyden, and there are some reports that he built and drove a full-scale one himself. This design of the first hot water rocket intended for the definite purpose of propulsion is the foundation of the modern hot water RATO (Rocket-Assist Take-Off).

As the eighteenth century continued, two Germans, Von Malinowski and Von Bonin, conducted the first example of systematic propellants research, and an Italian, Gaetano Ruggierei, put on what may have been the most gigantic display of fireworks in history. At the invitation of George II, the display was presented in Saint James' Park, London, on April 27, 1749.

AN EARLY CHINESE ROCKET LAUNCHING PLATFORM . . .

Ancient armies made use of field expedients. Here a large rocket has been set up on an improvised launching platform. Late in the period of Chinese development, the rocket became so destructive that it was no longer necessary to mount an arrow upon it.

During the course of the evening, some ten or twelve thousand rockets were sent aloft against a background of pinwheels, fountains, cannons, and war-like music. The event was climaxed by the firing of thousands of fireports, cascades, and volcanoes, and it established the Italian pyrotechnicians as supreme in their field.

Eleven years after this extravaganza the British faced rockets in a less pleasant encounter when Haider Ali, Prince of Mysore, India, and his 1200 men decimated the crack English cavalry at Guntor with barrages of vastly improved Chinese "fire arrows"—6- and 12-pound iron-barreled rockets with 10-foot bamboo sticks. When in 1799 his son, Tepper Sahib, again defeated the British at Seringopatam with a rocket corps, the British turned to experimentation in the field.

Early English experiments were indifferent, but by 1801 Sir William Congreve, a lawyer and a Member of Parliament, using the facilities of the Royal Laboratory at Woolwich, where his father was comptroller, had developed a highly successful war rocket which was first tested in action in an attack on Boulogne, the French channel-invasion port. One year later he fired 25,000 rockets to burn Copenhagen to the ground. It was Congreve who put war rockets on a practical basis by their use in the Napoleonic war. Congreve's rockets also were used in 1812 against the United States, and their use is preserved by Francis Scott Key in a phrase of our National Anthem.

Congreve had tremendous influence on European ordnance of the nine-teenth century, finally getting the range of his war rockets up to 3000 yards. And, until new ballistic discoveries such as the rifled barrel gave artillery

THIRTEENTH CENTURY ROCKET BARRAGE DEFEATS MONGOLS . . .

Mongolian cavalrymen were repeatedly repelled from Peking, China, by rocket barrages in 1232 A.D. The Mongols probably introduced rockets to Europe.

an uncomfortably high accuracy, rocket corps were found in the armies of every major military power.

An American, William Hale, endeavored to stabilize rockets by attaching curved flanges to the bottom of a stickless rocket so that the exhaust gases would impart a spin to the vehicle. Spin stabilization was an improvement but could not compete with rifled artillery barrels for accuracy, and rockets became a part of history as far as war use was concerned.

The eclipse of the war rocket lasted until the beginning of the twentieth century. Major developments occurred outside of the field of warfare. Signal rockets were improved; rocket harpoons were tried; and lifesaving rockets were perfected.

Captain Robert Jones of England, in a volume in 1776 entitled "Artificial Fireworks," detailed the manufacture of pyrotechnic rockets—how to select tubes and case material, make nozzles, and the ticklish task of adding just the right amount of powder by ladles and then applying the right number of hammer taps for even packing to prevent erratic propulsion. Some of these rockets must have been quite sizable indeed. "Larger rockets," he writes, "cannot be driven by hand, but must be rammed with a machine made in the same manner as those driving piles."

In 1807, a Prussian master weaver named Ehrgott Friederich Schaefer demonstrated the first lifesaving line-carrying rocket on the continent of Europe. This same year saw a similar experiment in England. One Henry Trengrouse, of Helston, Cornwall, conducted similar tests. This rocket might have been adopted by the Admiralty had it not been for a slightly

A FIFTEENTH CENTURY ITALIAN SURFACE TORPEDO . . .

In the early 1400's, the Italian, Joanes de Fontana, designed and constructed a surface torpedo which struck enemy vessels at the water line and set them afire.

A FIFTEENTH CENTURY ITALIAN ROCKET CAR . . .

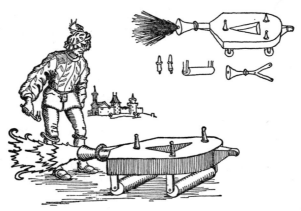

Another project of Joanes de Fontana was a rocket car. These ingenious devices were disguised as animals and used to attack enemy fortifications. The animal disguise was attached to the pegs protruding from the top of the device.

later demonstration of a line-carrying mortar invented by a man named Manby.

But rockets did win out about a generation later. In 1824, the Englishman John Dennet continued the experiments of Trengrouse on the Isle of Wight. In 1826, three lifesaving stations were established, the first of many throughout the United Kingdom equipped with these rockets. Dennet received a patent for his line carrier in 1838. By 1855, after further perfection of these rockets, these stations were made official, and saved possibly 15,000 lives on the English coast alone.

A FIFTEENTH CENTURY ITALIAN WHEEL OF FIRE . . .

A product of Leonardo da Vinci, the wheel of fire was self-propelled by a series of rockets. It was used to burn and scatter enemy soldiers.

Reaction-propelled airships were advocated both in the United States and Russia in the nineteenth century. There was talk in Germany of steam-propelled kite planes and railroad trains, while in France, Monsieur Ciaren drove a reaction-powered motorboat on the Seine. An Italian, Claude Ruggieri, sent rats and mice aloft in parachute rockets and was preparing to send a young French boy, Wilfried de Fonvielle, aloft when the police intervened and ended his plans. In 1895, another Frenchman, Dencesse, devised a camera-equipped rocket to be used for picture-taking at high altitudes.

In 1821, a Captain Scoresby is reported to have hunted whales with rocket harpoons. Suffering the same type of inaccuracies as war rockets, they were displaced by the first practical harpoon gun.

Other rocketeers devised crude rocket cars and a Mr. Phillips of England made a proposal for an astoundingly modern concept, a helicopter, and more astoundingly a modern power plant, a steam reaction system with thrust exerted at the rotor tips. Steam, which was the dominating energy source available in the nineteenth century, showed up again in 1867 in a proposal for another craft which was startlingly prophetic: a reaction-powered delta-winged aircraft. It was even proposed that rockets be used to power lighter-than-air craft.

Three events occurred in the 1890's which influenced the direction of twentieth-century rocket development. The first dealt with the space-flight concept. A German inventor, Hermann Ganswindt, prepared plans in detail for a trip to Mars in a space craft driven by successive explosions of dynamite.

A SIXTEENTH CENTURY CHINESE ROCKET PLANE . . .

The most picturesque legend in Rocketry is that of the Chinese Wan-Hu, who attempted the first rocket-powered flight in 1500. No two accounts give the same description of the event, but all agree that it was spectacularly unsuccessful.

This was one of the first systematic presentations of a reaction-propelled vehicle for interplanetary travel.

The close of the nineteenth century also found a then-obscure scientist, Konstantin Ziolkovsky, carrying on experiments in Russia on the principles of reaction propulsion and making detailed analyses for flight into space with rocket-powered craft. Ziolkovsky, probably as much as anyone else, is responsible for Russia's early interest in rockets and space travel and thus, indirectly, contributed much towards recent Soviet successes in these fields. Although Ziolkovsky made some rudimentary experiments, all of his great work was in the area of intellectual speculation and scientific calculation. In this respect his career was somewhat different from that of Goddard.

The third event occurred in Peru where a rocket motor was reported to have been made of vanadium steel, a material almost unknown at the time, and which operated on a liquid fuel and oxidizer rather than the conventional powder propellants. Pedro E. Paulet, an engineer, was the inventor. Since he did not report his work until 1927, and, even then, in a little-known Lima sheet, *El Comescio,* there always has been doubt as to the authenticity of his work.

The twentieth century opened with the science of rocketry off to a well-founded start. Newton's laws of motion had been formulated back in the seventeenth century, but no further serious work in the theory of rocket propulsion had taken place, although bits of progress, mainly of an industrial

INDIAN ROCKET BARRAGE DEFEATS BRITISH CAVALRY ATTACK . . .

The second era in the development of rockets opened with a rocket barrage fired by the Indians, repelling a cavalry attack against their walled city. The bitter defeat inflicted upon the British Colonial troops at Seringapatan in 1760 prompted Lord Congreve to develop a superior rocket which could be produced in large quantity. They enjoyed a short vogue until outclassed in accuracy by projectiles fired from cannons with refilled bores.

AN EIGHTEENTH CENTURY INDIAN ROCKET LAUNCHER . . .

In 1760, using rocket launchers of the type illustrated above, Indian Prince Haidar Ali organized a corps of 1,200 rocket warriors. By 1782, his son Prince Tepper Sahib had trained a 5,000 man rocket corps.

nature, are scattered throughout the preceding years. The great impetus to modern rocketry stemmed not from war, as in the Congreve era, but from man's quest for scientific knowledge.

Various new industrial materials and propellants were available at the start of the twentieth century and certain thermodynamic problems of heat engines had been studied and solved. With the rise of the scientific level of civilization, and with the all-important stimulus of possible space flight, reaction research had a new start. Ziolkovsky, in 1903, made the first specific liquid-propellant rocket engine proposal published in *The Scientific*

A DUTCH NINETEENTH CENTURY JET-PROPELLED CAR . . .

The steam reaction car illustrated above was designed by a Dutch professor, William Jakob s'Gravesande. It was never perfected, but a small model was constructed for classroom demonstration in 1821.

Observer. From then until his death in 1935 he turned out numerous designs for rockets to be used to explore space.

In America, Robert H. Goddard, a professor of physics, advanced the rocket from virtual obscurity to a prominent place in the technology of the early 1900's. In 1918, working with C. A. Hickman, he developed a basic "bazooka"-type rocket. Eight years later he engineered the world's first liquid-propellant rocket flight. By 1929, he had demonstrated the feasibility of sending instrumented rocket missiles into the upper atmosphere. In 1932, he fired a gyro-stabilized rocket and by mid-1935 he had fired a rocket faster than the speed of sound and another to an altitude of 7500 feet. In addition to his experimentation he made numerous inventions in the field of rocket propulsion and flight. Unfortunately Goddard worked alone for the most part, and it was thus many years before the world learned the details of his experiments and inventions.

Rocket development in Europe until the end of World War I was not very significant, except for the theoretical contributions of Ziolkovsky. Réné Lorin proposed the application of the ramjet power plant for aircraft propulsion; André Bing received a Belgian patent for a multistage rocket device; Professor H. Picard experimented with a rocket airplane model in 1912; and two years later G. Costanzi, an Italian pioneer in aerodynamics, discussing the fundamental problem of astronautics—escape from earth— prophesied that its solution would be obtained through the use of atomic energy. In 1912, also, Robert Esnault-Pelterie wrote his epochal essay on light rocket engines, reprinted in Appendix I.

Rockets were used sparingly in World War I, mainly for signaling, although the French did use ground-to-air incendiary rockets against German Zeppelins and a few air-to-air types to destroy moored enemy balloons.

Hermann Oberth's *The Rocket into Interplanetary Space,* published in Germany in 1923, helped to kindle European interest in astronautics and rocketry. Oberth believed that travel beyond the atmosphere to other planets was possible, and offered designs for space ships to accomplish this. It is Oberth who is credited with originating the idea of an artificial satellite, although the first recorded mention of a space station is found in a late-nineteenth-century book by Curd Lasswitz, *Auf Zwei Planeten.*

Later in the year that Oberth's book was published, General G. A. Crocco presented a paper suggesting the use of rapidly moving particles from disintegrating radioactive material to propel space ships. The particles were to be oriented in the proper direction by electric fields. Crocco's ideas anticipated, in a sense, modern research on ion rockets.

The interest created by Oberth's book led to the formation of the *Verein für Raumschiffahrt* (Society for Space Travel) in Germany, which grew with

ADVERTISEMENT IN WHALEMEN'S SHIPPING LIST AND MERCHANT'S TRANSCRIPT, NEW BEDFORD, AUGUST 8, 1865, OFFERS ROCKET HARPOONS. (Ordnance Corps Photo)

CHANTS' TRANSCRIPT. AUGUST 8, 1865.

BENJAMIN LINDSEY,
U. S. CONSUL, ST. CATHERINES, BRAZIL.

WILL furnish Beef. Vegetables, Groceries and other supplies for whaling vessels touching at that port, on the most favorable terms Letters forwarded to his care will be received and delivered as addressed.

—REFERENCES—

Messrs. David R. Greene. & Co.,
" Gideon Allen & Son.
" Swift & Perry.
" Henry Taber & Co., } New Bedford
" Thomas Knowles, & Co.
Edward C. Jones,
Jonathan Bourne, Jr.,
David B. Kempton.
Jy28'63   tf

WRIGHT & CO.,
COMMISSION MERCHANTS,
RIO DE JANEIRO, BRAZIL.
REPRESENTED BY OUR AGENT,
JOHN S. WRIGHT, ESQ., No. 69 Wall Street,
NEW YORK.
Je20-'65   6m

· C. BREWER & CO.,
SHERMAN PECK.............H. A. P. CARTER.
HONOLULU, S. I.

OFFER the services of their House, established in this place in 1828, as
GENERAL SHIPPING AND COMMISSION MERCHANTS.
AGENTS FOR
The Hana, Makee and Wailuku Plantations,
AND THE
Boston and Honolulu Packet Line.
REFER TO
Charles Brewer & Co., 67 Com'l Wharf, Boston.
James Hunnewell, Esq., 25 "   "
H. A. Pierce, Esq., 67   "   "   New York.
John M. Hood, Esq, " San Francisco.
McIver & Merrill, Hong Kong.
W. Pustau & Co., Manila.
Peele, Hubbell & Co.,
apl26-'64   1y

BURTON & TRUMBULL
E. W. BURTON.   J. H. TRUMBULL,
U S Consul.
SHIPPING & COMMISSION MERCHANTS,
TALCAHUANO—CHILI.
—REFERENCES—
Messrs. Samuel D. Crane & Co.,.... .Boston.
John Wheelwright, Esq..........New York.
Messrs. Loring & Co.......Valparaiso, Chili.
William G. Delano & Co........Conception.
dec7-'62—tf

COMMISSION HOUSE
AT HONOLULU, S. I.

FOR the transaction of a General Commission Business, at the above port, the undersigned have formed a connexion under the firm of
D. C. WATERMAN & CO.,
Especial attention will be paid to the whaling interests by the supply of funds, procuring of freights, and negociations of Exchange.
D. C. WATERMAN,
JOHN F. POPE.
REFERENCE TO—
Messrs. I. Howland Jr. & Co., } N. Bedford
Wm. G. E. Pope, Esq.,
Morgan, Stone & Co. San Francisco.

N S · PERKINS, Jr.,

PATENT ROCKET HARPOONS AND GUNS.

FASTEN TO AND KILL INSTANTLY WHALES OF EVERY SPECIES.

WITH PROPER LINES AND BOATS,
SUCH AS WERE USED BY THE OFFICERS OF BARK REINDEER IN 1864,
ALL WHALES ARE SAVED.
N. B.—Two Months' notice required to fill an Order for the Season of 1865.
——FOR SALE BY—— ·
G. A. LILLIENDAHL,- - - - - - - - - NEW YORK

J. & W. R. WING & CO.,
NO. 24 SOUTH WATER STREET—NEW BEDFORD.
MERCHANT TAILORS,
And dealers in Dry Goods, Clothing, Gentlemen's Furnishings of all description, Infitting and Outfitting Goods, &c., &c.,

ALSO a complete assortment always on hand of Broadcloths, Pilot and Beaver Cloths, German, French and American Doeskins, Cassimeres, Vestings, Ready Made Clothing, Furnishing Goods, together with all articles usually kept in a Clothing or Tailoring establishment. Garments made to order in the best style and warranted to suit, at short notice.
Also Seamen's Outfits and Infits on reasonable terms Believing from our long experience we can give satisfaction to all who favor us with a call, we invite our seafaring friends and the public generally to examine our well assorted stock before purchasing.
Feeling thankful for past favors in trade, we solicit a continuance of the same.
JOSEPH WING,
WILLIAM R. WING,
JOHN WING.
New Bedford, May 29th, 1860.

PELEG & FREDERICK SLOCUM.
NO. 15 SOUTH WATER STREET,
NEW BEDFORD, Mass.,

DEALERS in all kinds of English, French, German and American Dry Goods and Gentleman's Furnishings of every description, also a complete assortment of Cloths, Cassimeres Vestings, and Ready Made Clothing of all kinds together with
SEAMAN'S INFITING & OUTFITTING GOODS,
of the best quality, to all of which our seafaring friends and the public are invited to inspect. Garments of all kinds made to order in the best style, and warranted to set at short notice, feeling thankful for past favors, we would respectfully solicit a continuance of the same.
PELEG SLOCUM.   FREDERICK SLOCUM.

DOANE & WILLIAMS.
OF THE LATE FIRM OF A. H. POTTER. & CO.,
28 SOUTH WATER STREET, NEW BEDFORD,
MERCHANT TAILORS,

AND dealers in Dry Goods, Ready Made Clothing and Furnishing Goods, Infitting and Outfitting Goods. Also, a complete assortment of Cloths, Cassimeres, and Vestings of all descriptions Garments made to order, at short notice.
SIMEON DOANE.   THEODORE D. WILLIAMS.

astounding rapidity and encouraged unified experimental and theoretical work in this field.

In 1929, Oberth's book was revised, enlarged, and retitled, *Road to Space Travel*. The broadened text contained discussions of liquid-propellant rocket engines, multistage rocketry, space navigation, landing, guidance, and construction, and even proposed a transatlantic postal rocket which caused a stir on both sides of the ocean culminating in diplomatic level discussions. It was the precursor of the Intercontinental Ballistic Missile (ICBM).

In 1925, Walter Hohmann wrote a mathematical treatise on *The Accessibility of Celestial Bodies* which probed methods of escape from the earth, return to the earth, and the problem of circumnavigating and landing upon celestial bodies. In 1928, Franz von Hoefft revealed his rocket program which included sounding rockets, two-stage rockets, manned rockets, and space vehicles. Count Guido von Pirquet, of Austria, demonstrated the importance of the artificial space satellite as a takeoff base for planetary objectives and Von Ulinski proposed an electron-propelled space craft.

In France, another great pioneer, Robert Esnault-Pelterie, was carrying on valuable work. A well-known aeronautical scientist and manufacturer, he made remarkable contributions to the field during the early 1900's; in 1927, before the French Astronomical Society, he presented his famous paper, *Exploration of the Very High Atmosphere by Rockets, and the Possibility of Interplanetary Travel*. This was published in 1928, and in 1930 was enlarged under the title *L'Astronautique*. With André Hirsch, he established an annual astronautical prize, the first being awarded to Hermann Oberth. He was the first aeronautical scientist to use the concept of special relativity in the flight mechanics of rockets, a factor which cannot be overlooked in theoretical rocket ballistics, particularly in regard to long range, high speed, space flight.

To these pioneers the present-day men of rocketry owe their heritage.

FIG. 1   FIRST PILOTLESS AIRCRAFT PRODUCED IN 1916

The first pilotless aircraft, or flying bomb, was produced for the U. S. Army in 1916 by the Dayton Wright Testing Company of Dayton, Ohio. The aircraft was designed to carry explosives, similar to those carried by the *V-1* and the *V-2* missiles, behind enemy lines. The aircraft was vacuum-controlled in the air and proved to be successful.

FIG. 2   FIRST AERIAL TORPEDO PRODUCED IN 1917

The first aerial torpedo was produced for the U. S. Navy in 1917 by the Sperry Company. This missile was catapulted from a track by an accelerating device. It would climb to a predetermined altitude, fly on a predetermined course for a distance of up to 100 miles and then dive at the target, exploding 1000 pounds of TNT.

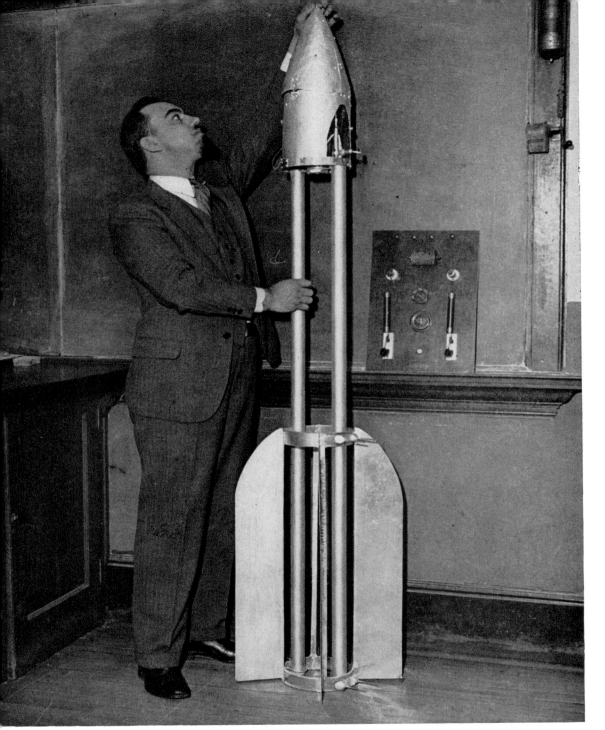

FIG. 3   IN 1932, EXPERIMENTAL ROCKETS WERE SIMPLY
CONSTRUCTED

G. Edward Pendray, Vice President of the American Rocket Society and Chairman of its Experimental Committee, examines the first high altitude rocket built in the United States.

18

FIG. 4   FIRST ROCKET UNDERGOING STRUCTURAL TESTS

Mr. Pendray is pictured with Franklin Pierce, engineer in charge of construction for the first rocket designed by the Experimental Committee of the American Rocket Society.   They are testing the balance of the rocket in the Physics Laboratory of New York University.

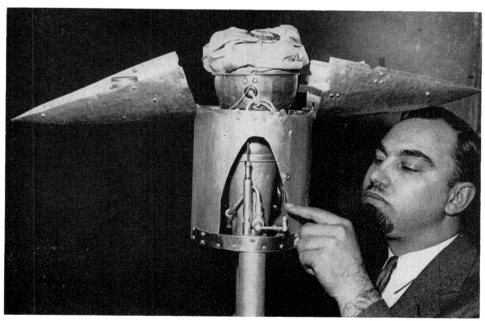

FIG. 5   FIRST ROCKET PRECISELY ADJUSTED IN THE
         LABORATORY

The first rocket produced by the American Rocket Society was equipped with an automatically operated parachute, designed to return the instrument to ground safely. The parachute was made by Mrs. Pendray and was contained in the sauce pan from her kitchen. Mr. Pendray makes last-minute adjustments of the rocket controls

FIG. 6　AMERICAN ROCKET SOCIETY'S FIELD WORKSHOP IN 1932

　　The American Rocket Society's 1932 field workshop, located at Stockton, New Jersey.　Mrs. Pendray wields the axe, Franklin Pierce feeds the fire, and Mr. Pendray adjusts the rocket.

FIG. 7   FUEL FOR THE FIRST ROCKET WAS POURED OUT
        CAREFULLY

The specially prepared liquid oxygen, used with gasoline for fuel, shattered a thermos bottle upon contact.   A coffee pot was successfully used to pour the fuel.

FIG. 8   FUELING THE FIRST ROCKET FOR FLIGHT

The rocket motor weighed only 1 pound, yet it developed 120 horsepower. Here, Mr. Pendray is fueling the rocket with his coffee pot.

FIG. 9 THE FIRST ROCKET BLASTS OFF

Franklin Pierce runs for cover after lighting the rocket engine with a torch. The first rocket provided useful data, but never actually flew.

FIG. 10 FIRST ROCKET ENGINE TEST IS RECORDED ON FILM

The successful ground test of the first liquid fuel rocket of the American Interplanetary Society was recorded on film in the above manner. Had the aluminum-magnesium alloy rocket been released, it would have reached a possible altitude of 10 miles.

FIG. 11   ROCKET NOZZLE BURNS THROUGH IN GROUND TEST

The heat of the liquid rocket proved to be above the endurance limit of the metal nozzle on this uncooled rocket engine.

FIG. 12   AMERICAN ROCKET SO-
CIETY'S THIRD ROCKET
PROVES SUCCESSFUL

In 1934, the American Rocket Society's third rocket is pictured just prior to a successful launching on Staten Island, New York. The Society had just been awarded the REP-Hirsch International Prize of 5000 francs for its rocket achievements.

FIG 13 PREPARING THE TORCH FOR A ROCKET LAUNCHING

Gasoline is used to prepare a torch for igniting the liquid propellant rocket engine.

FIG. 14 EARLY MEMBERS OF THE REACTION MOTORS CORPORA-
TION ARE PICTURED WITH THEIR FIRST LIQUID-PROPEL-
LANT ROCKET ENGINES

From left to right, the men are: Ed Cahill, Lovell Lawrence, L. Arata, John
Shesta, Franklin Pierce, Harry Smith, and Lester Collons.

FIG. 15   R. H. GODDARD DEMONSTRATES ROCKET IGNITER
IN 1935

R. H. Goddard, left, explains to Harry L. Guggenheim, financial sponsor of
rocket research, how the rocket igniter operates.   The rocket launching site in
1935 was near Roswell, New Mexico.   (H. L. Guggenheim)

FIG. 16   ROCKET IS RECOVERED BY PARACHUTE IN 1937

R. H. Goddard is shown fitting the cap and pilot parachute on the rocket after
rocket test on May 19, 1937.

FIG. 17   R. H. GODDARD DEVELOPS ROCKET FUEL PUMPS IN 1938

R. H. Goddard is shown in his shop at Roswell, New Mexico, working on a new rocket fuel pump in 1938.

FIG. 18   R. H. GODDARD MAKES ADJUSTMENTS ON ROCKET

R. H. Goddard is shown making adjustments at the upper end of the rocket chamber, in his shop at Roswell, New Mexico, in 1940. Around the chamber are small coils of copper tubing for vaporizing liquid nitrogen in order to produce pressure for the fuel tanks and for operating controls. Pumps were used for the fuel and oxidizer.

FIG. 19 GERMAN *A-3* MISSILE ON 1938 LAUNCHING PLATFORM

The *A-3* missile appeared in 1938. It was 25 feet high, weighed 160 pounds, and had a thrust of 3300 pounds.

FIG. 20 upper right: GERMAN *A-5* MISSILE IN
STARTING HUT

Propelled by liquid oxygen and alcohol, the *A-5* missile reached
an altitude of 40,000 feet.

FIG. 21 lower right: GERMAN *A-5* MISSILE BLASTS
OFF

The *A-5* missile leaves the launching platform during a test
firing.

FIG. 22 lower left: GERMAN *A-5* MISSILE HEAVILY
LOADED WITH INSTRUMENTS

The purpose of the *A-5* was to accumulate data for use in con-
structing the *A-4*, better known as the *V-2* missile. The *A-5* was
a heavily instrumented *A-3* missile used for test purposes.

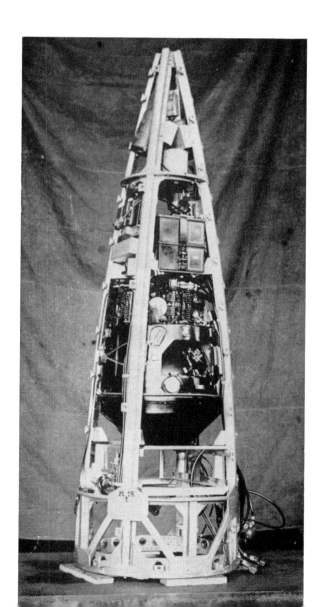

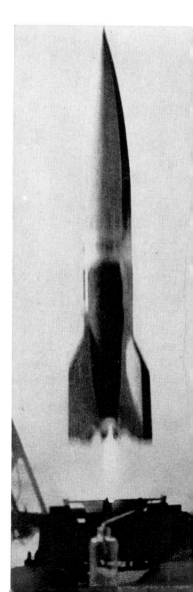

FIG. 23 GERMAN *V-2*
         MISSILES AT
         CHECKOUT
         POINT

Early *V-2* missile seg-
ments are shown in the
final checkout stage of production.

FIG. 24   GERMAN *V-2* MISSILES IN ASSEMBLY STAGE

Segments of the *V-2* missiles are shown on assembly platforms, ready for final
assembly.

2

Rockets and How They Operate

When the word "rocket" is used by the Congress in legislation how can one tell just what is involved? The Senate Committee which studied the original National Aeronautics and Space Bill demanded definite meaning for this word which was used thousands of times during the hearings. Dr. Glen P. Wilson, of the Committee's staff, said that he attached to the word meaning derived from his technical and scientific experience. Dr. Wilson used the word "rocket" to mean a self-propelled device which contains within itself the requirements for flight and which does not rely on the atmosphere but moves under the principles of Newtonian action and reaction. He defines the word in terms of its essential qualities. Any device which conforms to Dr. Wilson's definition would be a rocket whether or not it had a tail like an arrow or was used on the 4th of July.

The Committee on Astronautics and Space Exploration of the House of Representatives realized this ambiguity and saw fit to include in its Second Report a definition:

Rocket, n. 1. A rocket vehicle or rocket missile. 2. A rocket motor or a rocket engine, i.e., a motor or engine that moves itself forward by ejecting a stream of hot gases to the rear and is independent of the atmosphere for its operation. The rocket (sense 2) is a species of reaction engine, but differs from a jet engine in that the latter is dependent for oxidation upon air taken in from the atmosphere whereas the rocket can operate in outer space, either by carrying its own oxidizer or by relying upon some other system to produce a jet stream, as with a nuclear reactor working upon a fluid.

This definition captures the essence of the word and reflects the meaning that is at present ascribed to it.

Clearly related to the definition of the word "rocket" is the definition of the phrase:

Rocket engine. 1. A rocket propulsive device that is relatively complicated in its workings, as distinguished from a rocket motor; hence, the liquid-fuel rocket device. See note and see rocket (above) sense 2.

Note: The liquid-fuel engine with its elaborate pumping equipment, pressure chambers, fuel lines, electrical connections, etc. is more appropriately called an engine, as in sense 1, than the solid-fuel motor. The term "rocket motor" is preferred over "rocket engine" as the generic term. See rocket motor (below).

2. In less exact usage, a rocket motor or, generically, any rocket propulsive device.

These definitions are from a glossary which was prepared by the Air University Documentary Research Study Group and was published at Maxwell Air Force Base, Alabama, in March 1958.

Returning to the ramifications of the word "rocket" as defined in the glossary, one finds:

Rocket motor. 1. In exact usage, a rocket propulsive device that burns a solid self-oxidizing fuel, as distinguished from a rocket engine. 2. Generically, either the liquid-propellant rocket or solid-propellant rocket or, theoretically, the fission reaction or fusion reaction engine that emits a jet stream.

Note: In sense 1, the device consists essentially of a combustion chamber that houses the grain plus a nozzle and igniter.

One also finds:

Rocketry, n. The science or study of rockets, embracing theory, research, development, and experimentation: the art and science of using rockets, esp. rocket ammunition, either on the ground or in the air.

This is not an entirely satisfactory attempt since the last phrase indicates the frame of mind existing in 1956. Today as one looks into the future the "especial" character of the short range, tactical missile used in air-to-air or air-to-ground combat seems to be a minor concern of one engaged in "rocketry." It is interesting to note that the 1958 glossary does not attempt to define the word at all. An extremely broad definition of the word is found in the *New Military Naval Dictionary,* published in 1951:

Rocketry. A collective term for all activities connected with rocket theory, rocket development, rocket research, and rocket experimentation.

Neither Webster's *Universal* of 1936 nor the *New Twentieth Century* edition of 1951 has any entry for the word "astronautics." The definition contained in the Webster's *New International Dictionary,* 1957 edition, is:

Astronautics, n. The science which treats of the possibility of traveling through interplanetary space.

The Air Force glossary defines "astronautics" as:

1. The art, skill, or activity of operating space vehicles. 2. In a broader sense, the art or science of designing, building, and operating space vehicles.

Note: Because the prefix *astro* means "star," this term is, or may be, considered not wholly acceptable as defined. The term *spationautics*, however, has not been widely developed.

Throughout this book, the definitions of the Air Force will be used for the terms "rocket" and "rocketry." The Air Force definition for "astronautics" is satisfactory as far as it goes, but in this book "astronautics" will embrace the sum total of activities connected with man's adventure in outer space, including the related natural and social sciences, such as space medicine, space biology, space law, and the many other aspects of the arts and sciences which derive new meanings, new dimensions and new applications from vehicles in space and for man in space.

HOW ROCKETS OPERATE

Fill a container with a liquid or solid explosive. Ignite it. If the gases from the resulting burning (or combustion), at high temperature and pressure, are permitted to expand through an exhaust nozzle, the pressure and temperature are lowered, and heat energy is converted into energy of motion (kinetic energy). The resultant thrust will propel our container for a period of time in a given direction, an embodiment of Newton's principle of reaction which states: "To every action there is an equal and opposite reaction."

To illustrate this principle, a gun attached to a small rail car and then fired will send the bullet in one direction while the reaction or recoil jolts the car in the other. The recoil is the "equal and opposite reaction." A machine gun fired from the same car would cause a series of reactions to take place, and the car would accelerate until the supply of bullets was depleted. The heavier the bullets, the more used, and the faster fired, the greater will be the resulting forward momentum of the car. Thus *mass* and *velocity* of the matter expelled are the key factors in the performance of any reaction device.

The purpose of any rocket engine is to deliver the necessary thrust to propel a vehicle for a period of time in a given direction. The vehicle as a whole carries explosives or propellants, in liquid or solid form, and its thrust is produced by converting the chemical energy of the propellants first into heat energy in the combustion chamber and then into kinetic energy, in the exhaust nozzle.

The rocket's "machine gun bullets" are microscopic particles, products of the combustion of liquid or solid propellants. These particles are expelled from the combustion chamber at high velocities, providing the thrust, which is exerted largely at the forward end of the chamber, accelerating the vehicle in which the rocket engine is mounted.

Thrust is produced by the rapid discharge of combustion products generated from propellants carried entirely by the rocket. (These combustion products must contain a high concentration of energy. The propellants include both fuel and an agent for burning the fuel, i.e., an oxidizer.)

This exhaust stream is often called a *jet,* and properly so. The rocket engine is a jet engine, but to avoid confusion it is useful to specify the types of air-breathing jet engines (as turbojet, ramjet, pulsejet) to emphasize the fact they are not rockets. They do not carry their own oxidizers, but use the oxygen in the air through which they travel and thus are not like rockets which are self-contained systems. A rocket can operate where there is no atmosphere; a jet cannot.

If we take a chamber and fill it with compressed air the pressure is transmitted equally in all directions. Since everything balances, no movement occurs. A small opening at one end causes pressure forces to become unbalanced, and the gas (or compressed air), having nothing to stop it, will rush out. On the side opposite the hole, pressure forces will continue to act as long as there is any gas in the chamber and will thus "push" on the wall. This push will move the chamber and, if mounted in a vehicle, it will move the vehicle. The rocket designer, of course, refines this chamber by adding a nozzle and other accessories (i.e., "gas-replenisher"), and a rocket engine results.

As long as there is expanding gas in the chamber, propulsion will occur. To assure that there is gas in the chamber, continually exerting pressure against the wall, a solid or liquid fuel is burned which maintains a pressure difference between the inside and the outside of the chamber. A converging-diverging type nozzle at the open end of the chamber helps to control and direct the exhaust stream, providing at the same time approximately 25 percent extra thrust, compared to a chamber without an expanding nozzle. This utilizes a property of gases in motion which causes them to be accelerated at subsonic speeds by converging walls, and at supersonic speeds by diverging walls.

Unlike an artillery shell, a rocket with a constant thrust continually gains in speed, its mass decreasing during every second of operation. Thus a rocket may start its trip (upward, for example) rather slowly, but as its propellant supply is consumed, its acceleration will increase. This is significant in astronautics, since top speeds will thus occur when the vehicle is above the dense layers of the atmosphere and beyond the dangers of aerodynamic heating.

The greater the velocity and mass of the ejected propellant particles, the greater will be the reaction force, or thrust. To achieve a high jet velocity, it is necessary to generate as much heat or thermal energy as possible for conversion into kinetic energy. As the gas is accelerated, it loses most of this heat and exhausts at a lower temperature. To accelerate the gas, i.e., drive it out of the chamber to form the jet, a high pressure is needed in the rocket chamber. In summary, then, to produce a large thrust, we need high mass flow, high energy and high pressure.

SOLID PROPELLANT ROCKETS

Solid propellant rockets have been known for centuries. They are simple in shape, have no moving parts, and can be stored, transported, and fired easily. The solid propellant rocket consists essentially of a chamber filled with a powder charge, a nozzle, and an igniter device called a "squib." Its use was formerly confined to applications where high thrust and short firing-times are desired, since a tremendous amount of energy is released during a few seconds of firing. Because of this, we often find that solid propellant motors are used to boost vehicles to flight speeds, after which a "sustainer" motor provides the propelling power. A *booster* starts a missile in flight, and then drops off. A JATO (jet-assisted take-off) does the same thing for aircraft and may be designed to then drop off.

Interesting developments have recently taken place in solid propellant rockets that make it possible to use them as sustainers for long-range ballistic flights and for satellite launching. The slow-burning solid propellant rocket will become more prominent for use as a sustainer in the future.

The shape of the propellant charge in a solid rocket determines its thrust and firing duration. The simplest shape to manufacture is a cylinder, having a non-burning coating material on its outer surface and provision for combustion at the exposed end. This type of charge, burning like a cigarette, can be used to deliver a moderate thrust for a relatively long duration. For high performance flights it has severe disadvantages, despite its simplicity. The principal disadvantage is that the steel chamber containing the charge is exposed to the hot flame of the burning propellant for many seconds and must be constructed with a thick wall and be heavily insulated. The resulting weight is prohibitive for space flight. Although many aircraft JATO's of this type were used in the past, this type of charge is rapidly becoming obsolete.

High velocity solid rockets today generally use internal burning, hollow-bore charges. A charge of this type contains the hot flame entirely within the internal bore, thus shielding the walls of the container from the extreme heat of combustion. Except for the exhaust nozzle, the hardware of the rocket can be made of thin-walled aluminum, magnesium, or even light-weight reinforced plastic. The remarkable development of propellants that burn efficiently at low pressures and are adaptable to the light-weight hollow bore design has led to the growing importance of solid propellant rockets in the field of satellite launching and intercontinental missiles.

Only a few oxidizers are available for common use, but these are made into charges with any one of a fairly wide variety of fuels. Common oxidizers include ammonium nitrate, potassium nitrate, ammonium perchlorate, and potassium perchlorate. The earliest propellants were so-called black powders, with potassium nitrate ("saltpeter") as the oxidizer, to which were added varying amounts of carbon and sulfur (both fuels). Black powders have generally become obsolete except in firecrackers and simple signaling and lifesaving rockets.

Double-base, smokeless (nitroglycerin and nitrocellulose) compositions made up most of the successful World War II solid propellant combinations, of which "ballistite" was one. Such agents as coolants, stabilizers, and flash suppressors may be added. In addition, GALCIT (Guggenheim Aeronautical Laboratory (of the) California Institute of Technology) pioneered the development of composite propellants, generally based on potassium perchlorate and asphalt. The particular invention of the perchlorate-asphalt composition in 1942 is due to J. W. Parsons, a member of that group. In 1940 Von Karman and Malina first proved theoretically that stable burning of long duration solid rockets was possible, and gave propellant and design criteria for stability.

LIQUID PROPELLANT ENGINES

Once a solid propellant motor is ignited it is difficult to turn it off, a limitation not encountered in the liquid propellant engine. This lack of flexibility was one of the factors that led the early experimenters to investigate liquid propellants in an effort to devise an engine that could be shut off by valve action or throttled to various thrust levels. Furthermore, the "specific impulse" for many liquids was found to be higher than for ordinary solids, in some cases as much as 25 percent better. ("Specific impulse" is a measure of the jet velocity and equals the number of pounds of thrust obtained from an engine burning a pound of liquid propellant each second.)

Another advantage of the liquid rocket is that its firing time is theoretically limited only by the propellant tank capacity. The liquid rocket can operate with low tank pressures, using a turbopump to furnish propellants to the chamber where high pressures obtain. Solids, on the other hand, must be contained at combustion pressure, thus requiring heavier tankage. The cooling problem is somewhat easier to handle in a liquid rocket, since either the fuel or the oxidizer can be made to flow through a cooling jacket ("regenerative cooling"), thus taking up heat transferred from the combustion chamber and nozzle.

In a liquid propellant engine a fuel is generally burned in the presence of an oxidizer yielding heat. These propellants are stored in tanks from which they flow to injectors where they are atomized, mixed, and burned in the chamber. A much greater volume of propellant can thus be made available in a liquid system, since it is not limited to what can be placed in the combustion chamber.

There are two classic types of liquid propellant systems, those that use *monopropellants* and those using *bipropellants*. In the case of a monopropellant, the heat energy released from the rapid decomposition of the liquid (such as a concentrated solution of hydrogen peroxide) produces the thrust. Under storage-tank conditions, the monopropellant must be stable, or the serious explosion hazard would make it too dangerous to be used. Decomposition is induced by passing a typical monopropellant (such as hydrogen peroxide) over a catalytic material (such as calcium permanganate).

In the case of bipropellants, the action is one of combination rather than decomposition. The ignition of the fuel in the presence of the oxidizer is usually started by an igniter, but some propellants spontaneously ignite upon contact with one another. These propellants are said to be hypergolic with each other. If not hypergolic, they are sometimes ignited by the introduction of a small quantity of a third propellant that is hypergolic with one of the main propellants. This is called hypergolic ignition. Otherwise, an electrical system (glow plug, spark plug) may be used and is good for repeated operation. One technique used is to ignite electrically a small quantity of propellant in a miniature rocket chamber (igniter); then the heat given off by the little exhaust ignites the propellants flowing into the main combustion chamber. The valves and controls of the miniature chamber must be integrated into the over-all powerplant system. For a one-shot rocket engine, as in a missile, a solid squib igniter is usually found to be the simplest and most convenient.

In general, a bipropellant combination offers a greater amount of energy than a monopropellant. Typical oxidizers, or substances that act as oxidizers, are liquid oxygen; hydrogen peroxide; nitrogen dioxide; nitric acid; and others that support burning, such as the halogens (fluorine, chlorine trifluoride, etc.). The wide variety of fuels available include alcohol, hydrazine, kerosene, aniline, gasoline, liquid ammonia, liquid hydrogen, and some compounds of lithium, boron, and hydrogen.

There are a number of ways to conduct propellants to the combustion chamber, the method chosen usually depending on how much thrust is wanted, and for how long. If a moderate firing time is desired (a short duration firing time almost inevitably demands solid propellants) one should consider a pressurization system; a firing time of long duration, however, virtually dictates a turbopump arrangement.

Why do short firing periods suggest solids; moderate firing periods, pressurized liquids; and long firing periods, a turbopumping system? The answer is weight. As the length of time that a missile fires increases, the quantity of propellant available must also increase. In the solid field, where fairly high chamber pressures are characteristic, long burning periods require relatively heavy chambers, and the designer turns to pressurized liquids. Even in this case, with regenerative cooling techniques employed, tankage weight again steps in to limit the firing time. Long firing periods need large quantities of propellants, which require large and heavy propellant tanks and pressurizing gas cells. Beyond a certain firing time, one introduces the turbopump, which can handle a greatly increased propellant flow rate with a minimum of weight penalty. Tanks can be of much lighter construction since they do not need to stand up under heavy pressurization. Also, the gas (pressurizing) sphere required is much more modest than in the totally pressurized rocket system, and may even be eliminated.

In a pressurized rocket system, a gas such as nitrogen or helium alone is used to force the propellants from their respective tanks into the combustion chamber. In a turbopump system, the propellants are pressurized just enough to supply them to the pumps, which then furnish them to the combustion chamber. The pumps are directly coupled to a turbine which is driven, one way or another, by gaseous products of combustion, either from the main thrust chamber or an auxiliary combustion-type device. This can be clearly traced in the operation of a typical turbopump-powered missile, the *V-2*.

THE GERMAN A-4 (V-2): HOW IT OPERATES

In its simplest terms, the *V-2* missile consists of three main sections, warhead (in the nose), tankage (amidships), and powerplant (tail area). The vehicle is raised to a vertical position on the launcher and is supplied with nitrogen pressurizing gas, hydrogen peroxide, and propellants. The sequence of events that puts the *V-2* into operation, simplified as much as possible, is as follows:

A pyrotechnic black-powder device is placed in the throat of the thrust chamber and ignited. Both propellant valves are made to open under nitrogen gas pressure, allowing the propellants to flow in small amounts by gravity feed through the motionless pumps, and then, either directly or indirectly, into the thrust chamber through injector devices resembling shower nozzles.

The mixed propellants burst into flame upon striking the pyrotechnic device, and as soon as propellant burning occurs in the thrust chamber the propellant supply system begins to function. This reaction causes pressurized nitrogen to act on hydrogen peroxide, forcing it into a gas generator vessel. Upon coming into contact with a sodium permanganate catalyst, it decomposes violently, producing hot steam, which is directed against the blades of a turbine. Two centrifugal pumps attached to the same shaft as the turbine wheel are thus caused to rotate, supplying the mains to the thrust chamber with 275 pounds of propellant per second at a pressure of 350 pounds per square inch.

The fuel (alcohol), upon leaving the fuel pump section of the turbopump, circulates through a hollow ring at the rear of the nozzle and then enters the space between the double walls of the thrust chamber. While in this region, some of the fuel is permitted to flow through small holes in the inner wall into the thrust chamber. Not having access to oxygen, it fails to ignite but forms a film (rapidly forced out of the nozzle with the movement of the main body of gas), thus carrying away some of the heat which would raise the temperature of the inner wall. Some heat does get through this film, however, and is absorbed by the main mass of fuel flowing through the double wall. Enough heat is carried away in this fashion to make the thrust chamber cool enough to be well out of structural danger from melting.

Upon reaching the injectors, the fuel is mixed with the oxidizer (liquid oxygen) which flows directly into the injector with no preliminary circulation. The two propellants are then mixed in the proper proportions in a spray produced by the injectors and, upon striking the combusting material already there, this process sustains the operation of the thrust chamber until the propellants are exhausted or until the propellants' valves are closed.

With the development of pumping action, the flame in the thrust chamber stabilizes, and promptly builds up to the pressure required to produce usable thrust in the engine. This thrust is concentrated at the forward end of the thrust chamber, which is fixed to the framework of the missile airframe by thrust bearings, and thus transmits a push to the missile as a whole in a direction opposite to the exhaust. By design, this is straight noseward, and the thrust in building up to 56,000 pounds overcomes the downward weight of the missile, and the missile then rises.

A stabilization system, external to the powerplant proper, adjusts the position of heavy graphite vanes placed in the exhaust. This deflects the exhaust and moves the center of thrust in the forward end of the thrust chamber to some desired point off the longitudinal axis of the missile, which steers the missile, to a certain extent.

While the *V-2* rocket motor has a representative, "common" pump feed system, it is not the only one known. Propellants can be furnished to the chamber and raised to injection pressure by pumps whose turbine drive power is (1) "bled" off from the hot combustion gases in a firing chamber (*bleed turbine*), or (2) obtained by placing the turbine blades directly in the combustion products, either in or near the throat area of the combustion chamber itself (*topping turbine*) or in the exhaust stream at the end of the nozzle (*blast turbine*). Generally, the "bleed" gases are cooled by dilution before impinging on the turbine. In all cases hot gases impinge on the turbine wheels, and as temperatures are high, refractory materials and protective techniques must be employed to guard against blade burnout. All three types of turbine arrangement have the advantage of eliminating the need for a gas generator and its monopropellant; however, although they have been rather widely investigated in theory, they have not had much practical use.

ENGINEERING, MATERIEL, AND PROPELLANTS

It is not difficult to appreciate the problems facing the rocket engineer who must design engines involving gas temperatures of 5000 degrees (F) and up, pressures in 100's of pounds-per-square-inch, jet velocities of more than 1 mile-per-second, and the need for incredible reliability of every switch, valve, control, and seal. A combustion temperature of 4000–5000° F may exist, for example, only a few inches away from an oxidizer propellant valve handling liquid oxygen, the boiling point of which is lower than 290° below zero Fahrenheit!

While a rocket engine is theoretically simple in construction, it is evident that a vast array of problems confront the practical rocket engineer. A successful engine design suggests, for example, that all of the components, the successful operation of which means the success of the motor, must be made accessible to test, service, repair, and replacement. No propellant "traps"—places where fuels and oxidizers can accumulate—should exist to create the hazard of explosion. Instrumentation should be available to show the engineer how his engine actually works; hence a number of key "pickup" spots are needed on the engine where pressures, flow rates, and temperatures can be measured and evaluated. The propellant tanks must be designed so that the liquids will flow uniformly, even though the missile may be performing a variety of maneuvers. Bladder and compartmented tanks are frequently used.

High temperatures, chamber pressures, and flow rates (often measured in hundreds of pounds per second) require high material strengths. The materials must be extremely resistant, not only to heat and pressure, but to corrosion. In regeneratively cooled rockets they must be capable of rapidly transferring heat from the combustion chamber to the circulating cooling liquid (propellant).

Rocket engine performance is limited principally by the melting point of the construction materials employed and by the chamber design (in connection with combustion pressure). Unfortunately, high performance, or specific impulse, of a rocket engine requires high chamber temperature and a large expansion ratio (that is, the ratio of chamber pressure to exhaust pressure). Accordingly, high temperatures and high expansion ratios (implying high chamber pressures) are desirable from the performance point of view only.

In selecting propellant combinations, chamber pressures and temperatures must be considered, in addition to the density which regulates the size and weight of the tanks, freezing and boiling point, ignition properties, vapor pressures, and, above all, the experience gained from their use. It must be determined whether the propellant is corrosive, stable, economical, or costly. It is also necessary to determine viscosity, supply, and transportability in order to decide what propellants to select for a particular operation.

The rockets used to carry aloft the world's first artificial satellites were liquid propellant rockets. The guidance and stabilization gear of these rockets operated with near-perfect accuracy. The flow of propellants into the engines was synchronized to split-second precision. Complex ground facilities were required, including such service units as weather stations, communication centers, radar and camera observation posts, laboratories, fire departments—even field hospitals where men could be treated for injuries, such as burns from liquid oxygen, nitric acid, or other poisonous propellants.

Complex system facilities are currently in use at every missile and rocket launching base. As is the case with manned aircraft, ground support is an essential factor in rocketry. There is overlapping experience between missile weapon systems, such as the intercontinental ballistic missiles, and the designing, building, handling, and launching of earth satellite vehicles.

The relationship between satellite rockets and ballistic missiles is so close that the overall construction, propulsion, launching, and guidance techniques are almost identical. Whether it is a satellite-carrying rocket or an *Atlas* intercontinental ballistic missile, they both take off vertically from a concrete launching pad, under the impetus of a series of liquid rocket engines or a bank of multiple rocket motors in the lower stages of the missile. As the vehicle gains altitude it will begin to tilt. At a relatively low altitude, the first stage will drop away. Another set of powerplants in the second stage will push the now smaller missile still higher. In this way, the two or more stages are successively fired until the final portion—carrying either a satellite or a lethal warhead—hurtles through the outer atmosphere like a projectile.

*   *   *   *   *

These achievements are indicative of the developmental trends in today's rocket science—only 30 years after Robert H. Goddard fired his liquid propellant rocket to an altitude of 41 feet, traveling the distance of 220 feet at a velocity of 60 miles per hour.

Since then rocketry has become a science of its own. We are on the threshold of a new scientific age—not characterized by adjectives such as supersonic or hypersonic, but by the headings Space Flight or Astronautics.

3

Rocketry in the 1930's

If modern rocketry was conceived in the 1800's and born in the first quarter of the twentieth century, it started to toddle in the early 1930's and by 1940 was breaking into a run. Although the world was pre-occupied by the great depression, the 1930's established the basis for today's balance of power in international rocketry. This decade marked the end of a period of astronautical speculation with the emergence of concerted experimentation. Amateurs became professionals. Jottings on paper became hardware. Goddard, Von Karman, Malina, Parsons, Summerfield, Truax, Wyld, Oberth, Von Braun, Holloman, Dornberger, Sänger, Pendray, Shepherd, Cleaver, and many others, laid the foundations for the rocket industry of today.

The rocket already had become rather well established as the likely means for propelling space ships. The early "greats" never abandoned this goal, but in the decade before World War II they shifted their emphasis more and more to military missiles, realizing, no doubt, that money would be more readily forthcoming for weapons than for a sometime trip to the moon. They realized even then that to bridge the propulsion gap between early, small experimental rockets and the massive systems required for space travel would take vast sums of money, as well as a long, dedicated period of hard work.

Some experimenters, such as Robert H. Goddard of Clark University in Worcester, Massachusetts, had been at work for years, but the movement did not really gather momentum until this period, when two things happened: a popular urge developed to form rocket societies and to make and fire rockets "in the back yard"; and one government (Hitler's Germany) recognized the potential military significance of rockets.

Boats, automobiles, sleds, gliders and even human skaters were to become "fit" subjects for experiments in propulsion before prewar and wartime development culminated in the massed German *V-2* rocket attacks on Great Britain. Successes were moderate but significant. Some of the failures then, as now, were spectacular but less publicized. It was a short-but-productive interlude during which rockets were removed from the abstraction of technical papers and actually built and flown, in increasing numbers. With the advent of World War II, other national governments, including Great Britain and the United States, began to explore the possible uses of rockets for warfare, ignoring for the time being the lure of outer space.

The beginning of the popular movement which eventually aroused military interest can be traced back to the formation of the earliest rocket societies. The first of these was probably Russian and was a continuation of the early astronautical studies of space flight pioneer Konstantin Ziolkovsky. At least as far back as 1924 an interplanetary group existed in Moscow and the First International Exhibition of World Space Navigation took place there in 1927. In 1928 Nikolai A. Rynin published the first of nine volumes of a gigantic encyclopedia entitled *Interplanetary Communication*. Two astronautical societies appeared in Leningrad and Moscow the following year.

At the same time in Germany the German Society for Space Travel (VfR) was actively engaged in rocket experimentation. This society favored liquid propellants, but at least one member, Max Valier, visualized practical uses for solid propellants and developed, with the aid of automobile magnate Fritz von Opel, a rocket-propelled car which was demonstrated in 1928 in Ruesselsheim. Fast-firing rockets were used for acceleration, and slow-burning units were provided to sustain velocity. After several disappointing tests, the car reached 70 miles per hour and a second vehicle, Opel Rak II, was built. Driven by Opel himself it achieved 125 miles per hour; a third car, fitted with railroad wheels, reached 180 miles per hour. Later cars were less successful, which prompted Valier to turn to liquid propellants for fuel. Before he was able to perform any significant experiments, he was killed by the explosion of one of his own rocket engines in 1930.

A more auspicious beginning for the 1930's is found in Goddard's successful launching in 1932 of a liquid-propelled rocket to an altitude of 2000 feet with a velocity of 500 miles per hour. It wasn't until a year later that the Germans had their first liquid firing success. Goddard's first launching of a liquid rocket occurred in 1926. It was a bare success, burning for 2.5 seconds and achieving a velocity of only 60 miles per hour.

To Goddard and Colonel (now Brig. General) Charles A. Lindbergh goes the credit for getting the first really organized rocket research program going in the United States. It began in 1929 when a Goddard-launched rocket crashed in Auburn, near Worcester, Massachusetts, bringing out police and fire departments and a measure of ire directed at Goddard himself. Lindbergh heard of the incident and was impressed. A letter from him to Harry F. Guggenheim brought funds and facilities to Goddard to set up test stands, a launching tower, and other facilities for continuing his work in Roswell, New Mexico, close by today's great White Sands rocket proving ground.

However, Valier's work in Germany had demonstrated the propulsive power of the rocket to the man in the street, thus arousing further interest. He also demonstrated for the engineer the extreme difficulty of controlling the level of thrust of a solid propellant rocket.

On July 11, 1928, F. W. Sander (whose powder rockets powered the Opel-Valier car) achieved the first rocket airplane flight—a distance of 4000 feet in 70 seconds. In September, Von Opel bettered this distance by several hundred feet in a rocket plane of his own. The next year Sander fired a liquid rocket engine, and the Junker Airplane Company began experimenting with JATO-type units.

Other interesting experiments were conducted by a German engineer, Rheinhold Tiling, and an Austrian engineer, Friedrich Schmiedl. Tiling designed, developed and, in 1931, built an ingenious powder rocket equipped with folding wings, which automatically extended at the top of the trajectory and permitted the rocket to glide back to earth in a graceful spiral. In the same year, Schmiedl fired a mail rocket *V-7* in Austria from Graz. The public received demonstrations of these rockets with enthusiasm.

Back in Germany, a powder rocket fired by Karl Poggensee soared to an altitude of 2700 feet over Bremen, and Johannes Winkler launched a liquid-propellant rocket to 2000 feet over Dessau-Grosskuhnau. Chief Engineer Pietschof of the Heylandt Works produced an alcohol and liquid oxygen model of the Valier car. The idea of a reaction-powered car lingered on.

During this period Hermann Oberth was conducting rocket experiments at the German Chemical and Technical Institute, with an engine called the *Kegelduse*. Assisted by Willy Ley and Rudolf Nebel, Oberth was able successfully to operate the motor which delivered a 15-pound thrust at an exhaust velocity of 3000 feet per second.

Members of the German Society for Space Travel, using Oberth's work as a point of departure, embarked on the construction of a series of *Mirak* (minimum rocket) models to test the theories they planned to incorporate in later larger rockets. The *Miraks* were not really successful, but much experimental data were obtained. Among the scientists recording the data were such men as Riedel, Nebel, Ley, and Von Braun.

In May 1931, Riedel designed and fired a very simple rocket called the *Repulsor*. Stabilized by a single stick this rocket climbed to modest altitudes measured in the hundreds of feet. Later *Repulsors*, stabilized by two sticks, reached altitudes up to a mile. In 1933 Hitler seized power, and the Gestapo pre-empted the society's records, reports, and journals.

All these were then classified secret and turned over to the German Army. Members of the society were given the rather limited choice of quitting this work, going to jail, or continuing their rocketry work for the army under Captain Walter Dornberger. The then-young Wernher von Braun was among those society members who went to work for the army, and shortly, while still in his early twenties, became head of rocket experiments.

It took the army less than two years to realize that there was something big here and that it warranted more than a casual effort. In 1933, the German Army established the world's first coordinated guided missile research center at Peenemünde, on a desolate run of Baltic coastline. Here, in the next decade, would be gathered the cream of Germany's technical brainpower to work on every phase of research and experimentation that had any bearing on guided missiles, not the least important of which was rocket propulsion.

Walter Dornberger continued in command of the army's rocket-missile effort and, under the direction of Von Braun, W. Thiel and E. Steinhoff at Peenemünde, the Germans designed, developed, built and fired the *A-1*, the *A-2*, the *A-3*, and finally the *A-4* military rocket known to the rest of the world as the *V-2*. This 14-ton bird was 46 feet long, 5 feet in diameter, was powered by a 56,000-pound thrust liquid oxygen-alcohol engine and could deliver a one-ton explosive warhead 200 miles away in 5 minutes.

Meanwhile, though the German Rocket Society for Space Travel had been nationalized for military purposes, free-lance rocket work continued elsewhere. In Austria, Dr. Eugen Sänger developed fuel oil-oxygen, regeneratively-cooled rocket motors. Long interested in high altitude rocket-propelled airplanes, he also made significant advances in theoretical studies on the nature of combustion. In 1933, his definitive book, *Rocket Flight Technique,* was published. Dr. Sänger was nationalized in 1935 at Trauer for the German Air Force under Hermann Göring. Presented with what was probably the most extensive liquid rocket experimental facility in the world at that time, Sänger was given a go-ahead and ten years in which to develop a liquid propellant motor with a thrust of 200,000 pounds, a project interrupted by the war and an Air Force decision to concentrate on the *V-1*. Assisting him in this great effort was the noted physicist, Dr. Irene Bredt, a distinguished graduate of the University of Bonn. The German Army and Air Force jealously guarded their rocket secrets from one another. It is said that for a long time there was no intercourse between the two groups at all, despite the fact that Hitler had determined even then to launch on a military program of world conquest.

When Göring witnessed a series of unsuccessful exhibition *V-2* "launchings" (they didn't get off the ground) the German Air Force decided to build the inexpensive *V-1* "buzz" bomb, a subsonic missile powered by an air-breathing pulsejet rather than rockets. One of the most original German projects to stem from this period, and one of the most far-reaching in scope, was the Sänger-Bredt antipodal bomber.   Conceived in 1936, it remained only a paper project.

Sänger and Irene Bredt proposed to launch a rocket bomber, which would rapidly reach speeds of four miles per second at the top of a 162-mile-high trajectory.   Upon descending into denser layers of the atmosphere, the bomber would ricochet back into the tenuous border of space.   It would continue such a "bouncing" path much as a flat stone skips across a pond when properly thrown.   By this combination glide-and-ricochet path the bomber would continue in ever-decreasing "jumps" until its original energy had been consumed.

"The launching and climb of the rocket bomber have the purpose of giving it, with the minimum of fuel consumption, the high velocity necessary to carry it through its long glide path.   They are in the nature of an impulse which lasts only for a few minutes," wrote the authors.

For launching, Sänger suggested a "catapult-like, perfectly straight, horizontal starting-track, several kilometers in length," upon which a rocket-powered sled would ride with its antipodal bomber cargo imparting to it a 1000-mile-per-hour boost.   The bomber itself was to be 90 feet in length, have a 25,000-mile range and a maximum velocity of 13,500 miles per hour. Detailed plans for an attack on New York by such a bomber were drawn. Fortunately the end of World War II came before the development of such a bomber.

JATO (Jet-Assist Take-Off), too, found its beginning in the thirties.   As early as 1935 Dr. Hellmuth Walter began work on rocket engines in Kiel. In 1938 he found that by use of a turbopump rather than a pressurized gas feed system he was able to increase the chamber pressure and hence the thrust of his hydrogen peroxide-powered engines from 600 to 2000 pounds.   Still further thrust increases were subsequently obtained when the engines became bipropellant.   Instead of relying on the thrust obtained from the decomposition products of peroxide, a fuel was added to burn with the resulting oxygen.   To solve the problem of cooling, the fuel was first circulated in a cooling jacket before being injected into the chamber.   In 1938 a *Heinkel-112* took off with a liquid booster built by Walter.

In Great Britain, the British Interplanetary Society, founded in 1933 by P. E. Cleator, served as a nucleus for astronautical enthusiasts and rocket experimenters.   Later other societies appeared, but, despite wide interest, little actual experimentation took place, and this principally in Scotland. Members of the Manchester Interplanetary Society also carried on some short-lived work.   In 1936, Ralph Morris undertook some liquid fuel research, but was halted by the Explosives Act.   As a result of this legislation, only a minimum amount of rocket experimentation occurred in pre-war Britain.

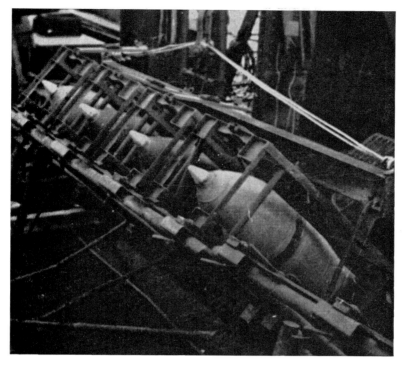

FIGS. 25 AND 26   GERMAN SUBMARINE MISSILE LAUNCHERS

The fabulous missile concept conceived by German rocket experts at Peene-münde during the war called for a launching mechanism to be mounted on the deck of a submarine. Each rack could hold four missiles. The Russians moved the equipment to the Soviet Union after the war and were reported to have continued development work on it.

FIG. 27   GERMAN "DO-WERFER" ROCKET LAUNCHER

An abandoned German "Do-Werfer" rocket launcher is shown after capture by the Americans in northern France (U. S. Army)

FIG. 28   REAR SECTION OF A GERMAN *V-2* ROCKET

A trainload of *V-2* missiles, apparently strafed by Allied planes while en route to a launching site, was found by the U. S. First Army at Bromkirchen, Germany. Note the spun glass insulator between the fuel tank and the outer shell of the rocket. (U. S. Army)

FIG. 29   GERMAN *WASSERFALL* MISSILE

Operating on a nitric acid-visol propellant, the highly advanced *Wasserfall* missile utilized a beam-rider guidance system, weighed 4 tons, and stood about 25 feet high.

FIG. 30   GERMAN PANZERFAUST 60-MM ANTI-TANK WEAPON

This German "bazooka-type" weapon came in two sections, namely, the firing tube with sights, and the grenade. The grenade, when fired, was guided by fins which flared out at the tail. The tube had to be discarded after being fired. (U. S. Army)

FIG. 31 GERMAN *X-4* AIR-TO-AIR MISSILE

The unique feature of this missile was the spiral propellant tank. Control was exerted on the missile through fine wires which unwound from bobbins attached to the fin tips as the missile shot forward.

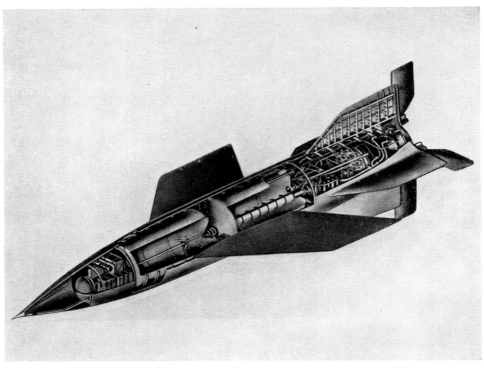

FIG. 32   CUTAWAY VIEW OF THE GERMAN *A-4b* MISSILE
(Gatland, *Development of the Guided Missile*)

FIG. 33 GERMAN *A-4b* MISSILE ON LAUNCHING PLATFORM

The *A-4b* missile was the forerunner of the *A-9* missile, which was modified with wings. The second of two flew successfully. (Gatland, *Development of the Guided Missile*)

FIG. 34   GERMAN DELTA-WINGED *A-9/A-10* MISSILE

The *A-9/A-10* missile reached the preliminary design stage at Peenemünde. Boosted by the giant *A-9*, the delta-winged (in this version) *A-10* would extend its natural range by gliding. With its potential target range of 3000 miles, Germany hoped to bomb New York City during the Second World War. (Gatland, *Development of the Guided Missile*)

In Holland, a rocket society was organized which tested postal rockets. From 1929 into the 1930's, the Italians, under General G. A. Crocco and R. M. Corelli, worked with gasoline-nitrogen dioxide motors which were regeneratively cooled. Later, with L. Crocco monopropellant studies were performed for torpedo and other applications. At a 1935 technical congress in Rome, N. A. Rynin read a paper on the thermodynamics of rocket motors. In France, L. Damblanc further developed the black powder rocket which later won the REP-Hirsch astronautical prize, and Esnault-Pelterie produced a liquid oxygen-gasoline motor with a 660-pound thrust. A Swiss, J. Stemmer, developed several liquid rockets. A Russian news dispatch in 1935 told of a stratosphere committee project to build an atmosphere exploration missile capable of reaching an altitude of 35 miles, at 2000 feet per second. In Australia and India, rocket groups did basic experimental work. In 1938 Franco's forces in Spain fired propaganda rockets, adapted from standard lifesaving rocket devices, against Loyalist positions.

Before 1940, most United States contributions to rocketry and astronautics, outside of the work of Dr. Goddard, were made within the American Rocket Society (ARS), organized in 1930 as the American Interplanetary Society. Under the direction of G. E. Pendray and H. F. Pierce, and with the aid of D. Lasser, N. Schachner, Dr. W. Lemkin, L. Manning, A. Best, A. Africano and L. Gregory, the society's first rocket motor took shape, based on the German *Repulsor* designs. It operated on gasoline and liquid oxygen, was pressure-fed, and produced a 60-pound thrust. It underwent a successful static test schedule in 1932. Under the leadership of Bernard Smith, Rocket No. 2 was constructed. On launching day in May of 1933, it fired for only 2 seconds, reaching 250 feet. An explosion in the oxygen tank caused the malfunction, but in spite of this, the experimenters were jubilant because a liquid rocket had at last left the ground.

Spurred by this success, new rockets were designed and built. Smith and Pendray prepared Rocket No. 3; John Shesta, No. 4. The Shesta motor had four nozzles, a feature designed to strengthen its construction, and it was water-jacket-cooled. This rocket reached a calculated velocity of 700 miles per hour.

The American Rocket Society also developed a "heat sponge" motor, wherein blocks of aluminum absorbed large amounts of heat. By 1935 a test stand was constructed, permitting motors to be thoroughly checked out before actual flight-firing. This facility led to further basic knowledge of rocket engine operation, which enabled the Society's members (J. Wyld and P. Van Dresser had been added to the original member list) to devise better and more reliable motors. Africano received the REP-Hirsch astronautical prize for his work on rocket motors. And despite the double-pronged Government-backed effort in Germany and claims of ambitious projects in Russia, the United States Government still exhibited little official interest in rocketry. The Navy exhibited some interest in pilotless aircraft and remote-controlled bombs in the late 1930's, and the Army's Colonel George Holloman realized the significance of guided missiles, but neither effort really recognized the ultimate possibilities of rocket propulsion. In 1932 L. A. Skinner of the Army Ordnance Department began tests on his own initiative, with limited funds and facilities, at Aberdeen, Maryland. He was primarily interested in the possibility of accelerating a shell by means of a solid or liquid propellant rocket motor. Skinner must be considered as one of the "greats" of rocketry. And so must R. C. Truax, who even as a United States Navy midshipman devoted his leave and pay to significant rocket experimentation.

While test-stand checkouts were steadily leading to more efficient, more practical rocket engines, the Society's experimental group tackled another basic problem, the airframe configuration. In organizing the research, a series of flight tests were made with a variety of aerodynamic sizes and shapes, using solid propellant charges.

It was also during this period that Robert Goddard developed a self-contained gyroscopic stabilization system for his test rockets, with jetavator vanes for missile control. He also launched the world's first supersonic rocket.

One of the more important results of what deserves to be called a motor development program was the regeneratively-cooled liquid propellant rocket. One was constructed in 1938 by H. W. Bull, in which gasoline was circulated through only part of the motor (the nozzle). Later in that year, James Wyld produced a design in which the complete thrust chamber was regeneratively cooled. This is generally regarded as America's first such engine and solved an irksome cooling dilemma.

Shortly thereafter, another regenerative engine, designed at Annapolis by R. C. Truax (then a midshipman), further established the superiority of this revolutionary concept. Other tests were taking place elsewhere in the country. Beginning in 1935, the Cleveland Rocket Society tested chrome-nickel steel, water-cooled motors at a specially constructed firing area. Under the guidance of E. Loeball, Chief Research Engineer of the Society, a series of propellant and rocket motor studies were made, using gasoline and liquid oxygen for most of the tests. On the West Coast, solid propellant rockets were tested in the late 1930's and early 1940's by the California Rocket Society. Maximum altitudes attained were about 1500 feet.

In 1936 F. J. Malina together with J. W. Parsons and E. Forman founded a rocket research group at CalTech. By 1938 the group included A. M. O. Smith, H. S. Tsien and Weld Arnold. Arnold gave a fund of $1000 to the group. In 1939 Malina received the last REP-Hirsch astronautics prize to be awarded for his work on the theory of operation of the rocket motor.

Finally, in 1940, the then-Army Air Corps launched a formal guided missile program, under the direction of Colonel Holloman. Its work, however, with such guided bomb projects as the *Azon,* the *Razon* and the *GB-1* glide bomb, was little concerned with rocketry. United States rocket weapons in World War II were largely concerned with small, aimed bombardment rockets, usually fired in great numbers from ships, ground-launchers, or aircraft.

Nevertheless, the rocket was emerging from its infancy, as Hitler Germany would soon demonstrate. It was this early start of a serious government interest in rocketry, rather than any particular genius exhibited during the war years, that put Germany so much in the lead in world rocketry by 1945. It is interesting also to note that Robert Goddard's results supplied to Hermann Oberth in the early years, when there was free international exchange of rocket information, provided much of the basis for the German work. Similarly, it was German knowhow captured at the end of World War II that provided both Russia and the United States with their individual points of departure for further work. To carry the parallel farther, it was Russia's all-out concentration on rocketry from the beginning of the postwar period that gave her lead time over the United States a scant dozen years later.

This was the prelude to the critical international race for space that developed following World War II.

4

Axis War Rockets

Hitler's management of Germany's wartime rocket program is one of several mistakes that worked in the Allies' favor. A number of military historians claim that, if the *V-2's* had been successful six to twelve months earlier, the course and even the outcome of World War II might have been quite different. Hitler insisted that costly steel-reinforced concrete installations be constructed as *V-2* launching sites, while his Peenemünde rocket experts argued that mobile launchers would be cheaper, more easily hidden and less subject to Allied air bombardment. It wasn't until his super-pillboxes were flattened and smoldering that Hitler approved a mobile launcher construction program. It seems likely, too, that Hermann Göring and the Air Force did much to delay the Army's work at Peenemünde. The decisive factors in the neutralizing of the German rocket offensive, were, of course, the British air attacks on Peenemünde and the British and American attacks on the launching sites.

Nevertheless, the German rocket program was fantastically successful, both in the case of the strategic *V-2's,* where there was strong emphasis from the beginning, and in the case of tactical (artillery and antiaircraft) rockets which came later in the war. It was a peculiarity of the German rocket program that the strategic ballistic missile was recognized even before the war, while development of smaller weapons for individual use by troops too often wasn't started until German troops found themselves confronted by such weapons in the field. The "bazooka" is a case in point. Similarly, it took overwhelming superiority of Allied bombers in the air to force a real drive behind antiaircraft rockets and rocket-powered manned inter-ceptors.

v-2, A STRATEGIC BALLISTIC ROCKET

Under the command of Colonel (later General) Walter Dornberger the German Army in 1932 began its highly secretive rocket development program, the first products of which were two vertically-launched liquid oxygen and alcohol rockets—the *A-1* and the *A-2.* The later model (*A-2*) incorpoed a heavy rotating steel container for gyroscopic stabilization. In 1938 the *A-3* appeared. This awesome weapon had automatic guidance vanes which "pressed" against the jet exhaust to provide control. The *A-3* development program, begun at Kummersdorf (Berlin) and completed at Peenemünde, was in many ways a precursor to the *A-4* missile, popularly known as the *V-2*. To test the design features of the *V-2* the Germans constructed and launched the smaller *A-5*, similar in dimensions to the *A-3*, and the first missile to use graphite vanes for guidance.

Walter Dornberger, army commander, Wernher von Braun, scientific chief, Walter Thiel, Ernst Steinhoff, and other top rocket experts were encouraged by the data and knowledge accumulated from the *A-5* flights; yet the design requirements for the *V-2* still seemed incredible. The range desired, 160 or more miles, was double that of the famed Paris Gun of World War I; velocities well in excess of 3000 miles per hour were required; thrust would be of the order of 25 tons. Launched at 45 degrees, such a rocket would travel outside the effective atmosphere of the earth. In addition, a 2000-pound explosive payload was called for to be delivered within 2 miles of the chosen target—an accuracy, incidentally, which was never reliably achieved. The finished rocket had to be small enough to travel on railroad cars through narrow German rail tunnels and on trucks along secluded country roads. Dr. Dornberger wrote recently of the initial conferences on the proposed *A-4* missile, "We were a bit uneasy, for we were up against a mass of new problems and quite aware that the step was really a little too ambitious." Yet the unsolvable problems were solved, and by the end of the war *V-2* rocket missiles were destroying targets 220–230 miles from the launching site.

When hostilities ceased the Germans had, under various stages of development, an *A-4b* missile (an *A-4* with wings attached) with an expected range of 360 miles, plus projected missiles with designation numbers up to *A-10*. The *A-9* missile, of *A-4* size, with delta wings was designed to be boosted to high velocity by the 87-ton parachute-recoverable *A-10* missile, and reach a speed of 6300 miles per hour at a peak altitude of 35 miles.

The *V-1* (officially designated *Fi-103*), the other well-known cross-channel bombardment missile, was subsonic in speed and highly vulnerable to fighter attacks. The *V-1* was not a rocket. It employed a pulsejet engine, carried a 2200-pound warhead, measured over 25 feet in length, and its take-off was accomplished on a launching ramp by means of a piston in a tube which was activated by the decomposition of chemicals, chiefly hydrogen peroxide. Several *V-1*'s fell into American hands, and in October 1944 the War Department ordered 2000 copies reproduced. Called the *Loon* in the United States, this missile was used for training purposes and to gain experience in manufacturing techniques.

Another surface-to-surface missile used by the Germans was the *Rheinbote* (Rhine Messenger), developed by the firm Rheinmetall, under the technical direction of Klein and Villiers. This four-step, solid propellant, 37-foot missile, launched from an inclined rack, could deposit its 88-pound warhead 110–140 miles away.

GERMAN SURFACE-TO-AIR MISSILE

As the air situation deteriorated for Germany, the antiaircraft missile program was pushed forcibly. By 1943 nearly 50 separate projects were under development. The number was soon reduced to a dozen.

The *Wasserfall* was one of Germany's most advanced and successful anti-aircraft missiles. Although never operational, except for experimental purposes, it was considered a finished product and ordered into mass production in 1945. The range of the *Wasserfall* was upward of 100,000 feet and it was reportedly capable of 1500 miles per hour.

A second important antiaircraft product of Germany's wartime Peene-münde program was the *Taifun*. Much smaller than the *Wasserfall,* it operated on liquid propellants, the oxidizer tank being contained inside the fuel tank. An exceptionally high acceleration of 31 g, and a thrust of 1900 pounds for 3 seconds would bring the 50-inch missile up to an altitude of 50,000 feet.

The *Rheintochter* (Rhinemaiden) was a most unusual missile in appearance, using 6 wings and 4 nose fins for stabilization, and a "wraparound" booster for take off. The missile was made by Rheinmetall-Borsing and operated on nitric acid and visol (a self-igniting hydrocarbon mixture based on vinyl isobutyl ether). It was not operational.

Another antiaircraft rocket employing the "wraparound" solid propellant booster and a liquid propellant motor was the *Schmetterling* (Butterfly) developed by the Henschel Company and the Bayerische Motoren Werke. Still in development at the end of the war, this small airplane-like missile flew at 500 miles per hour on a radio-controlled course.

Enzian (Gentian), a product of the Messerschmitt and Hellmuth Walter Companies, was unusual in that it combined metal and wood in its construction. It was stubby (11½ feet long), had a wing span of 13.1 feet, and was boosted by 4 straddling 3300-pound-thrust solid propellant units. It reached approximately Mach 0.9, had a range of 16 miles and a maximum altitude of 53,000 feet.

Two antiaircraft rockets that did not pass the experimental research stage were the *Feuerlilie* (Firelily) and the *Hecht*. Developed by Rheinmetall-Borsing, both rockets resembled small airplanes. The solid-propelled *Feuer-lilie,* constructed in 1941, weighed 265 pounds, was less than 7 feet high and

9½ inches in diameter, and developed 1100 pounds of thrust for 6 seconds. The 1942 version of the missile attained a speed of 1000 miles per hour and an altitude of 20,000 feet. This later version was larger than its predecessor and used liquid as well as solid propellants. The liquid-propelled *Hecht* weighed slightly more than the *Feuerlilie* and built up less thrust over a longer period. It accelerated to over 600 miles per hour.

GERMAN AIR-TO-SURFACE MISSILES

The best-known development of the war was a series of rocket-powered winged bombs which could be guided all or part of the way to the target. The best known of these glide bombs were designed, developed, and produced by the Henschel Company. The 12-foot *Hs-293*, weighing about 1700 pounds, was carried by Focke-Wulf, Junkers, Dornier and Heinkel bombers and was used against Allied ships with fair accuracy.

The *Hs-294* was capable of making short subsurface runs. A contact fuse prevented detonation upon impact with the water, thus permitting the bomb to be effective against the hulls of ships. The *Hs-293* powered by a single hydrogen peroxide rocket engine averaged 400 miles per hour, while the *Hs-294* used two such motors to propel it at 550 miles per hour from distances of 3 to 6 miles away. Still another device was the unpowered *Fritz-X* guided armor-piercing bomb, for use principally against ships. A *BV-type* glide bomb was developed to replace the *V-1*, but was never used for lack of the bombers to carry them.

GERMAN AIR-TO-AIR MISSILES

The German missile program resulted in highly effective air-to-air missiles, both solid and liquid propelled. In one battle toward the end of the war, rocket-firing *ME-110's* succeeded in bringing down 60 Allied bombers.

One rather unusual air-to-air missile was the *X-4*, a liquid-propelled, wire-guided rocket manufactured by Ruhr Steel Company and developed largely by Dr. Kramer of Bayerische Motoren Werke. The liquid propellants were contained in tanks coiled like tubes inside the missile. *X-4* was stabilized by 4 fins and 4 midship wings. Guide flares were attached to the two opposing wings with 3 to 4 miles of wire rolled in spools on the remaining two wings. Upon release, the spools unwound, enabling the pilot to guide its course by impulse. Smaller than the 78-inch *X-4* was the solid propellant, wire-controlled *X-7*.

The *R-4m*, a tiny (7-pound) solid propellant rocket carried by *Me-262* fighters and *Natter* rocket planes, and the solid propellant spin-stabilized *WGR-21cm*, adapted from a German Army surface-to-surface rocket, had speeds in the neighborhood of 700 miles per hour and ranges close to 30,000 feet; they were highly successful against Allied aircraft toward the close of the war.

ROCKET AIRPLANES

As the liquid propellant rocket engine improved in reliability, increased attention was naturally given to its utilization as an aircraft powerplant. Three possible uses were investigated: short-duration, high-speed power for fighter aircraft, manned missiles, and long-range rocket bombers.

As a result of his work in the 1930's, Dr. Hellmuth Walter produced a bipropellant hydrogen peroxide engine that developed more than 3500 pounds of thrust and was used successfully in two high-speed, short-range fighters—the *Natter* and the *Me-163*. Smaller Walter engines found application in glide bombs.

The *Me-163* was the most outstanding German rocket fighter. A midwing monoplane, with sharp leading-edge sweep-back, 20 feet in length with a 30-foot wing span, this craft could fly at top speeds of 600 miles per hour for roughly 10 minutes. Landing was effected solely on a sled arrangement since landing gear assembly was jettisoned upon take-off.

Junkers redesigned the *Me-163* and produced the *Ju-248,* of slimmer design and supposedly capable of reaching an altitude of 40,000 feet in 3 minutes. This craft, later called the *Me-263,* never flew. Other developments included a *DFS-228* rocket unit for a reconnaissance airplane and the *DFS-346* for a scout bomber. (DFS is the abbreviation of the "Deutsche Forschungsanstalt für Segelflug," or German Research Institute for Soaring Flight.) Objectives were 100,000-foot altitudes and 1700-mile-per-hour speeds.

Dr. A. Lippisch, in charge of design of these airplanes as well as a high-speed interceptor, *DFS-194,* also planned a heavily armored, streamlined, piloted rocket which would ram enemy bombers and then both pilot and rocket would parachute to earth. The plan was furthered by Dr. P. Karlson, but eventually was discarded in favor of a similar project—the *Natter* (Viper).

This half-missile, half-piloted airplane was constructed in 1944 in the Bachemwerke factory. The liquid-propelled *Natter* was vertically launched by 4 solid propellant boosters and climbed at a rate of better than 35,000 feet per minute. Made almost entirely of wood, the *Natter* could be built cheaply and rapidly. The pilot rode forward of the short wings and the powerplant was housed in the tail. When in position, the pilot would fire simultaneously the 24-to-33 *R-4M* rocket projectiles carried by the *Natter* and then bail out. The nose section was discarded and the motor was separated from the tanks and parachuted for reuse. *Natter* had a radius of action of about 25 miles and, although never used operationally, was subjected to many successful tests.

GERMAN ROCKET ORDNANCE DEVELOPMENTS

Perhaps the best-known solid propellant ordnance piece was the *Nebelwerfer 41,* which appeared on the Russian front in 1942. As the word meant "fog thrower," model of 1941, it was apparently conceived to be a smoke screen mortar. *Nebelwerfer* consisted of six short barrels, from which 40-inch long, 15-centimeter calibre shells were fired, simultaneously if desired. Rocket-powered shells fired from the *41* reached 3½ miles with fair accuracy. By 1943 a larger *Nebelwerfer* appeared, firing 21-centimeter shells with a 4-mile range.

Of the same calibre as the larger *Nebelwerfer* was another ordnance rocket device, *Schwere Wurfgerat* (heavy launcher) having two types of warhead, a 28-centimeter shell carrying 110 pounds of high explosive and a 32-centimeter shell carrying 110 pounds of inflammable jellied oil. The *Wurfgerats* were simply self-propelled incendiary bombs with rather short ranges of 1.5 miles.

An interesting 21-centimeter flare rocket, the *R-LG,* was developed by the German Navy and the Rheinmetall-Borsing Company. It was more than 40 inches long and could reach 16,000-foot altitudes. Upon attaining the maximum altitude, the illuminating material was parachuted slowly to the surface.

Following the appearance of American "bazookas" in the Tunisian campaign of the North African war, the Germans pushed the development of their *Panzerschreck* and *Panzerfaust.* They resembled American weapons in appearance, but were not as reliable and were even likely to explode at random due to inferior solid fuels.

Most German jet-assisted take-off (JATO) work was based on the hydrogen peroxide system first studied in 1933 at the Chemical State Institute in Berlin as a possible power source for submarines. It was on this basis that Hellmuth Walter did his JATO work in the 1930's.

Meanwhile the B. M. W. plant, testing nitric-acid-fuel combinations, developed an engine for the *Henschel 8-117* airplane. Eventually Walter mass-produced an 1100-pound-thrust, assist-take-off (ATO) hydrogen peroxide unit which was extensively used on *Heinkel III* and *Junkers 88* bombers. The spent units were parachuted to ground for reuse.

The two most important JATO engines were the HWK R1-209/109-502 and the BMW/109-718. The former burned its fuel with peroxide (T-stoff); the latter smaller-thrust engine used Salbei and appeared mainly on *Me-262* turbojet fighters.

By war's end the Germans were using JATO units extensively, and JATO had become a standard auxiliary powerplant.

WAR ROCKETS IN ITALY

In Italy, development programs began as far back as 1927, when the Italian General Staff commissioned General G. A. Crocco to perform work on solid propellants. Some of this work was carried on with L. Crocco, the Bombrini Parodi Delfino Chemical Company, and its director, Dr. Marenco. A constant-pressure type of solid motor was developed, incorporating a tubular charge of colloidal solventless powder. Chamber pressures were from 700 to 1400 pounds per square inch and specific impulses varied from 150 to 170 seconds duration.

At the Chemical Institute of the University of Rome, Dr. C. Landi and Dr. R. M. Corelli investigated a gasoline and nitrogen-dioxide propellant combination. Elsewhere, nitromethane studies were made. Solid propellant research ceased two years after it had begun.

In 1932 the Aviation Ministry sponsored monopropellant investigations under General Crocco and Dr. Corelli with rocket, torpedo and submarine applications in mind. This work was suspended in 1935. Little of this preparatory work was applied to weapon use in the Second World War. A few rocket-propelled bombs appeared, and a small company in Turin conducted experimental work on black-powder antitank rockets.

JAPANESE ROCKETRY DURING WORLD WAR II

Rocket developments in Japan during the war were not impressive, although a more or less sustained program was known to have been in progress, which began in 1935. All known types of Japanese ordnance were based on the solid phase. About all that was done was to convert existing bombs or shells into propelled missiles by adding a rocket motor. Ranges rarely exceeded 5000 yards. Japanese naval rocket developments were under the supervision of Lt. Commander Kumao Hino.

Two sizes of rocket-propelled bombs were devised by the Japanese—60 and 250 kilograms, indicating the weight of the bombs used before modification. A variety of general combat, antitank and antiaircraft types were developed, but they never reached an effective state. A depth charge with a reported range of 2735 yards was reported, its total weight of 76 pounds suggesting that it was of the *Mousetrap* variety.

By far the best-known Japanese rocket project was the *Baka* (fool) manned-missile airplane, the Japanese name being derived from its dangerously inadequate maneuverability. Outwardly, the *Baka* was somewhat similar to the German *Natter*, but it was propelled entirely by a solid propellant consisting chiefly of nitroglycerin and nitrocellulose. A monoplane constructed principally of plywood and aluminum, it measured only 19 feet, 10 inches in length. A minimum space was made available for the suicide pilot, and only the bare essentials in instrumentation were provided. The major assemblies consisted of three solid propellant rockets, the tail unit, the small stubby wings, and the warhead and fairing.

The *Baka* was air-launched from a mother aircraft, to which it was attached by a mounting lug and a series of slings. Using 3 rocket engines, it sustained powered flight for about 3 minutes. Two additional wing rockets were sometimes available, but their drag characteristics were unfavorable, and not much greater horizontal range was obtained from their use. The weapon achieved some success, but a large percentage were brought down by artillery and fighter planes.

A variation of the *Baka* was a ground-to-air missile, also pilot suicidal, which went into action against American B-29 bombers. It could reach an altitude of 32,000 feet in 3 minutes, attaining a maximum speed of 500 miles per hour. Flight time was approximately 7 minutes.

Some solid JATO units were developed, and enough had been learned from the Germans about the manufacture of hydrogen peroxide to begin development programs. At the Mitsubishi Seishi Kaisha plant, for instance, a liquid JATO unit for the Shusui airplane was investigated in 1944.

* * * * *

World War II proved rocketry in general, but German developments specifically demonstrated the feasibility of the large liquid-propelled missiles, both as weapons and as prototypes for space flight vehicles. When the war ended the Dornberger-Von Braun team at Peenemünde had plans in the works for a 2-stage ballistic missile with a range of 3500 miles and for a 3-stage development of this with space flight capabilities.

5

Allied War Rockets

While Germany led—and startled—the world with its big liquid-propelled rockets, the United States and most of its World War II Allies went solid and stayed small. Though the results were not nearly so dramatic as those from the *V-2*, unless perhaps one personally witnessed the predawn rocket bombardment of a Pacific atoll or the rocket assault on Normandy Beach, nevertheless they were every bit as influential on the course of the war.

Unfortunately, none of the Allied powers, with the exception of Russia, realized the importance of the big war rocket until several years after the war. Then, at the eleventh hour, the United States inaugurated in the early 1950's its first uninterrupted program for the development of Intercontinental Ballistic Missiles and Intermediate Range Ballistic Missiles—ICBMs and IRBMs—named *Atlas, Titan, Thor,* and *Jupiter.*

As late as September 1957, the United States assumed it had even then an unassailable lead in big missile development. But, on October 4, 1957, the first of a series of Soviet earth satellites was placed successfully in orbit. This dispelled much of the complacency that existed in America, and in other Western powers, as to their assumed superior strength in big rockets and the importance of space flight.

The story of Allied rocketry in World War II explains in part the failure of the United States, Britain, and others to appreciate the importance of these fields in the immediate postwar period. The Allies throughout the war treated rockets as conventional weapons for performing traditional tactical military tasks. The inaccuracy of the *V-2's* fired at Great Britain may have led Western planners astray as to the real potential of this concept when fully developed. The all-out Soviet effort beginning in 1945, on the other hand, is probably best explained by the fact that Russia had a popular appreciation of the practicability of manned space flight since the late nineteenth century. It did not take a genius even then to imagine what weapons might be developed on the way. But, in the West, with its conventional extension of World War II thinking, the rule was: Continued effort on traditional airpower concepts.

BACKGROUND TO UNITED STATES ROCKETRY IN WORLD WAR II

It was not until late in the decade immediately preceding World War II that the United States even began to think of providing official government support for any kind of rocket research. In 1940 C. N. Hickman, who had collaborated with Goddard in rocket research during the First World War, wrote to Frank B. Jewett, head of the Bell Telephone Laboratories and president of the National Academy of Science, listing the possible military advantages of the rocket. This letter was an important factor leading to the establishment of organized U. S. rocket research.

Shortly thereafter Section H, Division A of the National Defense Research Committee (NDRC) was formed. This new agency, set up at Indianhead, Maryland, concentrated between 1940 and 1943 on impulsive or fast-burning solid propellant motors and their application to conventional aerial bombs.

In the spring of 1941 a rocket motor to augment the penetrating power of a 14-inch shell was completed. Considering the scarcity of basic information on the internal ballistics of rockets, this was a remarkable achievement.

Activities were later transferred to the Allegany Ballistics Laboratory at Cumberland, Maryland, operated by George Washington University under the direction of Dr. R. E. Gibson.

The Indianhead effort was coordinated closely with the British, who had discovered that rockets could be effective as high-altitude aircraft weapons. As a result of the visit of a British scientific mission, headed by Sir Henry Tizard, a valuable interchange of rocket information began. Dr. C. C. Lauritsen, Vice Chairman of Division A of the NDRC, examined rocket establishments in England in the summer of 1941. Further convinced of the military value of rockets, he sent a memorandum to Dr. Vannevar Bush which led to increased rocket activities.

Under the direction of Lauritsen at the California Institute of Technology (CIT) a fast-burning solid propellant motor was developed. A motor of this type propelled the *Tiny Tim* aircraft rocket.

By 1942 rocket research was being conducted at George Washington University, the University of Wisconsin, the University of Minnesota, Duke University, Budd Wheel Company, Budd Induction Heat Company, Hercules Powder Company, and Bell Telephone Laboratories.

Experimental work in the early 1940's utilized only solid propellant systems since no practical liquid propellant systems were available. "Ballistite" (60% nitrocellulose and 40% nitroglycerine) was the most widely used solid propellant and once manufacturing experience was obtained in making large, long-burning, thick-webbed grains (needed to insure a long range and high velocities), large-scale production was possible. In 1944, for example, the Hercules Powder Company set up the Sunflower Ordnance Works to supply the Soviets with extruded dry powder for their rockets.

ROCKET VERSUS SUBMARINES

In 1943 a *Minnie Mouse* rocket, supplied with a 2.5-inch (diameter) grain, was designed by CIT to counter enemy submarines. These projectiles, based on the British "Hedgehog" idea, were launched from a rail, elevated at 45 degrees. Once in the air their paths fanned out in such a way that the rockets would fall in a straight line across the bow of a ship at some distance ahead. The fuse was armed under hydrostatic pressure and would explode only upon striking a solid object. The launcher became known as the "mousetrap" because of the similarity between its launching rails and a cocked mousetrap. This weapon was inexpensive to produce and immediately found wide application, notably on submarine chasers and cutters.

THE RETRO-ROCKET BOMB

A novel antisubmarine weapon was the "retro bomb." Aerial bombing usually requires a standard aiming-run, but submarines, when submerged, are often invisible until the bomber is almost directly overhead. Procedure turns in preparation for such a run often resulted in losing track of the submarine. A bomb which could be dropped vertically on the spur of the moment improved the chances of U-boat kills.

NDRC and CIT tackled the problem and, in short order, came up with a low-powered rocket bomb, launched rearward from rails under the wings of the airplane. Upon being launched, it stopped abruptly in mid-air and dropped straight down. Projectiles of three different speeds (to coincide with three ranges of airplane speeds) were equipped with 35-pound warheads fused like *Minnie Mouse*.

The initial test-firing of these bombs, the first firing of any kind of an American rocket weapon from a plane in actual flight, was made from a *PBY-5a Catalina* in July 1942. Similar retro bombs, with flares added, were developed for use by night patrols, to spot submarines before they attacked with a regular barrage of retro bombs.

FORWARD-FIRING AIRCRAFT ROCKETS

Hickman had proposed 4-inch, forward-firing aircraft rockets as early as 1918. These rockets, to be fired from tubular wing launchers, had an arrangement permitting both the warhead and the engine to explode, giving added destructive power. The idea aroused interest in this country, but no action was taken until 1941 when Army Captain L. A. Skinner developed and fired a weapon with a proximity fuse. This was the birth of the 4.5-inch *M-8* rocket. Captain Harry L. Donecht supervised the development of a three-tube launcher, and on July 6, 1942, an AAF fighter discharged a volley of 4.5-inch folding fin rockets at Aberdeen Proving Ground surface targets.

This was the first launching of a forward-firing American aircraft rocket from a plane in flight. Improvements in the *M-8* rocket led to the *T-22* rocket which proved highly successful against both planes and ground installations.

The first destruction of a submarine by American forward-firing aircraft rockets occurred on January 11, 1944, when carrier-based airplanes chanced upon a surfaced German U-boat. They carried 20-pound, solid steel warheads, with 3.5-inch diameters designed by CIT specifically for this use.

The British developed this weapon first. Experiments had shown that long, shallow, underwater trajectories up to 50 feet under water would result in a punctured submarine. Frequent targets for these rockets were conning towers, just before or after they submerged. Spurred by excellent British results in the Mediterranean, CIT boosted this type of weapon to top priority. It was but a short step to the production of similar rockets with high-explosive warheads. This 3.5-inch rocket had a total weight of 54 pounds.

Because of the pressing need for more installations, the Naval Ordnance Test Station (NOTS) was established at Inyokern, with Fleet Wing 14 (AIR) which had tested rockets for CIT forming the nucleus of Ordnance Development Unit No. 1 at that station.

Introduced in action in Burma in 1944, aircraft rockets began to be used shortly thereafter in the Pacific and European areas. Less damaging but more accurate than bombs, weight for weight, they soon supplanted the 75-mm cannon formerly used in the B-25 Mitchell bomber. These rockets were effective against ships up to destroyer-size, as well as airfields, oil and ammunition dumps, tanks, trains, light field guns and pillboxes.

By December 1943, CIT had produced a 5-inch motor with 8 nozzles and a rupture disk for safety against high pressures, which was used in one of the most famous rockets of the war, the HVAR (high velocity aircraft rocket). Christened the *Holy Moses,* it went into combat in July 1944.

Meanwhile, Allegany Ballistics worked on a similar 4.5-inch rocket using a smokeless powder of greatly improved temperature characteristics to replace the older and slower *M-8* charge. This became known as the *Super* 4.5-inch rocket. Designs were frozen in December 1944, but the war ended before it saw combat. Stabilized by 4 large fins, its semi-armor-piercing nose could penetrate 5 inches of homogeneous armor plate. A sister model had 8.5 pounds of explosive, or three times that of the *M-8*.

In February 1944, CIT decided to construct a larger rocket which could be used against strengthened Japanese fortifications. Over 10 feet long and nearly 1 foot in diameter, this rocket was to weigh 1284 pounds, including a 590-pound warhead. By April, a complete round had been dropped from a regular bomb rack and fired by lanyard. This rocket, the last and the largest produced by the CIT-NDRC-Navy team, was called the *Tiny Tim,* an ironic name for a rocket which added the power of 12-inch guns to a medium bomber. It saw action in Okinawa.

Aircraft rockets had a variety of targets, but they were especially successful as tank destroyers. CIT produced 100 HVARs a day, which were flown in relays to *P-47s* in Europe. Enemy troops reportedly fled vehicles for ditches when the rocket planes approached. The Navy also used aircraft rockets in Pacific operations, Atlantic antisubmarine campaigns, and during D-Day in Normandy. Marine squadrons in the Pacific sometimes developed make-shift launchers in order to equip planes with these rockets when regular launching equipment was scarce. Some enterprising grasshopper pilots even fitted "bazookas" to the wingstruts of their light planes.

Most Japanese islands in the Pacific experienced rocket-strafing. Rockets could reach caves, blockhouses, and pillboxes. They were particularly adaptable to underwing mounts on fighter planes. Dive bombers first silenced antiaircraft batteries with rockets (and other targets at the request of ground forces) and then dropped in at low altitude with their bombs. Air coordinators often flew in beforehand, selecting ground targets and firing smoke rockets which left long, white lines leading down to pinpoint positions.

In reviewing the pioneer rocket efforts in the United States one is overcome by a feeling of not being able to give adequate credit to the great workers in the Army, Navy and Air Force, in educational institutions and in industry, who made the original contributions. Missing from this narrative of rocket pioneers by sheer force of logical classification are such great names as those of Robert A. Millikan, of California Institute of Technology, and his notable son, Clark B. Millikan; Trevor Gardner, who was the production genius at CIT; H. S. Seifert; Louis G. Dunn; Charles F. Bartley; William H. Pickering; Bruce H. Sage; Henry L. Thackwell, Jr.; Simon Ramo; George P. Sutton; and many others. In the Bureau of Aeronautics the working pioneers included Calvin M. Bolster; John S. Warfel; James S. Russell; Benjamin H. Coffman, Jr.; and, of course, the Annapolis group which is discussed elsewhere herein. In the Air Force both at Headquarters and at Wright Field, the pioneering group included General Benjamin Chidlaw; General F. O. Carroll; General James F. Phillips; Colonel Paul Dane; Weldon Worth; and, again, scores of others. And not to classify but simply to mention a few others, one cannot forget the contributions in those days of Edward H. Heinemann; R. E. Marquardt; Samuel K. Hoffman; Brooks T. Morris; M. J. Zucrow; Chandler C. Ross; H. N. Toftoy; C. C. Furnas; Lawrence D. Bell; Elmer Wheaton; Roy Healy; Paul F. Winternitz; Charles W. Chillson; William C. House; James A. Van Allen; William Avery; William L. Gore. It is hoped that the succeeding narration will accommodate to a reasonable degree the names of those who made great contributions during the succeeding two decades, although some of the valuable efforts of indefatigable workers, such as Mrs. Billie Slade and James J. Harford of the American Rocket Society, can only be implied.

FIG. 35　FLYING BOAT TAKES TO THE AIR WITH HELP OF JETS

A U. S. Navy *PB2Y-3* is shown making a jet-assisted take-off (JATO) from San Diego Bay in 1944.

FIG. 36　AEROJET LIQUID PROPELLANT ROCKET ENGINE

Flight testing on an *A-20* by Colonel Paul Dane of the Aerojet AL-1000 liquid propellant unit. Inspecting the installation is A. G. Haley, then president of Aerojet, and David Young, now chief coordinator of the Advanced Research Projects Agency (ARPA).

FIG. 37   AIRCRAFT FLARE AND AIRCRAFT ROCKETS

Roy Healy is pictured with a "bazooka," a 3.5-in. aircraft flare rocket, and a 4.5-in. aircraft rocket.   (M. W. Kellogg)

FIG. 38   COL. LESLIE SKINNER INVENTS THE "BAZOOKA" IN 1943

Col. Skinner is shown firing the first production model at the Aberdeen Proving Grounds.   (Col. Leslie Skinner)

FIG. 39 4.5-INCH "CALLIOPE" MULTIPLE ROCKET LAUNCHER

It is shown mounted on the *M4A3* medium tank for experimental use by the Marine Corps during World War II. While its "saturation" firepower was greater, it was not as hard hitting as the larger 7.2-inch rocket launcher. (USMC)

FIG. 40   NORTHROP AIRCRAFT'S "FLYING WING" *JB-10* MISSILE

Jet-powered, the *JB-10* missile could carry two tons of high explosive. Preset guidance control was used, but the project remained experimental. Here it is shown at take-off. (USAF)

FIG. 41   *VB-3 (RAZON)* GUIDED MISSILE

The *VB-3 (Razon)* guided missile, designed with a radio set constructed in its tail section, could be pin-pointed on such targets as bridges, railroads, etc. Dropped from a bomber, the missile was guided by the bombardier with the aid of a colored flare from the tail section. (USAF)

FIG. 42   THE BELL AIRCRAFT CORPORATION'S *TARZON* GUIDED
BOMB

The 12,000-pound *Tarzon* radio-guided bomb was produced for the United
States Air Force.   The bomb was launched by heavy bombers of the *B-29, B-50*
and *B-36* variety.   *Tarzon* was equipped with controls similar to an airplane's
rudder, elevators, and ailerons.   Its descent from the launching plane was remotely controlled (via radio) by the bombardier, even to the extent of altering
the angle of approach to a target.   (USAF)

FIG. 43   4.5-INCH MULTIPLE ROCKET LAUNCHER, *T45*

The *T45* multiple rocket launcher could be mounted on trucks or jeeps. It was used to support infantry operations in World War II with saturation bombardment. (U. S. Army)

FIG. 44   "BAZOOKA" ANTI-TANK MISSILE LAUNCHING

An early U. S. war rocket was the 3.5-inch "bazooka" shown here at a night firing. (U. S. Army)

FIG. 45 AIR FORCE *VB-10 ROC* RADIO-GUIDED MISSILE

Development by the Douglas Aircraft Corporation, the *VB-10 ROC* missile can be guided to its target through a television eye in its nose, while controlled from a mother plane or a ground station. (USAF)

FIG. 46 ROCKET BARRAGE

Illustrating the barrage effect of rockets, this unique night sky pattern was made at the Ordnance Department's Aberdeen Proving Grounds, Maryland. Nine 4.5-inch rockets, each packing the wallop of a large artillery shell, were fired at half-second intervals from a light-weight launcher hidden by the glare of firing. A similar launcher, nicknamed the "Xylophone," is shown in the foreground. (U. S. Army)

FIG. 47   LANDING SHIP EQUIPPED WITH ROCKET LAUNCHERS
          FOR INVASION

British Combined Operations Headquarters test a rocket-equipped LST at
Portsmouth Harbor, England.   British officers are shown inspecting the rocket
launchers from the bridge of the LST.   (U. S. Army)

FIG. 48   ROCKET BARRAGE LAUNCHED FROM LST

Rockets are shown in mid-air, after being launched from the LST.   (U. S.
Army)

FIG. 49 *TINY TIM* MISSILE FIRED AT NAVAL PROVING GROUND

The *Tiny Tim* missile blasts off from a ground launching rig at the Naval Proving Ground, Dahlgren, Virginia, in 1946. Experiments of this type may have introduced the "Honest John" philosophy in rockets. (U. S. Navy)

FIG. 50   *P-47* FIGHTER PLANE FIRES *5-INCH HVAR* ROCKETS

A *P-47* dives at a ground target releasing *5-inch HVAR* rockets during World War II.   (M. W. Kellogg)

FIG. 51   ROBERT C. TRUAX AND HIS MEN AT THE ENGINEERING
EXPERIMENT STATION, ANNAPOLIS, MARYLAND, IN THE
SUMMER OF 1945, WERE ENGAGED IN THE DEVELOPMENT
OF LIQUID PROPELLANT ROCKETS, PULSEJETS AND UNDER-
WATER PROPULSION DEVICES

Front Row (*seated*): Lieut. (jg) Richard Simmers, Lieut. (jg) Robertson Young-
quist, Lieut. James R. Patton, Jr., Lieut. Howard Hart, Lieut. Commander Robert
C. Truax, Lieut. Jack Speer, Lieut. Greenberg, (Unidentified), Lieut. (jg) Ralph
F. Fearn. *Second Row* (*standing*): Lieut. (jg) Richard Frazee, W. O. Gilpin,
Ensign Joseph L. Gray, Ensign William L. Green, Ensign Ira Hull, C.P.O. Ken-
neth Omang, Ensign Leonard Edelman, Ensign William C. Cooley, Ensign N.
MacRae Nyborg, Ensign John E. Gray.

FIG. 52 *V-2* MISSILE ASSEMBLY LINE

Three *V-2* missiles are shown in the final assembly stage at White Sands Proving Grounds. (C. F. Green, *Rocket Exploration of the Upper Atmosphere*)

FIG. 53 *V-2* MISSILE UNDER TEST

A *V-2* missile is shown under test in the assembly building at the White Sands Proving Grounds. (C. F. Green, *Rocket Exploration of the Upper Atmosphere*)

AMPHIBIOUS WARFARE

Beach-head operations, perhaps the most difficult of all types of mass combat, were a natural for rocket barrages which could be launched from nearly every type of air- or water-borne vehicle. In 1943, CIT developed a 120-pound launcher for the 2½-ton amphibious "duck," a 10-round launcher for jeeps, and an 88-round launcher for the LCM. Most important was the 12-round, lightweight launcher which was gravity-fed and side-loaded, that could be mounted on practically any structure. About 20,000 launchers had been made by August 1944. Barrage rockets were first used in the Pacific in New Guinea and were launched from barges, "ducks," and as a field expediency from trailers taken into mountain areas. About 60 PT boats were also equipped with rocket launchers for harassing fire along the shore-line.

The LCI rocket ships wreaked such havoc at Iwo Jima that the Japanese, expecting an imminent landing at Okinawa, moved their first line of defense out of the range of these ships. Nonetheless, four Navy rocket ships (LSMRs) managed to find targets for 30,000 spinner- and fin-stabilized rockets during the first twelve weeks of the Okinawa operation. These new rocket ships, unlike their predecessors, were custom-built for the operation, including ten remotely controlled magazine-launchers firing 300 rockets per minute per ship.

In developing the spinner-stabilized rocket, CIT had begun by producing an 1100-yard barrage rocket adapted from the 5-inch aircraft rocket, and then proceeded to test a whole series of spinners, with ranges up to 11½ miles.

Spinner rockets had long been expected to provide greater accuracy and ease in handling. This had been obvious even in 1865 when the Hale spinner rocket was created. The beauty of the spin rocket was that it had the same stability in flight as the artillery shell fired through a rifled barrel. The spinner can be made to spin by using two or more canted nozzles, by firing it from a rifled launcher, or by mounting small auxiliary spin rockets tangential to the circumference of the rocket body, which are fired at launching.

The development of its modern counterpart by CIT and Army Ordnance began in 1943. CIT's first spinner was of 3.5-inch caliber and was designed to replace the Marine pack-howitzer; however, it was discarded in favor of a 5-inch spinner, adapted from the 5-inch aircraft rocket. This resulted in a barrage rocket with an 1100-yard range. Provision was made for launching 16 rockets, 8 rockets from each of 2 launchers, in PT-boat combat against armored barges. CIT then proceeded to test spinners with ranges up to 11½ miles.

For the Navy, CIT developed a 5000-yard, 5-inch rocket late in 1943. The Navy felt that the successful performance of this rocket warranted the construction of a special ship to launch it. Specifications drawn up a year later resulted in the super LSMR's that bombarded Okinawa.

A whole new family of spinning rockets grew out of the LSM specifications. Of identical size and performance (except for range), they all used the same launcher to achieve ranges of 1250, 2500 and 5000 yards. Over 70,000 of the 5000-yard rockets were produced by CIT for the Navy. After initial saturation-fire, rocket ships harassed shorelines or supported land artillery.

BAZOOKAS

Rifle grenades, developed by the Army in 1941, produced too much recoil. A small rocket motor was substituted. When it was discovered that the weapon could not be fired from a rifle, a 54-inch-long launching tube was developed. This was the world famous "bazooka."

Initial models, rushed through production to support North African landings, proved dangerous in cold weather. Low temperatures resulted in longer burning times and caused a serious backflash in the operator's face. A metal gauze screen was used as a temporary safety measure until a faster-burning charge developed at NDRC's Division 8 eventually eliminated the problem. This "hand cannon" with a 200-yard range gave the infantryman a new and deadly weapon for use against tanks, bunkers, concrete pillboxes, and armor-plate.

Later developments in the "bazooka" included easily carried hinged launchers, better sights, trigger magnetos to replace batteries, and eventually a 700-yard-range "super-bazooka."

MULTIPLE LAUNCHERS

During the course of the war small assault rockets went everywhere. Army Ordnance developed a variety of multiple launchers capable of discharging 8-to-60 of the 4.5-inch folding-fin aircraft rockets from tanks, trucks, jeeps, or "ducks." Although these rockets lacked velocity, their dispersion when fired in large numbers made them very effective at ranges up to 4000 yards.

Xylophone launchers, firing eight rockets, were mounted singly or in pairs on Army trucks, while 60-rocket *Calliope* launchers permitted Sherman tanks to lay down their own preliminary artillery barrage. The *Honeycomb,* a 24-tube launcher on a two-wheeled carriage, eventually replaced the *Xylophone,* while the 36-tube *Hornet's Nest* took the place of the *Calliope.* For use in inaccessible areas a 60-pound tripod launcher with a 4-foot expendable plastic tube was developed. The *Grand Slam* truck-mounted launcher was used to fire a barrage of 24 smokescreen rockets. These were modified versions of the 3000-yard range, 7.2-inch chemical rocket.

JET-ASSISTED TAKE-OFF

The Air Force started work on jet-assisted take-off (JATO) units in 1939 through the Guggenheim Aeronautical Laboratory of the California Institute of Technology (GALCIT). In July 1940, Theodore von Karman and Frank J. Malina established the now famous Jet Propulsion Laboratory as a part of GALCIT, to develop JATO for heavy bombers. The program was carried out along two lines: (1) the development of long-burning, large thrust, solid propellant JATO, and (2) the development of large liquid rocket engines based on any oxidizer except liquid oxygen (which the Air Corps regarded as impractical for field use).

Diligence and imagination were rewarded with early success. In August 1941, the first solid propellant JATO, whose propellant was developed by J. W. Parsons, was successfully flight tested on a small liaison type airplane. In April 1942, liquid propellant JATO utilizing nitric acid and aniline, developed by M. Summerfield, was successfully tested in an exhaustive series of flights on an A-20 attack bomber. These flights were the first jet-assisted take-offs carried out in the United States. Many other persons were involved in these efforts and their contributions have been noted in other chapters of this book.

The Air Force, formerly the Army Air Corps, was interested in further development of JATO for a bomber program, and ordered additional liquid propellant JATO from the Aerojet Corporation. This was the first production order for JATO in the United States. The Navy was also interested in JATO for flying boat and carrier aircraft programs, and heavily supported initial procurement of both liquid and solid types.

The Navy, meanwhile, had begun work of its own under R. C. Truax on JATO at Annapolis in 1941. About the same time, Reaction Motors, founded by the leading experimenters in the American Rocket Society of the 1930's, was incorporated to carry out development in the JATO field. The Navy asked Reaction Motors to undertake the production of a liquid oxygen type JATO for use on flying boats. After much testing, the Navy selected the 12-second, 1,000-pound thrust Aerojet solid fuel unit as suitable for most operational needs, and it was produced on a large scale. In 1944, Section H of the Allegany Ballistics Laboratory perfected a unit with little smoke, better low-temperature characteristics and a shorter firing time, but this was never used.

An engine similar to the JATO unit, the booster, made its appearance through Research Division 8 of NDRC and the Monsanto Chemical Company. Huge propellant grains weighing 120 pounds produced a fierce thrust for 2 seconds, long enough to launch the *Loon,* the U. S. copy of the German *V-1* "Buzz Bomb."

OTHER ROCKET DEVELOPMENTS

The Navy Bureaus of Ships and Ordnance developed a "window" rocket. This 3.5-inch aircraft rocket was fired from surface vessels, and at peak trajectory discharged metallized strips of many lengths. These were designed to jam enemy radar. During the Normandy invasion, PT boats launched these rockets when the massed Allied landing fleet was on the verge of discovery by German radar. Enemy searchlights and gunfire promptly went aloft to fire uselessly into what their radar reported as an air raid.

On order from the Bureau of Ordnance, CIT modified the 4.5-inch barrage rocket to a smoke rocket, tested it, and delivered the first one in two weeks. Maximum range was 1100 yards. A tetryl "burster," to improve smoke dispersion, was perfected, as well as a smoke head for the 3.5-inch HVAR. Beginning in March 1945, the amphibious forces received them at the rate of 10,000 a month.

Army Engineers and Ordnance, with Section H (Allegany), developed an improved version of the German *Donnerkeil* (thunder-wedge) which drove a 1-inch rod, 6 feet long, far enough into the ground so that primacord could be inserted in the hole and detonated, making a hole large enough to hold a telephone pole—a marked improvement over shoveling.

The *Snake,* developed at Allegany Ballistic Laboratory, pulled a 100-foot ski train laden with TNT to detonate enemy mine fields. A "Detonating Cable Kit" with a 2-nozzle, U-shaped motor, carried primacord over mine fields, this was a custom-made version of an earlier field expediency which accomplished the same purpose with dummy-headed "bazooka" rockets.

Not ordinarily thought of as rocket weapons were recoilless rifles. Three types were used briefly during the closing months of the war. Both 57-mm and a 75-mm type were developed by Army Ordnance. A 4.2-inch mortar was produced jointly by Section H (Allegany) and the Chemical Warfare Service. All three were mounted on machine-gun tripods.

PHASE-OUT

By the time V-J Day arrived, the Army was receiving $12,500,000 worth of rockets a month, and the Navy relied upon over a thousand plants to produce its rocket ordnance. After the war, OSRD transferred many of the experimental facilities to permanent Army and Navy agencies. The Naval Ordnance Testing Station (NOTS) at Inyokern, organized in 1943 to test all kinds of Navy ordnance, gradually began to specialize in rockets, as CIT equipment and operations were transferred to Inyokern. This transfer was completed in December 1945. Allegany Ballistics Laboratory was absorbed by the Navy, but Hercules Powder continued to work on existing contracts.

BRITISH ROCKETRY DURING WORLD WAR II

The achievements made by the Allies in liquid propellant systems were relatively insignificant when compared to German development. It was in the solid propellant field that the Allies excelled, and it was Britain who was the first of the Allies to appreciate the potentials of the rocket.

Spurred by intelligence reports of German military rocket activity, top British officials late in 1935 ordered the Research Department of Woolwich Arsenal to initiate a rocket program. In 1936 systematic rocket research was begun in four principal types of equipment: antiaircraft, heavy artillery supplement, shipboard antiaircraft and aircraft rockets. The most vigorous supporter of British rocket and missile development was Sir Alwyn D. Crow, who was placed in charge of the Technical Services of the British Ministry of Supply.

One of the first results of the rocket research program was a two-inch antiaircraft rocket which was test-fired by the thousands during 1937 and 1938. Rocket priorities were lowered when World War II began, because of more urgent needs elsewhere, but, before long, rockets were again being mass-produced in Britain.

Investigation of cordite smokeless powders eventually led to a new type of unrestricted burning motor yielding a high terminal velocity for short burning times. The high combustion pressures involved required thick walls, and the high (2500° F) combustion temperatures taxed the then-current knowledge of metallurgy. A 2-inch rocket was made workable after many difficult pressure and temperature problems had been solved, principally by loose-loading the web and by the use of silica-gel nozzle liners. Later 3-inch rockets were turned over to the Americans for further development. A 5-inch rocket appeared and became a standard piece of armament. Impact fuses were used at first but were soon replaced by time fuses so that rockets which missed their aerial targets would not explode upon friendly territory below.

Grindell-Matthews snare rockets were used for the defense of small ships against low-flying planes. Using a conventional black-powder charge of about 4 pounds in weight and a 17-pound thrust for 2.8 seconds, they attained altitudes of about 500 feet.

Most of this early antiaircraft work was done under the code name of U.P. (unrotating projectile) Development. The first of these, 3 inches in diameter and fired from "Z-Gun" launchers developed under Sir Alwyn Crow, were used effectively during the Battle of Britain and well into 1942.

For regular shipboard antiaircraft defense, the *Briefcase Column* launcher delivered as many as 20 rockets in salvo. Guided by an operator seated inside the column, the device had the rapid elevation and traverse qualities of small-caliber antiaircraft cannons.

British aircraft rockets, launched from Beaufighters, Hurricanes, Typhoons and other airplanes, measured 4 feet in length and 3 inches in diameter. They were stabilized by 4 large fins and ignited by special platinum-wire fuses. Some Beaufighter configurations used 8 larger rockets, 5 feet long and 5 inches in diameter, against shipping, submarines and selected ground installations.

British work in the JATO field was confined to small units used on shipboard fighter planes like the *Seafire.* Mounted in the wing-fairings, pointing 10–12 degrees downward and 30 degrees outward, they permitted take-off in as little as 190 feet.

British barrage rockets for land warfare were fired from *Land Mattress* launchers, a kind of rectangular German *Nebelwerfer,* but containing more rockets per loading. Three-inch rockets firing through rifled barrels were spin-stabilized with a resulting 50-percent reduction in dispersion. A 32-barreled launcher announced near the war's end was reported to have fired rockets weighing 100 pounds with a target destruction capability comparable to that of 5.5-inch guns. An antitank projector named PIAT and weighing 33 pounds was shoulder-operated.

For barrage work, England produced several effective rocket ships by converting LCTs, which were twice as large as American LCIs and fired more and bigger rockets.

RUSSIAN ROCKETRY DURING WORLD WAR II

The Russians, traditional proponents of massed artillery, have long been interested in rockets for military purposes. They saw in the barrage rocket a means of simultaneously increasing mobility and fire volume. They began a serious, organized military rocket research program during the middle thirties. This led in World War II to the introduction of two basic types of launchers for mounting on the ground, trucks or tanks. The best known was the *Stalin Organ,* which fired from 16 to 60 *Katyusha* rockets, weighing 17 to 31 pounds each with ranges from 3 to 6 miles. They went into action shortly after the German *Nebelwerfers* in 1941.

The *Katyusha* was invented by military engineer Andrei Kostikov, with the assistance of General of the Artillery V. Aborenko; I. Gvai, engineer; and V. Golkovski, a designer. Kostikov received a 100,000-ruble Stalin Prize for his rocket, which was used in the defense of Stalingrad and later at Kharkov. This 6-foot, fin-stabilized projectile employed a relatively slow-burning, double-base cordite powder, and was fired in clusters. Calibers of 3.25 inches were first used, but later 5.25-inch and even 11.8-inch rockets appeared. The last size approximated that of the American *Tiny Tim*.

A rocket-propelled penetration bomb appeared in 1943, used by sturdy *Stormovik* fighters. Using a 2.2-pound solid propellant charge, this 13.4-pound bomb measured nearly 2 feet in length by 3.25 inches in diameter. Its percussion fuse was armed with an airstream propeller and it achieved a velocity of 1150 miles per hour en route to the target. Larger bombs of roughly similar design, weighing 220 pounds, were used as early as 1941, and earned the title *Black Death* with Nazi tank crews.

OTHER EUROPEAN ROCKETRY

Outside of the United States, Great Britain and Russia, wartime Allied rocket research was not extensive. In France, R. Esnault-Pelterie worked with the Armament Fabrication Technical Services at St. Cloud, near Paris. Using a light alloy motor, he began a long series of experiments in 1934 on gasoline-ether and liquid-oxygen propellant combinations. Some of these rockets were fired at the French Army Proving Ground.

Rougeron investigated rocket-propelled bombs, but work came to an abrupt halt when the Germans invaded France. Reportedly, Major J. J. Barre conducted secret static tests on an *EA-41* rocket during 1941, and I. M. Tercet worked secretly on small powder rockets.

Thus, even though the Allies expended a relatively massive effort on rockets during World War II, at no time was any serious work conducted on the big strategic ballistic rocket. Rockets were always thought of as supplements to field artillery, to aerial bombs or to the cannon and machine guns of aircraft by the military services. No one at any point, except the Germans, thought it practicable to try to develop a rocket or missile that would substitute for a big bomber or a naval task force. Neither did anybody (outside of the Germans) foresee that the big rocket would one day change the whole concept of warfare. The one exception to this conclusion may well be the theoretical work of Fritz Zwicky at Aerojet, 1942–1945, when, during his morphological study of all rocket uses, he included systems which later proved to parallel the *V-1, V-2, ICBM,* and indeed systems-concepts still in the "whispered" stages.

6

The War's Heritage

Fortunately, Allied investigation of the German missile program was pressed vigorously at the end of World War II. Interrogation teams questioned German scientists on their wartime research and persuaded many to join research groups abroad. The Russian Army, occupying Peenemünde, discovered that the commanding general, Dr. Walter Dornberger, had evacuated his staff, including Von Braun, to the Oberammergau area where they were captured by United States forces within a few weeks, in May of 1945. Underground *V-2* production facilities occupied by U. S. forces during this period were subsequently turned over to Soviet troops, after roughly 100 *V-2* missiles had been removed for study.

Much of the early postwar *V-2* firing research program was conducted by such agencies as the Naval Research Laboratory, Naval Ordnance Laboratory, Air Research and Development Command, and the U. S. Army Signal Corps, working in cooperation with the General Electric Company. In November of 1944 U. S. Army Ordnance had awarded G.E. a broad research contract under the code name *Hermes* for the investigation of many areas of missile research, development and manufacture. One of the major phases of research involved the development of large, surface-launched tactical missiles.

Missile tracking for these tests was supervised by the Ballistics Research Laboratory of the Army's Aberdeen Proving Ground, the Signal Corps, and the New Mexico College of Agriculture and Mechanical Arts. Radio-sonic equipment developed by the Naval Research Laboratory in 1946 was used to collect data. Data not amenable to telemetering were recorded on recoverable equipment which was exploded from the missile for parachute descent to earth.

These were times of limited budgets and minimal (often primitive) facilities. Nevertheless a few hardy pioneers had set out to learn what they could about the German *V-2* and to proceed from there. On December 17, 1946, at White Sands, New Mexico, a team of rocketeers including Milton Rosen, Ralph Havens, Herbert Karsch, Ernst Krause, William Foley, Carl

Seddon, Edward Munnell, J. Preston Layton, C. H. Smith, H. C. Hanks, and others babied a *V-2* to the single-stage record altitude of 114 miles—a record not exceeded for five years. It was a gratifying moment. Ten months later, a *V-2* was successfully launched (though it failed shortly after take-off) from the deck of the United States Navy aircraft carrier, *Midway*. February 24, 1949, another *V-2* (*Bumper*), acting as a first stage for a *WAC-Corporal*, enabled the combination to make the first successful flight into airless space, setting a new world altitude record for rockets of 242 miles.

For the so-called successful missiles (i.e., those that reached 50 miles or higher), the average peak was 61 miles, the highest 132.5 miles. It is of interest to note that greater than designed payloads (2200 pounds) were carried on 71 percent of the *V-2* missiles, the increased load averaging 47 percent in excess of rated capacity by 1949. Because of its tremendous carrying capacity, the *V-2* became known as the "workhorse" missile.

But for most purposes the *V-2* was too big, and the *WAC-Corporal* was much too small. As a result, Johns Hopkins University's Applied Physics Laboratory, working with the Aerojet-General Corporation, developed the *Aerobee*. Most *Aerobee* manufacturing was by Douglas Aircraft. A variation of the *Aerobee* known as *Aerobee-Hi* was also developed. To date nearly 200 of the *Aerobee* series have been fired. Another research rocket of this period was the *Deacon*. To learn how these came into being and how the postwar effort of the United States got its start, we must return once again to the 1930's.

Daniel Guggenheim, the Guggenheim Fund, and later the Guggenheim Foundation maintained an interest in the field of rocketry going back to the original Guggenheim grant made to Goddard in 1930. As a result of the Guggenheim Foundation's interest in rocket research, aeronautical schools were established at New York University, Stanford University, the Massachusetts Institute of Technology, the Georgia School of Technology, the University of Michigan, the University of Washington and the California Institute of Technology.

Establishment of the Guggenheim Aeronautical Laboratory of the California Institute of Technology (GALCIT) was a factor which influenced postwar missile activity in the U. S. almost as much as the *V-2* experiments. Rocket research at CalTech had started in 1936 and was initiated by F. J. Malina, J. W. Parsons and E. S. Forman. Early participants in the work included A. M. O. Smith, H. S. Tsien and Weld Arnold. Arnold gave $1000 to support the work of the group in 1937. The organization of a rocket research project received the attention and accord of the renowned aerodynamicist, Theodore von Karman, head of the Guggenheim Aeronautical Laboratory at the Institute.

The early research projects of GALCIT included thermodynamic problems, the reaction principle, flight performance analyses, as well as tests of fuels, thrust measurements and nozzle shapes. Von Karman, C. B. Millikan and E. E. Sechler were advisors in this early work.

Apparently the first private enterprise to realize the need for some kind of assisted take-off unit to get airplanes off the ground more rapidly or from restricted runways was the Consolidated Aircraft Company. Its president, Reuben Fleet, requested the GALCIT scientists to submit a report outlining the advantages of jet-assisted take-off. In 1938 the report, prepared by Malina, recommended the use of the rocket motors as an auxiliary powerplant.

Late in 1938 General H. H. Arnold of the Army Air Corps requested the Committee for Air Corps Research of the National Academy of Sciences to sponsor general rocket research, and JATO work in particular. In July 1939, following consideration of a report prepared by Malina for the Committee, the National Academy of Science sponsored the formation of the Army Air Corps Jet Propulsion Research Project by awarding a $10,000.00 contract to GALCIT. Von Karman was appointed director of the project. The Army took over sponsorship of the research program at CalTech in 1940 under the initiative of Major B. Chidlaw, who later became Commanding General of the Air Materiel Command and later Commanding General of the Air Defense Command.

In 1941 and 1942 GALCIT underwent a rapid expansion. The Army Service Forces and Ordnance Department, collaborating with the Air Materiel Command, initiated a rocket research program at CalTech in 1944. The rocket research group was reorganized as the Jet Propulsion Laboratory and was governed by the Executive Board of the California Institute of Technology. In December, C. B. Millikan became acting Chairman of the Board, Malina acting director and L. G. Dunn assistant director of the Laboratory in the absence of Von Karman, who was on leave to assume the post of Expert Consultant to the Commanding General of the Army Air Force. Further growth of the rocket research program took place under the Army, and liaison was expanded to include the Signal Corps, the Army Ground Forces, and the Naval Bureau of Ordnance (BuOrd).

By 1946 the Jet Propulsion Laboratory was equipped with a 40-acre tract on the outskirts of Pasadena, California. Included in the installation were about 80 structures—test beds for liquid rocket and ramjet work, laboratories for high-temperature-resistant material research, solid-propellant development facilities, a towing channel for underwater missile research, and sheet-metal, welding, and machine shops. The staff had reached 385 personnel and the value of the installation was estimated at three million dollars. All of the CalTech facilities, the Guggenheim wind tunnels, the

Chemical Engineering Department, Muroc Air Force Base and, by subcontract, many industries in the United States were involved in the gigantic program.

LIQUID PROPELLANT ROCKETS

Liquid propellant rocket development began at CalTech in 1936. In 1940 the Army Air Force ordered a 1000-pound thrust liquid JATO that would run for one minute. The first three test models exploded, but the fourth, tested on the Fourth of July, was a success.

Meanwhile, a group at the Naval Experiment Station, Annapolis, Maryland, had experienced the same difficulty with gasoline-acid combustion that caused CalTech's JATO to explode. Aniline was proposed as a gasoline additive to overcome the trouble. Then, at the suggestion of Malina, aniline was used as the motor fuel. Acid-aniline motors were developed at CalTech and subjected to long testing in an *A-20A* airplane through the winter of 1941–1942. These tests, conducted at the A.A.F. Muroc Bombing and Gunnery Range, led to the acceptance of the design by the Army Air Forces, and the Aerojet Corporation was assigned the task of designing and manufacturing the production unit.

JATO DEVELOPMENTS

The early work of Goddard and the GALCIT group, and an exhaustive survey of problems associated with the fundamental properties of propellants, had paved the way for work on increasing the burning time of solid propellants. Firing period durations of between 10 and 30 seconds were desired.

One plan specified the firing of motors in series, but since the difficulty of timing the ignitions to coincide exactly with the burnout of the previous units was a serious one, the plan was abandoned. Another approach was taken—the same general magnitude of propellant grain was loaded into one shell and restricted to burn only on the end, thus maintaining a prolonged thrust.

An early motor was constructed from a steel cylinder 2 feet long, 5 inches in diameter, and with walls 1-inch thick. A solid charge was moulded under very high pressure by a hydraulic press to prevent cracking. This charge was inserted into the cylinder and a seal was placed between the charge and the cylinder wall to restrict burning to the end nearest the nozzle. The nozzle was attached by bolts to the cylinder at a flange connection and ignition was accomplished with an electric squib.

In 1941 a small unit was placed in limited production. The dependability of the motor and the charge had been reasonably established; testing remained. The motor produced 28 pounds of thrust for 12 seconds with a 2-pound charge of GALCIT-27. This propellant consisted of an amide powder pressed in 22 separate increments into the shell under 18 tons of pressure.

An *Ercoupe* (light plane), fitted with two 3-unit assemblies under each wing, was test-flown during August by Captain H. A. Boushey. Results showed that flying distances and times were cut approximately in half. One hundred and fifty-two firings were made without a failure, and the pilot reported that the JATO made the control of the plane generally much easier.

GALCIT-27 propellant was improved in its ability to be stored. The Navy then granted a contract in 1942 for the development of a unit to deliver 200 pounds of thrust for 8 seconds. At this time a new propellant, GALCIT-46, made its appearance. Its storage life was better than GALCIT-27, but it required too narrow a range of storage temperatures to be reliable for use in a wide range of climates. Ballistite (nitrocellulose and nitroglycerin) was considered, but, like GALCIT-46, it was known to be subject to serious variations in burning time caused by variations in the storage temperature.

A new propellant, solving most of the shortcomings of previous types, appeared in the same year. Designated GALCIT-53, it contained an asphaltic fuel which was oxidized by white potassium perchlorate powder. It had both chemical and physical stability. Manufacture was simple and the ingredients were plentiful. It could be stored, and the ambient temperature operability range had been widened in comparison with previous propellants. A GALCIT-53-burning motor, measuring 13 inches long and 5½ inches in diameter, was developed for the Navy Bureau of Aeronautics. In 1943 the Navy granted a contract to the Aerojet Engineering Corporation of Pasadena, California for a number of the 200-pound thrust motors based on GALCIT-53. These were successfully tested and a large order was placed for not only the 200-pound unit, but also for larger units, scaled up to 500 and 1000 pounds. The Aerojet Corporation and GALCIT collaborated on this project. Further improvements were made and newer propellant versions appeared, notably the GALCIT-61C, which was widely used by the Navy during the latter part of World War II.

THE ORDCIT PROJECT

In 1944 the Army Service Forces, in response to a memorandum sent to the Ordnance Department by Von Karman, Tsien and Malina, awarded the first contract in the United States for research on long-range jet-propelled missiles. Allied Intelligence having reported that the Germans were in the advanced stages of a similar program, Major General G. M. Barnes pressed the Jet Propulsion Laboratory to begin studying long-range jet-propelled missiles at once.

The first step was the *Private "A."* Stabilized by fixed fins, and booster-launched from a truss-type rectangular steel boom 36 feet long, it ascended four guide-rails. With its flight stability already achieved, it dropped the booster before leaving the boom. Testing was carried out at Leach Spring, Camp Irwin, Barstow, California, and 24 shots were made during the first half of December which averaged 18,000 yards each.

While *Private "A"* tests continued, a *Private "F"* was developed, equipped with stubby wings of 5-foot span and two stabilizers near the nose having a total span of less than 3 feet. The launcher was changed to accommodate the wings, and tests took place at Hueco Range, Fort Bliss, Texas, during the first half of April 1945. Seventeen were fired and were tracked by radar and cameras. Despite successful firings, one point was clear—missiles with wings needed flight control equipment.

In 1944 the Ordnance Department, upon a proposal by Malina, authorized the ORDCIT project to study the matter of producing a sounding rocket capable of carrying a 25-pound payload to 100,000 feet or more. To save complex control development, tower-launching was selected, and a one-fifth-scale model (the *Baby WAC*) was built and then tested in July 1945, at the Goldstone Range in California. Booster designs and the feasibility of 3-fin control were found to be successful. The full-scale rocket, of which this was the prototype, was the now famous 16-foot long, 665-pound *WAC-Corporal*. (The *WAC-Corporal* served also as a scaled down model of the *Corporal* missile whose design had been initiated earlier in 1944 under the ORDCIT project.) With a modified *Tiny Tim* serving as booster, firing tests took place from September 26 to October 25, 1945, at the White Sands Proving Grounds in New Mexico, six months before the first U. S.-launched *V-2* probed the upper reaches of the atmosphere.

THE ANNAPOLIS GROUP

Although rocket ordnance using solid propellant systems was more fully investigated during the war, a considerable amount of progress was attained in the field of liquid propellant devices. At the United States Naval Engineering Experiment Station (USNEES) in Annapolis, project TEDEES 3401 was initiated in July 1941 by Rear Admiral C. M. Bolster of the Bureau of Aeronautics. Under the direction of Lt. Commander R. C. Truax, Ensigns R. C. Stiff, J. F. Patton, W. Schubert and R. Youngquist developed a liquid propellant rocket-assist take-off unit for large flying boats, especially the *PBY-2*. By 1942 tests were made on 1500-pound thrust chambers, the largest liquid propellant thrust chambers in the United States at the time.

Early tests resulted in failure as a result of the same gasoline-acid dilemma experienced by GALCIT. Aniline, which is hypergolic with nitric acid (i.e., spontaneously ignites upon contact), was again substituted for gasoline and a second motor, the OU-1, attached to the wing struts of a *PBY-2,* worked successfully, decreasing the normally required take-off run by 60 percent. At that point the job of completing the development of the motors and preparing them for production was turned over to private industry.

The USNEES group also tested a nondroppable liquid-oxygen JATO unit designed for the *PBY-2* by Dr. Goddard. Results were unsuccessful. A liquid oxygen-gasoline, 60-second motor, made by Reaction Motors, was successfully tested on a Martin *PBM.* Chief test pilot Marine Captain W. L. Gore also tested the Aerojet 38LDW1500 liquid engine. Results were favorable, and 100 units were built. These were mainly used by the Coast Guard. Solid propellant JATOs from the Aerojet Corporation and GALCIT were also tested. Rocketry in America owes an immense debt to the skill and intrepidity of test pilot "Bill" Gore.

The Naval Aircraft Factory required a motor for a projected radio-controlled antiaircraft missile for bomber defense. Under the direction of Lt. William Schubert, a 350-pound thrust, 500-mile-per-hour, liquid propellant unit, the *Gorgon* missile, was made available within a month and a half. Toward the end of 1945, the Annapolis group terminated its work and moved to the newly formed Naval Air Missile Test Center at Point Mugu, California.

HIGH ALTITUDE ROCKETS

Following a meeting of experts in January 1946 at the Naval Research Laboratory, the Upper Atmosphere Research Panel was established. In 1948 this panel became known as the Upper Atmosphere Rocket Research Panel.* This body had a vital influence on the development of big missiles for the exploration of airless space. Before the war ended, orders had been placed for the General Electric *Hermes* and the highly successful Martin *Viking* research rockets. It was a *Viking* that on the morning of August 7, 1951 topped the *V-2* missile single-stage altitude record by peaking at 135 miles.

Like the *Viking* missile, the General Electric series of *Hermes* missiles provided the United States with much of the knowhow it needed in order to go on to larger and better rockets. *Hermes A-1,* originally considered a surface-to-air vehicle, but later modified to a surface-to-surface short-range

---

* Members included L. A. Delsasso (Aberdeen Proving Ground), W. G. Dow (University of Michigan), M. Ference, Jr. (Evans Signal Laboratory), C. F. Green (General Electric Company), G. K. Megerian (General Electric Company), H. E. Newell, Jr. (Naval Research Laboratory), M. D. O'Day (Air Force Cambridge Research Center), W. H. Pickering (California Institute of Technology), J. A. Van Allen (State University of Iowa) and F. L. Whipple (Harvard College Observatory).

bombardment missile, was similar in design to the German *Wasserfall*. It weighed about 8000 pounds, was 25½ feet long, and built up about 10,000 pounds of thrust. From this came the *Hermes A-2* (25,000 pounds) and the *A-3* (12,000 pounds), all with relatively short range.

Hermes C-1 was to be a surface-launched, 3-stage test vehicle, with a range potential of several thousand miles. The final stage was to be designed for hypersonic gliding. *C-1* was turned over to Redstone Arsenal in Alabama where Army Ordnance experts continued development.

Other research rockets of that era include the *Private A* and *Private F*, *Baby-WAC*, *WAC-Corporal*, *Aerobee* and *Aerobee-Hi*. These were highly satisfactory missiles for beginning the study of upper atmosphere conditions. The *Private* series were developed during the war by CalTech's Jet Propulsion Laboratory. These were small (36 feet long) solid rockets with a useful altitude of about 20 miles. Further CalTech developments, the *Baby-WAC*, was a one-fifth scale model of the *WAC-Corporal*—whose 16 feet of length tipped the scales at 665 pounds. The *WAC-Corporal* fired in September, 1945, was America's first liquid-propelled missile built with government funds. It is interesting to note that preliminary plans for the *WAC-Corporal* had already been initiated in 1936 by the GALCIT rocket research group. It took almost 10 years for the opportunity to appear for the successful completion of these plans. The final design of the *WAC-Corporal* was made under the direction of Malina by Meeks, Stewart, Mills and Sandberg. Its construction was carried out in cooperation with the Douglas Aircraft Co., the Aerojet Engineering Corp., and the Consolidated Steel Corp.

The missile and upper-air sounding programs were hampered by the limitations of their working equipment. The *WAC-Corporal* missile could not carry enough fuel and could not reach the altitudes desired by physicists. The altitude of the *V-2* rocket was limited by the fact that, for reasons of stability, it had to carry at least a ton payload in its modified warhead where instruments were placed. High-altitude research scientists, in their search for new facts, did not always choose to send up a ton of instrumentation. Sometimes a small payload and a high altitude flight were desired, or vice versa. In short, the *V-2*, a war rocket, was not sufficiently flexible for use in a basic research program.

THE VIKING MISSILES

American *V-2* missile pioneers Rosen, Krause, Smith and other members of a small guided missiles branch of the Naval Research Laboratory had long planned a large American upper atmosphere research rocket, but plans to develop and build such a vehicle were postponed for a short period when it was learned that *V-2* missiles would be available in this country. As it became clear that the supply of German rockets would not last much longer than five years, work was resumed on several designs. The rocket that was accepted, based largely on Rosen's early designs, showed not only the strong influence of *V-2* characteristics, but of some of Goddard's work.

In August 1946 the Glenn L. Martin Company of Baltimore received the country's first large missile contract. In all, ten automatically stabilized rockets were planned. This number was subsequently increased to 14. The Reaction Motors Corporation was awarded a contract to develop a liquid propellant powerplant. Thus the Viking missile was born.

Work on the motor began in 1946 at the Reaction Motors Corporation under the guidance of J. Shesta, one of the founders of the company. The first motor was completed by October 1947 and underwent test at the Navy-RMI facilities located near the plant. The first test was somewhat encouraging and the motor ran five times before it burned out. The second motor was ready in December and was very successful, firing up to 3 minutes at a time.

Meanwhile, progress was rapidly being made at the Martin plant, and by December 1948 *Viking-1* was assembled. In January 1949, it began its long trip to the White Sands Proving Ground where static and flight tests soon began.

For a country with no previous big rocket experience, the *Viking* program was enormously successful for the United States from several points of view. It showed the feasibility of many new powerplant and missile techniques. Measurements of atmospheric density, composition, temperatures and high altitude winds, of cosmic ray intensity, and of the abundance of meteorites in space were all made. The solar spectrum was even analyzed from data supplied by *Viking* firings. *Viking-11* rose to 158.4 miles, the highest altitude as yet reached by a one-stage rocket missile.

On May 11, 1950, the *Viking-4* missile had been successfully ship-launched from the *USS Norton Sound* to an altitude of 106 miles. The *Viking* missiles were used intermittently all the way up until 1957 when they acted as the first test vehicles for the official United States satellite program, *Project Vanguard*.

The *Viking* missile has undergone a variety of design and component changes. The early *Viking* stood 48 feet, 3 inches high and had a diameter of 2 feet, 8 inches. Its launching weight was generally around 10,000 pounds, and its maximum velocity was 4100–4300 miles per hour.

The *Viking-8* missile was quite different, however, from the earlier models, with a propellant capacity increased by 50 percent, its length shortened to just under 42 feet and its diameter increased. Slight modifications were also made to the *Viking-9*, which have been carried into the final models.

Other upper atmosphere rockets are being tested and used in the United States at the present time. One of these is the *Deacon* missile, which is launched either from the surface or from a balloon. For the balloon launch,

(continued on p. 121)

FIG. 54 *NATIV* MISSILE ADJUSTED FOR FIRING TEST

At Holloman Air Force Base, New Mexico, F. A. Lane, technician with North American Aviation, Inc., of Los Angeles, adjusts a connection on an early experimental liquid rocket, the *NATIV*, whose name comes from its lengthier designation, "North American Instrumentation Test Vehicle." (USAF)

FIG. 55 *HERMES A-1* GUIDED MISSILE READY FOR FIRING

Each cubic inch of the *A-1's* interior is crowded with delicate instruments, to enable it to do its research and development job more efficiently. The *A-1,* an early postwar liquid rocket, was designed and developed by the General Electric Company. (General Electric)

FIG. 56 *CONVAIR 774* SUPERSONIC ROCKET BLASTS OFF

One of America's first supersonic self-launched rockets, the Convair 774, is pictured during firing at the White Sands Proving Grounds, New Mexico. The firing cable is shown breaking away from the missile as it begins its ascent. (Department of Defense)

FIG. 57   A *BUMPER* MISSILE IS INSTALLED ON A LAUNCHING PAD

A *Bumper* missile is shown being readied for firing at the Cape Canaveral launching area of the Air Force Missile Test Center.   The *Bumper* missile was a *V-2* vehicle with a WAC Corporal second stage.   The nose of the *WAC Corporal* has not yet been installed.   (USAF)

FIG 58 *WAC CORPORAL* MISSILE

The *WAC Corporal* missile is pictured with her "father," Frank J. Malina. The rocket was developed by the Jet Propulsion Laboratory, GALCIT, California Institute of Technology, in 1945 for the Ordnance Department, ASF.

FIG. 59   LOCKHEED TEST MISSILE READY FOR LAUNCHING

Early postwar rocket work in the United States included various test missiles similar to this one produced by the Lockheed Aircraft Company, here shown ready for launching. (Lockheed)

FIG. 60 BOEING *GAPA* MISSILE READIED FOR FIRING

This photo shows details of the Boeing *GAPA* research missile, as one was prepared for firing at Alamogordo, New Mexico. The early supersonic test program was started by the Boeing Airplane Company in 1945, under contract to the U. S. Air Force, and was concluded in 1949. (Boeing)

FIG. 61 *CORPORAL* MISSILE READY FOR LAUNCHING

This is the U. S. Army's 75-mile range, liquid propellant, guided artillery missile *Corporal* on its launcher. (U. S. Army)

FIG. 62 *VANGUARD* MISSILE TEST IN 1957

A high-altitude separation test of the launching vehicle for a scientific earth satellite was fired May 1, 1957. This shot was part of Project Vanguard. The *Viking* missile, however, was developed shortly after World War II, based on *V-2* missile technology, and enabled American researchers not only to explore the upper air but to learn much about rocketry as well. (U. S. Navy)

FIG. 63   RYAN *FIREBIRD* MISSILE IN FLIGHT

An early U. S. antiaircraft missile was the rocket-powered Ryan *Firebird,* shown here in flight.   (Ryan)

FIG. 64 FIRST FIRING OF THE *TINY TIM* ROCKET

The first firing of the *Tiny Tim* air-to-surface bombardment rocket was made from a Douglas *A-26* bomber on February 14, 1945. (USAF)

FIG. 65 RYAN *FIREBEE* MISSILE TAKES OFF

The Ryan *Firebee* missile, a rocket-boosted, turbine-powered target drone, is shown just after zero-launch take-off. (Ryan)

FIG. 66 SCORPION *F-89D* BARES ITS STING

From its wing-tip pods, this U. S. Air Force Northrop Scorpion *F-89D* unleashes
a barrage of deadly air-to-air rockets. A total of 104 devastating 2.75-inch rockets,
capable of downing the largest bomber with a single hit, makes the Scorpion
F-89D one of America's most heavily armed fighter-type aircraft. Advanced electronic aiming and automatic triggering equipment enable a two-man crew to
seek out invading aircraft despite darkness or inclement weather and envelop
the enemy target in a barrage of rockets. (Northrop)

FIG. 67 *HONEST JOHN* MISSILE READY FOR FIRING

A rocket launcher is shown carrying the *Honest John* fully elevated while being checked for performance. This solid propellant powered weapon, capable of carrying a nuclear warhead, is an aimed, spin-stabilized ballistic missile with a range of about 20 miles. (U. S. Army)

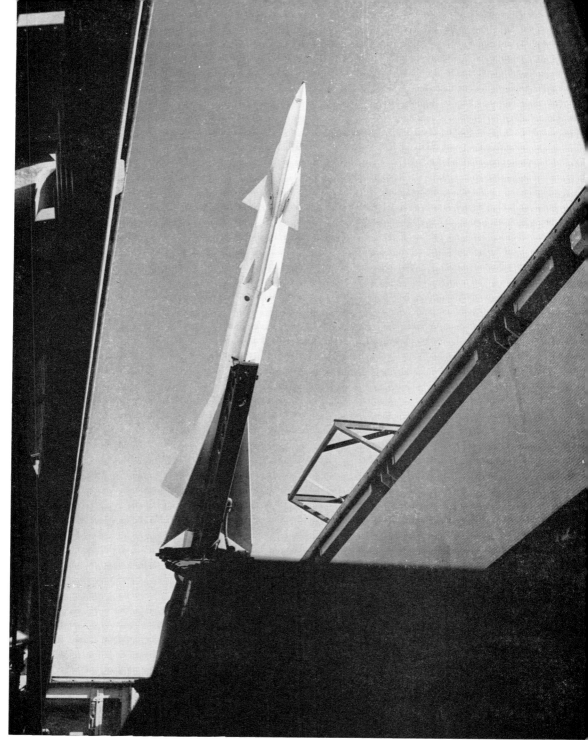

FIG. 68   THE *NIKE-AJAX* MISSILE IS READY FOR DEFENSE

A *Nike-Ajax* antiaircraft guided missile is raised up on an elevator from an underground storage area to a launching site. *Nike* missiles now guard most large U. S. cities. (U. S. Army)

FIG. 69 THE *REDSTONE* MISSILE IN FLIGHT

A giant *Redstone* missile, manufactured by the Chrysler Corporation for the U. S. Army, is shown in flight. The 200-mile *Redstone* missile uses an 80,000-pound liquid propellant rocket motor; is radio-inertially guided; and carries a nuclear warhead. It is now in use by the Army. (Chrysler) the *Deacon* is carried on a 100-foot cord beneath a *Skylark* polyethylene balloon up to perhaps 50,000 feet. It is fired automatically and then soars 40, 50 or more miles under the power of its own solid propellant, 5700-pound thrust motor. The *Deacon* is a product of the Allegany Ballistics Laboratory. If launched from the surface of the earth, the *Deacon* would ascend to only 15 or 20 miles. The small missile is 9 feet long, fires for 3½ seconds and undergoes 60 *G's* acceleration.

The *Deacon* missile program is sponsored by the Office of Naval Research and the Atomic Energy Commission, with the aid of the University of Iowa. At Iowa, J. A. van Allen and R. M. Missert have been particularly active in the program. The *Deacon* missile now plays an important role in the International Geophysical Year and is being bought in quantity by the United States Weather Bureau for upper air sounding.

A 2-stage missile that uses a *Deacon* as the second step is called the *Dan*. An Air Research and Development Command project, it has been tested at Wallops Island, Virginia. The *Dan* missile can reach an altitude of 70 miles, but the ARDC hopes eventually to attain an altitude of 100 miles. The *Nike* missile is used as the first-stage booster.

AEROBEE PROGRAM

The *Aerobee* rocket was specifically designed for upper air research. This rocket filled the need for a relatively cheap vehicle for upper air research. It was useful for training crews in rocket-handling and laid the basis for a possible future antiaircraft weapon.

After three dummy missiles (booster-lifting deadweight models) were fired, the first live-firing of the *Aerobee* missile occurred on November 24, 1947. The Air Force ordered 60 *Aerobee* missiles and fired the first of its own series from Holoman Air Force Base on August 16, 1949. Thirty colleges, universities, and research institutes were participants in the Air Force study program on the relationship between weather and solar activity.

More recently an improved *Aerobee* missile, called *Aerobee-Hi,* has been developed. Empty weight has been lowered (loaded weight is slightly over 1100 pounds), overall length increased, firing time lengthened, and velocity increased from Mach 4 to Mach 6. On April 28, 1955 an *Aerobee-Hi* missile, carrying 230 pounds of instruments (a load record), reached a peak altitude of 124 miles. The rocket is seeing wide use during the 1957–58 International Geophysical Year.

At the same time that the *Viking* missile program was under way, the Reaction Motors Corporation received an Air Force contract for the development of a rocket motor for the *MX-774* missile. This missile, built by Consolidated Vultee, was planned to be the second stage of a long-range multi-step configuration. The Reaction Motors Corporation improved its 6000-

pound thrust, 4-chamber, X-1 and D-558-2 engine to 8000 pounds of thrust. On September 17, 1947 the first of three *MX-774* missiles carried upper air research and other instruments aloft. The engine was unique in that each of the 4 combustion chambers could swivel independently of each other for altitude stabilization.

A recent Navy research rocket designed to investigate the upper atmosphere is called the *Rockair*. This rocket which reached a 17-mile altitude, upon vertical launching from a fast-climbing jet airplane at an altitude of 30,000-feet, was first tested at Chincoteague Naval Air Station in Virginia.

Since World War II an intensive missile development program has been promoted by the services. Thirty or more military missile projects are known to be under development in the United States at this time, and expenditures in the field have risen from $21,000,000 in 1951, to $295,000,000 in 1953, an estimated $518,300,000 in 1955, and to over $2,500,000,000 in 1958. As a matter of fact, the rocket industry, including missile systems and associated gear, is now the largest industry in America both in dollar volume and size of labor force. Financial circles are beginning to recognize this fact and investments in the field are no longer looked upon askance. For example, the investment banking house of Ira Haupt & Company has recently underwritten a public offering by Missiles-Jets & Automation Fund, Inc.

7

Post-War Rocketry in America

Peace came in 1945, and, with it, demobilization. To rocketry it meant different things in different places. In Germany it meant the end of an era. The world's greatest concentration of big rocket and missile knowhow and the people who developed it became the spoils of war. They were spirited away to Great Britain, Russia, the United States and France. The United States, by a swift move known as Project Paperclip, got the top personnel, including such names as Wernher von Braun, Ernst Stuhlinger, Ernst Steinhoff, etc.—nearly 150 in all. Germany, as a nation, was to be out of the rocket business for some years to come but always latent with genius to come back.

To Russia, with many captured facilities, *V-2's* for study and test, and a few German scientists whom they soon returned to the Fatherland, it meant a chance to develop really big, long-range strategic ballistic rockets and to continue plugging towards Ziolkovsky's half-century-old dream of reaction-powered space flight. The Soviet Union gave its rocket and space-flight programs top priority and cloaked them in the strictest secrecy. As a result, early post-war efforts at rocket-development cooperation between the United States, Great Britain, France and Russia quickly failed.

Neither the United States nor Great Britain officially recognized the potential proximity of manned space flight through rocket propulsion. Nor was either apparently aware that what the Germans had begun in rocket weaponry with the *V-2* was amenable to further rapid progress. They assumed that Russia's refusal to cooperate indicated a lack of pressing interest in missiles and space flight. The belief (now dramatically proved falacious) persisted that without outside aid Russian technology could never match the West's.

In the early post-war years, the Congress repealed the legislation that provided for full and free exchange of technological and scientific knowhow among the Allies. As a result, the Big Three of the Free World went their individual ways in the fields of rockets and missiles, as in others. Any real sense of urgency was lacking. Ironically, with the exception of the efforts of a few dedicated persons and institutions, the West's efforts in rocketry were

123

academic or even casual. That this was a near-fatal error in judgment has now been demonstrated.

The United States began its post-war rocket efforts in 1945 with a handful (100 rockets, compared to the 5100 rockets the Germans produced during World War II) of captured *V-2's,* thousands of left-over small solid propellant barrage and air-to-air rockets, and a fairly well-developed JATO capability. Its interest in rockets at that time seemed largely to be split between an academic curiosity in how the Germans had done what they did and a desire to study the upper air. To a limited extent, top military planners saw a future in missiles, even large missiles, but habit and lack of foresight led them to think first in terms of "air-breathers." This accounts for the rash of "air-breathing" interceptor and long-range cruise missile projects initiated in the 1945–1950 period, resulting in such operational birds today as Northrop's subsonic 5000-mile *Snark* missile, the long-range interceptor missile *Bomarc,* the 1000-mile *Matador* missile and the *Regulus* missile series. It also meant some costly cancellations, such as the $700,000,000 North American Aviation Company's *Navaho* missile, and the multi-million-dollar McDonnell Aviation Company's *Triton* missile, whose actual cost up to cancellation has never been released.

The value of large, strategic rockets was freely admitted in planning talks about the distant future, and manned space flight was admitted grudgingly by some as a possibility "some day." In a word, the United States officially stuck to a conventional step-by-step approach to the evolution of weaponry, blind to the fact that an era of revolution in technology had already started.

Aside from the *V-2,* the *Viking,* and the *Hermes,* no "big" rockets were made in the United States before 1950. And, even these early research and test vehicles cannot be considered large in contemporary (1958–60) terms. Nevertheless, they and the smaller rockets, like the *Aerobee,* provided valuable experience. Also, of course, they were constantly teaching us more and more about upper atmosphere conditions, a valuable asset in itself.

SURFACE-TO-SURFACE MISSILES

The Army's Redstone Arsenal group began thinking about larger and better rockets for performing military missions. In the late 1940's and early 1950's a variety of projects were initiated. The most ambitious of these resulted in the *Redstone,* a 300-mile, inertially guided ballistic missile, with nuclear warhead capabilities. In both range and accuracy it was an appreciable step forward from the *V-2* missile. In charge of its technical development was Peenemünde rocket expert, Wernher von Braun. The *Redstone* missile is 69 feet tall, 6 feet in diameter (fin-span, 12 feet) and powered by a 75,000-pound thrust, North American Rocketdyne engine. It is manufactured by the Chrysler Corporation and uses inertial guidance provided by the Ford Instrument Company. Propellants are liquid oxygen and alcohol. The *Redstone* missile is now in service with United States forces.

Other Army surface-to-surface missiles include the 762-mm *Honest John*, an unguided artillery rocket with a range between 20 and 30 miles, now in squadron service with Army forces in Europe and the Far East, and the *Corporal*. The aerodynamic and engineering studies of the *Honest John* missile began at Redstone Arsenal in May 1950. The first firing was made at the White Sands Proving Grounds in August 1951. It was placed into production by Army Ordnance at the Douglas Aircraft Company in 1953. It is aimed and spin-stabilized at take-off and has a Hercules Powder Company solid propellant motor.

The history of the *Corporal* missile SSM-A-17, also in active service with the Army, goes back to 1944, when the GALCIT group started the *Private* and *Corporal* series of missiles. It is radar beam-guided, operates on a bi-propellant liquid motor, and is designed to carry an atomic warhead. A long-range, artillery-type, ballistic missile, it is considered to be accurate up to at least 75 miles. It is currently in production at the Firestone Tire and Rubber Company. The guidance work is handled by the Gilfillan Brothers Company and the rocket engine by the Ryan Aeronautical Corporation. The *Corporal* probably will be replaced by a solid propellant *Sergeant* missile by the year 1960. The *Sergeant* uses a 50,000-to-70,000-pound Thiokol Chemical Corporation rocket engine and is manufactured by the Sperry Gyroscope Company. It has a range approximating that of the *Corporal* missile.

Other important post-war small surface-to-surface missiles include the *Lacrosse,* designed by the Cornell Aeronautical Laboratory and manufactured by The Martin Company. Now in production for the Army, it utilizes a solid propellant motor. It is a highly effective pillbox buster. Another recent addition to the Army's arsenal is the *Little John* missile. Only 12 feet long, it is one of America's smallest missiles with an atomic warhead capability. Its range is believed to be under 20 miles. It is manufactured by the Douglas Aircraft Company in conjunction with the Emerson Electric Manufacturing Company. Not to be forgotten is the Utica-Bend Corporation's antitank rocket, the *Dart,* utilizing optical and electrical pulse guidance through trailing wires (after the French SS-10). It is in production for the Army.

Another well-known, surface-to-surface missile, the Air Force's TM-61 *Matador,* is simply a jet-propelled pilotless bomber with sweptback wings. It has a 600-mile range at near sonic speeds. Rocket boosters aid its take-off, and sustainer power is provided by a J-33 turbojet engine. Its guidance is either radio-controlled or self-homing, and it is supersonic in its dive on a target. The *Matador* missile is in squadron service in Germany at the present time.

The Navy's *Regulus I* is an operational surface-to-surface missile that can be launched from shore, ship and submarine. First announced in 1953, it resembles a sweptwing fighter. Development began in 1948, and tests were made in 1950 at the Navy's Point Mugu Air Missile Center. It was first flown at Edwards Air Force Base in the same year. Four types of *Regulus* have been announced: training missile, tactical missile, target missile, and experimental missile. Designated the XSSM-N-8, it is a Chance Vought Aircraft Corporation product, currently in production at Dallas. The *Regulus* missile is operated on a J-33 turbojet, with rocket boosters for take-off, like the *Matador*. It can be landed on its tricycle undercarriage landing gear after flight. When launched from shipboard, it is catapulted or zero-launched with JATO units, followed by the jet engine. The submarines "Tunny" and "Babero" were the first to be modified to launch the *Regulus* missile. Now others, including atomic-powered submarines, have *Regulus* missile launching capabilities.

Aside from getting an effective ship-launched surface-to-surface missile in operation, in a minimum of time, the *Regulus I* project served another unusually useful purpose, namely, to enable a missile system to be perfected with a minimum of worry over the reliability of the actual hardware. In this respect, what was essentially an unmanned aircraft had its advantages, and it resulted in the development of a trouble-free transition to the supersonic *Regulus II* missile, now undergoing advanced flight tests. The *Regulus II*, like its predecessor, can be zero-launched with the Aerojet Corporation's solid propellant boosters.

One of the first surface-to-surface "air-breathers," for which development was ordered, was the 5000-mile Northrop Aircraft *Snark* missile. It is a subsonic, self-guided intercontinental cruise missile, with nuclear capabilities. It is now being incorporated into the Strategic Air Command of the United States Air Force, as an interim weapon, until the ICBMs are operationally available. The *Snark* missile weighs roughly 38,000 pounds. It combines the Northrop Company's celestial and inertial guidance system and is powered by a Pratt & Whitney J-57 turbojet engine with 11,000 pounds of thrust. It is zero-launched with two Aerojet solid propellant rocket boosters, each having 33,000 pounds of thrust.

Another aerodynamic cruise missile which reached advanced stages of development before cancellation was the ramjet-powered *Navaho,* made by the Missile System Division of the North American Aviation Company. Flight test prototype for this missile was NAA's *X-10,* powered by two turbojet engines. Its configuration approximates that of the actual *Navaho* missile, with its small delta wing placed well aft, and a "V" tail and canard stabilizers forward. The *Navaho* missile was designed for a 5000-mile range, with speeds up to Mach 3.5, and altitudes of 70,000 to 80,000 feet. It would have carried a nuclear payload. Weighing an estimated 200,000 to 300,000 pounds, it was zero-launched by three NAA liquid propellant rocket engines, with a total thrust of 450,000 pounds. Ramjet sustainers (an estimated 4 feet in diameter) were made by the Curtiss-Wright Corporation. Ironically, the *Navaho* missile made successful transitions from rocket boost to ramjet sustainer flight after the Air Force had cancelled its development.

America's important large missiles, however, both from the point of view of weaponry and eventual space flight, are its strategic ballistic missiles: the ICBMs, *Atlas* and *Titan;* the IRBMs *Thor* and *Jupiter;* and the Fleet Ballistic Missile (FBM), *Polaris*. All of these missiles have been placed on order relatively recently. Three of the missiles—*Atlas, Thor* and *Jupiter*—have made successful complete unit flights. Successful test vehicle flights have also been made by the *Titan* and *Polaris* missiles.

These are startling weapons. They require massive thrust for take-off. They are guided (inertially, and therefore are unjammable) for only the first few minutes of powered flight. When their rocket engines cut off, their lethal nose cone separates from the missile body and continues its trajectory to a peak altitude hundreds of miles in outer space, and then makes a free-fall reentry into the earth's atmosphere at speeds ranging up to Mach 20. These nose cones glow white-hot from the friction heat of reentry, but nevertheless detonate their lethal payload within a few miles (close enough for a thermonuclear warhead) of a predetermined target point, 1500 to 5000 miles from the launching site. Considering the late start the United States made in beginning work on these missiles, it is a credit to its scientific and engineering capabilities that these weapons are in such advanced stages today.

The Air Force *Atlas* is manufactured by the Convair-Astronautics Division of the General Dynamics Corporation. It has two side-mounted liquid propellant rocket boosters of 135,000 pounds thrust each, and a 100,000-pound thrust liquid sustainer rocket, supplied by NAA Rocketdyne. Its inertial guidance system is supplied by the American Bosch-Arms Company. The General Electric Company supplies the reentry nose cone. The *Atlas* is some 70 feet high, over 8 feet in diameter, and has a take-off weight somewhat over 200,000 pounds. The predecessor to the *Atlas* was the on-again, off-again, Air Force *MX-774* project, first founded in 1947, and carried on for a time at the Convair Corporation's own expense.

The Air Force *Titan* is under development by the Martin Company and is designed to be a successor to the *Atlas* missile. Like the *Atlas*, the *Titan* is an intercontinental ballistic missile with a designed range of over 5000 miles. Unlike the *Atlas*, it is a 2-stage vehicle having in the first stage a 300,000-pound thrust, liquid Aerojet-General Corporation engine, and in the second stage a 60,000-pound thrust, liquid engine made by the same company. It is being developed at The Martin Company's new $20,000,-000 Denver plant, and initial flight tests have begun at the Cape Canaveral missile test center. The Army supplies the guidance system and AVCO Manufacturing Corporation supplies the reentry nose cone for the *Atlas* missile.

The two IRBMs, the Air Force *Thor* manufactured by Douglas Aircraft Company and the Army *Jupiter* manufactured by Chrysler Corporation, are parallel development projects. Both have made successful flights on a number of occasions. They are both designed for a target range of 1500 nautical miles. They both use a NAA-Rocketdyne liquid propellant single-stage powerplant, with a thrust of 135,000 pounds. The AC Spark Plug Company and Bell Telephone Laboratories supply *Thor's* guidance. The Ford Instrument Company supplies *Jupiter's* inertial guidance system.

The Navy's FBM, *Polaris,* is one of America's newest projects. It is different from the other two development projects in that it utilizes solid propellant motors exclusively. The Navy insists on solid propellants because of the relative difficulty in handling liquid propellants in a submerged submarine, for which the *Polaris* is primarily intended. Lockheed Aircraft Corporation's Missile System Division holds the prime contract. The Thiokol and Aerojet Corporations are slated to supply the powerplants. Preliminary descriptions of the *Polaris* indicate that it will have a first stage of three solid propellant motors, clustered around a single second-stage motor; each of the motors will be in the general thrust category of 50,000 to 70,000 pounds.

In recent years, the large missiles have been subject to bitter interservice rivalry over who shall be allowed to use them in combat. One result was the famous Roles-and-Missions memorandum promulgated by Defense Secretary Charles E. Wilson, which turned over operational responsibility for all surface-to-surface missiles with ranges above 200 miles to the Air Force, the Navy's *Polaris* excepted. Within 18 months, the Wilson memorandum was reconsidered and materially modified, because of the influence brought about by the Russian Sputniks.

After all the political furor over the use of *Jupiter* and *Polaris* missiles as weapons, the advent of Soviet space flight advances also emphasized their importance as potential space exploration vehicles. For example, a rocket system consisting of either a *Thor* or a *Jupiter* missile as a first stage and clustered *Sergeant* missiles for second and third stages was quickly calculated as being able to place an 1100-pound satellite in orbit. An *Atlas* or a *Navaho* booster first stage could send the rocket even higher.

Future large projects in rocketry include: television camera carrying satellites, proposed by both the Air Force and the Army; moon rockets; manned satellites; and boost glide bombers. Nearly all of these projects have at least study contracts behind them. Some, such as the reconnaissance satellites, have been ordered into development. The go-ahead signal has been given to see what can be done in the way of adapting military hardware to space flight and upper atmosphere research projects. Prior to Sputnik, use of military hardware for this purpose, generally, was prohibited. Project *Vanguard* was conceived and managed as something aside and distinct from military rocket programs. This concept was maintained because the attitude of the other nations toward earth-circling objects was not known, and the *Vanguard* effort—at least until the Sputniks were launched—could not have any military connotation.

AIR-TO-AIR MISSILES

Air-to-air missiles are those that are launched from an airplane or a missile against another airplane or missile. Some of these missiles are guided, and some are not. A few air-to-air missiles have homing devices, but the majority possess proximity fuses. Because of their desirable dispersion, their flat trajectory and their relatively long range, air-to-air missiles are gaining increasing favor as aircraft armament.

One of the best-known air-to-air rockets is the *Mighty Mouse*. Resembling the *Mighty Mouse* is the *Aeromite,* an Aerojet-General Corporation product adapted for use on standard launchers. Twelve of these missiles can be fired in less than ¼ of a second.

Another aimed air-to-air rocket is the Navy's 5-inch diameter *Zuni,* a folding-fin missile weighing 107 pounds and having a length of 110 inches. It achieves velocities in the realm of Mach 3.

In 1947, the Navy Bureau of Aeronautics and the Sperry Gyroscope Corporation commenced work on project *Hot Shot*. The result, announced in 1954, was the 300-pound, Mach 3 *Sparrow* missile, now produced by the Douglas Aircraft Company, as well as by the Sperry Corporation. The beam-riding and terminal homing system incorporated into the missile were developed by the Sperry and Raytheon Corporations. Several versions of the 5-mile range missile have been successfully used against target aircraft.

Two other successful missiles bear the names: the *Falcon* and the *Firebird*. The former, designated GAR-98 by the Air Force, is made by the Hughes Aircraft Company and the Philco Corporation. Under development since

1947, it was first tested in 1950. The *Falcon* has a solid propellant motor, a 3-to-5-mile target range, and either a radar or an infrared target-homing guidance system.

Falcon models II and III, now being developed, are expected to extend the target range and speed at which an air-to-air attack could be made. The *Falcon* is 6 feet long, 6 inches in diameter, and weighs 112 pounds.

The *Firebird* (XAAM-A-1 in military terminology) is older than the *Falcon*. Research was completed in 1949, and the missile was in service a year or so later. Built by the Ryan Aeronautical Company, it is radar-controlled by the carrying aircraft until it nears the target, at which time a target-homing device goes into operation. It has a double cruciform wing arrangement and a bipropellant rocket motor with a booster. It can be fired alone or in groups of two or four.

An even earlier air-to-air missile, the rocket-propelled KU2N-1, *Gorgon IIA,* was directed by radio control from a mother plane, using information obtained from a television camera carried by the missile.

The Philco *Sidewinder* (XAAM-N-7) is another air-to-air missile in the Navy's arsenal. Reportedly, it is available in two versions. It is pod-mounted in Navy jet airplane wing tips and is being produced by the Martin Company. It was developed by the Naval Ordnance Test Station at Inyokern under the able direction of W. B. McLean, at a reported cost of about $1000 a round. The *Oriole* AAM-N-4 was a Martin Company development missile, powered by a solid rocket motor. It weighed about 1500 pounds and was apparently capable of Mach 2 speeds. This project was cancelled by the Navy in 1954.

Yet another Navy air-to-air rocket family is found in the *Sparrow* series, ranging from I through III. *Sparrow-I* was developed and produced by Sperry Farragut Company. It has a target range of 5 miles and reaches Mach 3 velocities. *Sparrow-II* was developed by the Douglas Aircraft Company but cancelled. *Sparrow-III* is a Raytheon development, ordered into production at the Sperry Farragut Company plant, under Raytheon direction. The Aerojet Corporation supplies the motors. Radar is used as the basis for the guidance system.

One of the latest air-to-air missiles had a variety of popular names, ranging from *Ding-Dong,* through *Bird Dog* and *High Card.* The final designation, which has stuck, is *MB-1.* It is manufactured by the Douglas Aircraft Company, and the guidance system is supplied by the Hughes Aircraft Company. It gives air-to-air rocketry nuclear warhead capability. It has been successfully tested at Yucca Flats, Nevada, and has been ordered into production. Both liquid and solid propellant versions of the *MB-1* missile have been tried.

Another air-to-air missile concept involves defense of America's high and far-flying strategic bombers. The *Goose* missile, made by the Fairchild Engine and Airplane Corporation, is designed to be fired ahead of a raiding bomber force in order to draw the fire of intercepting aircraft and missiles. It has made several successful flights. Rockets play no part in this bird, which is powered by a small turbojet engine.

SURFACE-TO-AIR MISSILES

One of the earliest and most successful of a long series of surface-to-air missiles was the Navy's CTV-N-9 *Lark,* an automatically guided weapon, powered by a reliable Reaction Motors Corporation rocket engine. It was first revealed to the public in 1949.

Two separate combustion chambers were used in this novel liquid engine. One chamber provided 220 pounds of sustainer thrust, and the other chamber provided 400 pounds of initial thrust. The second combustion chamber went into operation when speed dropped to Mach 0.85.

Lark missiles, used primarily as training vehicles, were launched from shore (particularly from Point Mugu) and shipboard. Another early shipboard launched vehicle was the *Little Joe* (KAN-1). It was catapult-launched with the aid of standard solid rockets and was radio-controlled.

A contemporary surface-to-air missile is the *Terrier* (SAM-N-7), a Convair and Bendix development, dating from 1945. It is already in service with the fleet. The *USS Mississippi* was the first ship to fire missiles operationally, although they were tested on the *USS Norton Sound* in 1951. The *Terrier* missile's range is reported to be about 20 miles. It is detonated by a proximity fuse. Its history goes back to the Section T contract placed by the Navy Bureau of Ordnance with the Applied Physics Laboratory of the Johns Hopkins University, and the project *Bumblebee* from which it grew. It was put into production in January 1953, at a Naval Industrial Reserve Ordnance Plant operated by Convair.

The *Bomarc* missile, a name derived from the Boeing Airplane Company and the Michigan Aeronautical Research Center (now the Willow Run Research Center), is a formidable weapon designed to attack bombers up to 250 miles away at a speed of Mach 2.5. Measuring 46 feet long and weighing 15,000 pounds, it is powered by two of the Marquardt Company's ramjets, which in turn are rocket-boosted by two of the Aerojet-General Corporation's liquid rocket engines. Later versions of the *Bomarc* missile will be boosted by solid propellants. The *Bomarc* missile is *SAGE* programmed. *SAGE* is an aircraft interception system, similar to the Army's *NIKE* system. The first flight test of this interceptor missile was made in 1954. It has been ordered into production, and a selection of sites around American cities has been made.

The *Bomarc* missile grew out of a long series of missile test programs, carried on by the Boeing Aircraft Corporation and the Air Force under the name of *GAPA* (Ground-to-Air-Pilotless Aircraft). This project, which lasted from 1945 to 1949, was primarily concerned with testing ramjet and rocket missile characteristics. The largest missile built under the project measured 22 feet long and was 8 feet in diameter. About 100 vehicles were launched, often from towers, and speeds in excess of Mach 2 were realized.

A project in some ways similar to *GAPA* was *Nativ* (North American Test Instrument Vehicle). The purpose of *Nativ* was to gain information on missile aerodynamics and control, and to teach handling and launching crews the techniques of modern rocketry. The *Nativ* missile was tower-launched by its own liquid propellant powerplant, no booster being employed. The supersonic missile had 4 fixed fins and 4 movable aerodynamic control surfaces.

The mainstay of antiaircraft ground defense until recently was the *Nike Ajax* (SAM-A-7), built by the Western Electric Division of the Bell Telephone Company and the Douglas Aircraft Company, as well as by the Army Ordnance Missile Plant in Charlotte, North Carolina. This missile is powered by an Aerojet-General Corporation liquid propellant rocket motor, plus a solid booster. *Nike* (which means "Victory" in Greek) is an Army missile and was first test-fired as far back as 1946. The missile is command-guided and houses a homing system which responds to target reflection from a surface-based radar station.

Latest addition to the United States air defense arsenal is the *Nike Hercules* missile, an all-solid propellant development growing out of the *Nike Ajax* missile. Using a 3-motor first-stage booster (all *Nike Hercules* motors are made by the Thiokol Corporation), the larger, heavier *Nike Hercules* missile reaches speeds over 2000 miles per hour. It carries (when desired) a nuclear warhead and has an effective range of some 70 miles. The *Nike Hercules* missile is capable of reaching any known bomber altitude. It is being supplied to *Nike* bases in 1958.

The *Talos* (SAM-N-6) missile, developed by the Bendix & McDonnell Aircraft Corporations, is in production for shipboard use by the Navy. It is also being assessed by the Army for point contact defense on land. Like the *Terrier* missile, it originated in the *Bumblebee* project, and a guided missile ship will be outfitted to handle it. The missile is being built by the Bendix Aircraft Corporation at its Mishawaka, Indiana plant. The Bendix Aircraft Corporation also builds the *Loki* missile, an unguided barrage-type rocket, powered by a rocket engine made by the Grand Central Rocket Company.

The *Hawk* missile, an Army-sponsored Raytheon Corporation development, using a liquid rocket motor, has a slant range of 15 to 20 miles. It is particularly useful for low altitude defense. Some 16 feet long, 14 inches in diameter (fin-span, 47 inches) and highly supersonic, the *Hawk* missile is very mobile, being designed primarily to give ground troops close protection against tactical airpower. Its guidance system is unusual and based on radar. It has been mentioned as a possible bomber defense missile.

Another surface-to-air missile under advanced development for the Navy is the *Tartar;* like the *Terrier* missile it is an outgrowth of the original *Bumblebee* project. The Convair Aircraft Corporation is the manufacturer. It uses a solid propellant motor made by the Allegany Ballistics Laboratory.

AIR-TO-SURFACE MISSILES

As the effectiveness of the ground-launched antiaircraft missile increases, bombers will be forced more and more to attack their targets from a distance. This requirement leads to the guided bomb utilizing radar, television, infra-red, or inertial terminal guidance system techniques.

The Bell Aircraft Corporation is one of the major organizations engaged in air-to-surface missile development. The *Rascal* missile, in production at Niagara Falls, has undergone successful flight-testing, demonstrating pin-point accuracy at up to a 300-mile target range. The powerplant for this missile, developed by Bell Aircraft Corporation, consists of a 3-chamber liquid propellant rocket. Using the *Shrike* missile as a prototype, the *Rascal* (GAM-63) program made rapid headway. The *Rascal* missile, designed to carry an atomic warhead from *B-47* and *B-52* type of jet bombers, can be launched well outside the normal main line of enemy antiaircraft defense.

Less spectacular air-to-surface missiles include the *Bullpup* and the larger *Bulldog,* the discontinued *Gorgon V* and the early *Gargoyle* (KUD-1). The *Bulldog* missile is a Navy-Martin Company project now entering production. The *Bullpup* missile is in production at the Martin Company's Orlando, Florida plant. The *Gorgon* missile was developed by both the Martin Company and the Fairchild Corporation. The *Gargoyle* missile was a carrier-aircraft-launched glide bomb, holding a 1000-pound explosive charge for use against enemy ships. Two other missiles, the *Dove* (XAUM-N-4) and the *Petrel* (XAUM-N-2), were used for the same purpose. The *Petrel* missile is a Fairchild development, using a Fairchild J-44, 1000-pound thrust jet engine. It is properly classified as an air-to-underwater missile. It has a range of about 20 miles, a weight of 1500 pounds, and a subsonic speed. The *Petrel* missile incorporates an underwater, self-homing device. It is launched from such patrol airplanes as the Lockheed *P2V,* the Grumman *S2F,* the Martin *P5M,* and can possibly be launched from helicopters. The prime contractor for the *Dove* missile is Eastman Kodak Company. All except the *Bullpup* and *Bulldog* missiles have been discontinued.

ROCKET AIRPLANES

In the earliest attempts at rocket-propelled flight in the United States, solid rockets were attached to gliders which then took off for successful but very short flights. The first genuine rocket plane, the *MX-324*, was a military craft designed as an interceptor by Northrop Aircraft Corporation. It was built secretly during the middle of World War II. The piloted *MX-324* made its first flight on July 5, 1944 at Harper's Dry Lake, near Barstow, California, with A. G. Haley and E. J. Vogt of the Aerojet Corporation being the ground crew for service of the rocket engine.

The Army Air Force then asked the Bell Aircraft Company to design a research plane, the *SX-1* (later shortened to *X-1*), which was needed to investigate, at transonic and supersonic speeds, the odd reversals of aerodynamic control forces experienced by pilots of conventional airplanes in fast dives. Bell Aircraft at first conceived the plane as a turbojet-rocket combination aircraft, using a turbojet engine for climb, and rockets for speed. Closer inspection revealed that rocket power, though expensive, provided a highly competitive rate of climb. A consideration of various propellant combinations (bearing in mind that the vehicle was piloted) eliminated all but alcohol and liquid oxygen, and the task of developing a suitable engine was handed to the Reaction Motors Corporation of Rockaway, New Jersey.

The engine provided by the Reaction Motors Corporation was one of the classics of modern rocketry. Designated the *6000C4* engine, it weighed 210 pounds and developed 6000 pounds of thrust with four 1500-pound thrust chambers which could be fired one, two, or three at a time in any combination, or all at once, thus permitting an elementary control over the speed of the mounting aircraft. By conventional rocket engine standards, the engine could be fired for incredible periods of time before overhaul.

B-29 bombers were adapted to carry the *X-1* plane aloft. Ten glide tests were made in 1946 at Pine Castle, Florida, and powered flight tests were begun in December at Muroc Dry Lake. On October 14, 1947, Captain Charles E. Yaeger, USAF, became the first pilot to exceed the speed of sound in level flight. The plane consumed 588 gallons of propellant at the rate of 3.9 gallons a second, resulting in 2½ minutes of powered flight at full throttle.

In January 1949, Captain Yaeger took the *X-1* aircraft off the ground. After 2300 feet of take-off run, at maximum thrust, he nosed the plane up and reached an altitude of 23,000 feet in 100 seconds. In August 1950, after having proved that an airplane with nonswept wings could fly faster than sound, the *X-1* was retired to the National Air Museum in Washington, D. C.

While the Bell Aircraft Corporation worked on the *X-1*, the Douglas Aircraft Corporation was working on a graceful counterpart to the *X-1* airplane, to be known as the *Skyrocket*. Built for the Navy and the National Advisory Committee on Aeronautics (NACA) as a part of the D-558 Program, the *Skyrocket* was originally a turbojet-rocket combination with a Westinghouse Corporation 24C turbojet engine and a Reaction Motors Corporation 6000-pound thrust engine. Later, the turbojet engine was abandoned because of windmilling under rocket power. The airfoil of the *Skyrocket* plane was made subsonic to determine the effects of this shape at supersonic speeds. This experiment proved subsonic airfoils do not perform well at over-Mach 1 speeds.

On December 12, 1953, Captain Yaeger was able to exceed his former speed record by attaining 1635 miles per hour in another Bell Aircraft Corporation rocket plane, the *X-1A*. The plane carried a doubled propellant supply, which was made possible by the use of a light-weight turbopump instead of a gas pressurization system. It weighed 9 tons loaded. The rocket engine fired for about 4.2 minutes, and then the plane glided in for a landing at 150 miles per hour. In 1954, the *X-1A* rocket plane climbed to over 90,000 feet.

The *X-1B* rocket plane, sixth and last of the *X-1* series, is identical with the *X-1A* except for instrumentation (1000 pounds of it). It is used by the United States Air Force and the National Advisory Committee on Aeronautics, to obtain aircraft and missile data. Measuring 35 feet 7 inches in length, 10 feet 8 inches in height, and 28 feet in wingspan, the *X-1B* rocket plane weighs 8 tons loaded. It is of very sturdy, polished Duralumin construction. It has a jettisonable Plexiglas canopy, an ejection seat, and a tempered-glass windshield.

The *X-2* rocket plane, built by Bell Aircraft Corporation, was larger, heavier and faster than any of the *X-1* series. It had swept stainless-steel wings and a nickel-alloy fuselage. Powered by a variable-thrust, Curtiss-Wright Corporation *XLR-25* rocket engine developing an estimated 16,000 pounds of thrust, it exceeded 2200 miles per hour and gained 127,000 feet of altitude before going out of control in its first flight test. It crashed due to a turn made at too great a speed. It was equipped with a refrigerated cockpit, to protect the pilot against aerodynamic friction heating. The first of the two *X-2* rocket planes exploded over Lake Ontario in May 1953.

The *X-3* rocket plane, designed by Douglas Aircraft Corporation to explore the speed realm of Mach number 3, has two turbojet engines and a rocket booster. Reportedly underpowered at first, it now uses two Westinghouse Corporation *J-34-17* turbojet engines for normal flight. It is a flying aerodynamic research laboratory, carrying 1200 pounds of instrumentation.

Recently the second *X-1* rocket plane has been modified to replace the *X-2*, until the highly advanced *X-15* rocket plane reaches flight stage. It is called the *X-1E* rocket plane, and its main difference from the original *X-1* is that it employs a much thinner wing.

The *X-15* rocket plane, built by North American Aviation Corporation, will be America's first manned space vehicle. It is designed specifically to study the problems of transitional control, from aerodynamics in the atmosphere to jet tip reaction systems required in airless space. It is to be powered by a 60,000-pound thrust, liquid propellant motor, made by Reaction Motors Corporation. The *X-15* rocket plane is supposed to have an initial altitude capability of over 100 miles. Later versions of the rocket plane are supposed to go even higher. This rocket plane looks in some respects like the ill-fated *Navaho* missile, with a small delta wing placed well to the rear. The *X-15* rocket plane, designed for research, is supposed to be flying before 1960.

Surpassed by guided missile progress, the plans for a piloted interceptor rocket plane were not very fully developed. The nearest thing to it was an attempt by the Republic Aviation Corporation to convert an *F-91* fighter plane into an interceptor, by adding the *X-1* rocket plane's 6000-pound rocket engine. This thrust, added to the 5200 pounds available from the afterburning *J-47* rocket engine, was calculated to provide a sudden burst of very high speed, at crucial moments in combat. The airplane was refrigerated and had a swept, inverse-taper wing, with an adjustable angle of incidence. The first flight test was made in May 1949. Late in 1952 the craft exceeded sonic speed in level flight. It was the first combat plane to do so, but it never got beyond the study and test stage.

ROCKET SLEDS

The rocket-powered sled is the only practical vehicle known that can accurately test human reactions to high speeds, accelerations and decelerations, and ejection seat techniques. Such sleds as the *Free Air Facility Track* (FAFT) and the *North Track,* both at Edwards Air Force Base, the *Muroc Dry Lake rocket sled,* the 4-mile *SNORT* (Supersonic Naval Ordnance Research Track) at Inyokern, California, and the *SMART* (Supersonic Military Air Research Track) at Hurricane Mesa, Utah, are playing important roles in the development of new missiles.

Sleds are powered by solid or liquid propellant motors and attain incredible speeds. North American Aviation Corporation has a 50,000-pound thrust, liquid oxygen-alcohol, water rocket motor, with a firing time at full thrust of 4½ seconds. The supersonic Cook Research Laboratory sled uses this engine.

FIG. 70 *MATADOR*, PILOTLESS BOMBER TAKES OFF

A USAF *B-61* Martin *Matador* pilotless bomber roars away from its launcher leaving a fiery trail. The *Matador*, powered by an Allison turbo-jet engine, is already in service in Europe. With a powerful blast from its engine and aided by a rocket-assist-take-off bottle, it is fired from the "world's smallest airport," a highly mobile roadable launcher no bigger than the *Matador* itself. (USAF)

FIG. 71 *GAR-2A FALCON* AIR-TO-AIR MISSILE

The *GAR-2A Falcon,* air-to-air guided missile developed by Hughes Aircraft Company for the Air Force, is an infrared-seeking missile. The *GAR-2A* is designed to team up with the Hughes *GAR-1D,* radar-guided missile, for use by jet interceptors like the *F-102A* in background.

FIG. 75 *TERRIER* MISSILES DEFEND NAVY

Needle-nosed Convair *Terriers* point skyward in their launchers aboard the *USS Boston,* the U. S. Navy's first guided missile cruiser. The *Terrier* is a surface-to-air antiaircraft guided missile produced in quantity by Convair Division of General Dynamics Corporation at the U. S. Naval Industrial Reserve Ordnance Plant in Pomona, California. (Convair)

FIG. 76 *REGULUS* MISSILE JOINS SUBMARINE FLEET

The Navy's Chance Vought *Regulus I* surface-to-surface guided missile nestles, wings folded, in its cocoon on the deck of a submarine. *Regulus I* carries a nuclear warhead 600 miles. It is rocket-boosted and sustained in flight by a jet engine. (U. S. Navy)

FIG. 77 *REGULUS II* MISSILE ON LAUNCHING CART

The *Regulus II* guided missile is shown on a launcher cart used when the Navy missile is launched with the aid of a jet-assist bottle. The single bottle is installed beneath the *Regulus* and boosts it upward and forward. Chance Vought Aircraft manufactures the *Regulus II*, a supersonic attack missile designed for firing from submarines, carriers and other vessels. (Chance Vought)

FIG. 78 TEST PILOT AND *SIDEWINDER* MISSILE

Not a space traveler of the 25th century with a missile of the future, but rather one of today's guided missile test pilots, Lt. G. A. Tierney, of the U. S. Naval Ordnance Test Station and the Navy's latest guided missile, the *Sidewinder*. The pressurized suit allows the pilots to fly to extremely high altitudes where the *Sidewinder* is infrared-guided. (U. S. Navy)

FIG. 79 *LA CROSSE* MISSILE IS BLOCKHOUSE BUSTER

LaCrosse at Army Blockhouse area, White Sands Proving Grounds. *LaCrosse* is a tactical precision blockhouse buster, now operational with Army troops. (U. S. Army)

FIG. 80   TWO NOSE CONES MOUNTED ON SINGLE ROCKET

An NACA test rocket does double duty by carrying two experimental nose cones to test high-speed aerodynamic phenomena.   (NACA)

FIG. 81 *HAWK* MISSILES ON MOBILE LAUNCHER

The Army's Raytheon *Hawk* is designed to intercept low-flying attack aircraft in a tactical situation. The *Hawk* is highly mobile and is especially interesting to rocket men because it is a two-stage bird, even though it doesn't look it. The second-stage, forward rocket fires through center of first-stage via a blast tube. (U. S. Army)

FIG. 82 *TALOS* MISSILE ON AUTOMATIC MISSILE LAUNCHER

The Navy's *Talos* missile is shown on the land-based automatic missile launcher. *Talos,* equipped with a mechanical brain known as the steering intelligence system to direct it to its target, can travel at supersonic speeds and at an altitude higher than any known bomber can reach. It can carry either a high explosive or a nuclear warhead. *Talos* is primarily a shipboard bird.

FIG. 83 *NIKE-HERCULES* MISSILE ON LAUNCHER

The *Nike-Hercules,* the U. S. Army's new surface-to-air guided missile, on launcher at the White Sands Proving Grounds. Much faster and higher and possessing nuclear capabilities, *Nike-Hercules* is replacing *Nike-Ajax.*

FIG. 84 *THOR* MISSILE HURTLES INTO SPACE

Belching flame, an Air Force *Thor* reaches for the sky above its firing pad at the Air Force Missile Test Center, Cape Canaveral, Florida. Developed for the Air Force by the Douglas Aircraft Company, Inc., the intermediate range ballistic missile is being manufactured at the Santa Monica, California, plant. Missile has a 1500-mile range.

FIG. 85 THE *ATLAS* IS LAUNCHED

These sequence photos record the launching of an *Atlas* intercontinental ballistic missile from the Air Force Missile Test Center at Cape Canaveral, Florida. *Left*, twin incandescent jets from the powerful rocket engines become visible as the *Atlas* climbs clear of its wake of flame and steam. *Center*, the huge missile soars skyward, as expendable launcher tubing on pad still burns. Plume of flame spurting from missile base at (*right*) is exhaust from fuel system turbopumps. The *Atlas* is in pilot production at Convair, Astronautics' plant at San Diego, California. (Convair)

FIG. 86 *VANGUARD* SATELLITE ROCKET

Firing of the Navy's *Vanguard* Rocket, Cape Canaveral, Florida, February 5, 1958. Unfortunately it later broke in two, failing to place a satellite in orbit. Notice ice and frost falling away from around liquid oxygen tank in first stage. (U. S. Navy)

FIG. 87   SATELLITE READIED FOR LAUNCHING

Aspects of U. S. Army satellite program shown by Jet Propulsion Laboratory (California Institute of Technology) and Army Ballistic Missile Agency.   Missile technicians at the Army Ballistic Missile Agency assemble the satellite and final-stage rocket, designed to orbit as a single unit.   (U. S. Army)

SKOKIE AND CHEROKEE TEST MISSILES

An odd missile is the subsonic free-flight test vehicle, the 2500-pound *Skokie I*, developed by the Cook Electric Company. Designed as a recoverable parachute test vehicle, this unpowered missile is dropped from airplanes flying at about 30,000 feet and parachuted to the ground. The missile lands on a long spike protruding from the nose, which reduces landing damage.

For supersonic parachutes a *Skokie II* missile was developed, which is powered with three JATO units of 11,000 pounds thrust each. Air-launched, the *Skokie II* missile reaches a speed of Mach 2. Its free weight is 3000 pounds.

Still another missile in the Cook series is the *Cherokee,* designed for the checkout and testing of Air Force ejection seats. Top speeds involved are Mach 1.5 at 20,000 feet. The powerplant of the missile consists of a 3-second, 50,000-pound thrust, solid propellant unit. It is air-launched, parachute recovered, and like the *Skokie* missile, it incorporates a landing spear.

MISCELLANEOUS USES OF ROCKET POWER

Rockets have been proposed, and used, for several less heralded purposes than those already discussed. Research rockets are used to take instruments to high altitudes and through atomic mushrooms and tropical hurricanes. The mail rocket crops up perennially as a standard mail carrier, and something may conceivably yet come of it. In the meantime, postage stamps printed and surcharged or cancelled especially for these rare mail-shooting events bring rather high prices in the philatelic world.

Target practice is available with the *Pogo* rocket developed by the Physical Science Laboratory of the New Mexico College of Agriculture and Mechanical Arts under a Navy contract. The *Pogo* rocket has four square tail fins and is fired from a portable launcher. At peak altitude, a parachute contained in the nose opens, and the 13½-foot-long, 6½-inch diameter *Pogo* rocket drifts slowly to earth, being used as a target en route.

Rockets show great promise as a main or secondary power for helicopters. Ramjet and rocket engines installed in helicopter rotor tips have resulted in dramatic increases in climbing and carrying capacity. Since power is applied directly to the rotor, heavy transmissions are eliminated. The high fuel consumption problem is being solved, and the United States Navy is working with rocket-powered or -assisted helicopters, made by the Sikorsky, Kellett, and Rotocraft Corporations.

JATO has become well established in the aviation philosophy, but its cousin, the rocket auxiliary for surge power in combat, has not fared well. Braking rockets (reverse JATO) have been tried for shortening landing runs. Placing JATO bottles on wingtips for spin reversal has been attempted with somewhat promising results. Rocket power has been applied to all manner of vehicles (boats, gliders, automobiles, motorcycles, sleds, rail cars and even human skaters) with spectacularly poor results. For slow speeds rocket power is extravagant, but it is conceivable that some application might have military significance, if it provided a tactical advantage which ignored expense. Such an exception is the rocket sled, used in Air Force medical experiments, but here the element of transportation is incidental.

Sometimes the rocket takes the form of an igniter, which is really a miniature rocket engine. It is about the size of a fountain pen and extends into the interior of a thrust chamber to light the incoming propellants in some preliminary mixture ratio, which will not respond to sparkplugs soon enough to avoid a chamber explosion. Rocket propellants are sometimes burned in confined chambers called gas generators, and the resulting high-speed gas jet is applied to turbine wheels that drive propellant pumps or generators that generate hydraulic or electric power for short periods of time during missile flights.

Since a rocket engine operates on a principle similar to the oxyacetylene torch (except that it goes to great pains to have a sonic nozzle), it is a logical candidate for metal and even ground drilling. With adaptation, it could be used to inflate rafts made of balloons. The high energy available from a rocket engine can provide motive power for airplane launching catapults. Although typically massive devices, aircraft catapults may be modified to increase their transportability for expeditionary use.

Rocket engines, or similar devices, might be used to power turbine-starting systems. Liquid propellant artillery pieces are conceivable. A rocket flame could be used for hot-spraying layers of ceramic materials on the inside of thrust chambers, or on other devices using refractory surfaces. Little-known and rather mysterious to the layman is the potential of the rocket principle in the chemical industry for speeding reactions or making possible others through the addition of enough energy or heat at the right time and place.

Lifesaving rockets have been in use for a century. They are used to carry cables to grounded ships and to other highly inaccessible places. A recently developed 3.25-inch rocket hurls a 7-foot pike, trailing a ¼-inch cable a distance of 1171 feet. With this device it is not necessary to use a lighter line to draw the main cable out to the stricken ship. If the cable falls on the stricken ship it may be secured immediately, and a breeches-buoy can be installed on the cable for immediate use.

The smallest rocket engine ever likely to be constructed is one recently developed by the University of Southern California at Los Angeles. Using a 0.005-inch nozzle and propelled by the detonation of a small wafer of nitrosoguanadine, the new supersonic hypodermic "needle" delivers injections to tumors and internal organs at a speed of about Mach 1.75.

These are welcome incidental benefits being derived from rocketry. The real future, however, of reaction-powered flight lies in outer space, with chemical rockets, nuclear rockets, ion rockets, photon rockets and—who can really foretell?—other kinds of rockets.

Now that the Russians have shown their power, it seems certain that the thinking of departments, agencies and commissions in Washington must be reorganized and centered on one basic long-term plan—to put the United States in first place in space exploration. This will be one of the most difficult struggles this country has ever faced—a struggle that cannot be won by brawn and dollars alone. It requires not only an acceleration of this country's superb rate of technological achievement, but also the proper mobilization of that achievement. It is perhaps here that Americans are most lacking.

The Soviet Union beat the United States with the first earth satellite, not because this country failed to spend enough money, or because Americans lacked any of the technological knowhow, but because the United States chose to be beaten. However, Congressional committees and government agencies have been established to guard against repeating the errors of the past. These committees are (with their chairmen): House Democrat Leader, John W. McCormack, and his "Select Committee on Astronautics and Space Exploration," together with the Committee Staff, headed by George J. Feldman, Chief Counsel and Director; Senator Lyndon B. Johnson and his "Special Committee on Space and Astronautics," together with the Senate Committee Staff consisting of Edwin L. Weisl, Consulting Counsel; Cyrus Vance, Consulting Counsel; Dr. Homer Joe Stewart, Scientific Consultant; Dr. Glen P. Wilson, Coordinator of Technical Information and Mrs. Eilene Galloway, Special Consultant.

The future of astronautics in the United States is in the capable hands of the military and in two essential non-military organizations, namely, Advanced Research Projects Agency (ARPA), and National Aeronautics and Space Administration (NASA).

The principal officers of ARPA are: Roy W. Johnson, Director; Lambert L. Lind, Special Assistant to the Director; Rear Admiral John E. Clark, Deputy Director; Dr. Herbert F. York, Chief Scientist; James O. Spriggs, Special Assistant to the Chief Scientist; Lawrence P. Gise, Director of Office of Program Control and Administration; William H. Godel, Director of Office of Foreign Development.

The principal officers of NASA are: T. Keith Glennan, Administrator; Hugh L. Dryden, Deputy Administrator.

8

Rockets and Missiles—
An Industry

A great industrial change is taking place in the United States. The aircraft industry, which long considered missiles as a small department, now finds itself becoming a part of the large missile and space flight industry. It is an elemental evolution. An industrial change is upon us comparable to the advent of mercantilism.

Any discussion of guided missiles and rocketry inevitably becomes a discussion of the industry that, in most cases, designs, develops, manufactures, and tests the articles and components. The military establishment that supports the project in most cases provides the ultimate system test facilities, and in many cases the production plants where the products are made. Whatever the relationships between various enterprises and the armed forces, close liaison is invariably present.

The present emphasis on the weapons system concept usually results in extensive subcontracting. For example, the prime contracting company may build the airframe, other companies may build the motor and the guidance system, while still other companies provide various avionic (aviation electronic) parts. It is not unusual to find the whole affair under the technical supervision of a relatively small contractor or perhaps a university laboratory.

Specialists in the rocket engine field include the Reaction Motors Corporation, the Grand Central Rocket Company, the Aerojet-General Corporation, and the Thiokol Chemical Company, while others, such as the North American Aviation Corporation and the General Electric Company, develop rockets as only one phase of a wide field of missile activity. The listing of all aircraft and avionic manufacturers working in some phase of rocketry or missile development would fill a book in itself.

More and more non-aircraft companies also occupy extremely important places in the missile industry, examples being the Westinghouse Electric Corporation, the Raytheon Company, the Bell Telephone Company (its subsidiary the Western Electric Company developed the *Nike* missile), the Diversey Engineering Company, the Cooper Development Company, the Chrysler Corporation, and the Olin Mathieson Chemical Corporation. Obviously it is impossible to discuss more than a selected few representative companies in this activity, and even here only capsule accounts are feasible.

THE NEW COMPANIES

Today, most aircraft companies active in missiles have established guided missiles divisions, generally with their own separate facilities. One of the oldest is the Fairchild Engine and Airplane Corporation, whose Guided Missiles Division has been in operation since 1945. It received one of the first complete missile system contracts in the country. The missile division of an aircraft company is capable of handling many phases of missile engineering—electronics, servomechanisms, aerodynamics, test, and related activities. Up-to-date computer facilities permit the rapid solution of complex problems.

The Fairchild Corporation's Guided Missiles Division is best known for its *Lark* missile project, which originally began during the war as a defense against Japanese *kamikaze* planes. The Navy's Bureau of Aeronautics initiated the program and gave Fairchild the job of designing and building an airframe. By December 1945, the first test missile was made available to the Navy, and by the following year the *Lark* project expanded to include guidance systems. In 1950, after well over a hundred tests were fired, the *Lark* missile was released for production for the Air Force and the Navy.

The rocket engine pioneers are, of course, the Aerojet Corporation and the Reaction Motors Corporation. The former produces both liquid and solid propellant motors, while the latter has emphasized liquid developments.

The Aerojet Engineering Corporation was organized in 1941 by a group composed of Theodore von Karman, F. J. Malina, M. Summerfield, J. Parsons, E. Forman, and by Von Karman's attorney, A. G. Haley. The last-named individual supplied the initial capital to achieve the formal incorporation of the company in the spring of 1942. The group pooled their financial resources to accumulate eventually a capitalization of $68,000. It soon became apparent that, in order to do the job envisioned by the Armed Services, the company would require adequate testing grounds. A site was selected by Haley at Azusa, California, and he was able to obtain Defense Plant Corporation financing for most of this project. However, the dollar volume of the contracts for liquid and solid propellant JATO units and for many other developments, including items of basic research, mounted so fast that it was quite impossible for the financial authorities in the Army and Navy Departments continuously to provide what amounted to almost 100% financing of the operations of the company.

Early in 1944, the financial officials of the Armed Services advised Haley that they could not continue to grant contracts in terms of millions of dollars when the Aerojet Corporation did not have the basic 10% of its own capital with which to perform the contracts.

The dilemma became quite obvious—all of the work of the Aerojet Corporation was classified either as confidential or secret and Haley's hands were tied in discussing the company's activities, even with the most respected of financial institutions. In the meantime, he and his colleagues had recruited hundreds of outstanding scientists, engineers and technicians from all over the United States and had moved them to the Pasadena-Azusa, California, area. No sacrifice was too great to protect these people.

Haley finally got permission from security officials to discuss financing with a former client of his Washington law firm, The General Tire & Rubber Company. The officials of that company were alert and farsighted enough to supply the necessary financing and, eventually, to take over control of the corporation. They also exercised a high degree of wisdom in retaining the key employees originally recruited by Von Karman, Summerfield and Haley. These key men still form the official nucleus of what is now the Aerojet-General Corporation.

The story of the ultimate disposition of the founders and original owners of the Aerojet Corporation is paralleled by the story of the Reaction Motors Corporation, and the Power Jets Corporation, the organization formed by Captain Whittle in England. The fate of each group was inexorably the same. Lovell Lawrence and his colleagues at the Reaction Motors Corporation, and Captain Whittle and his colleagues at the Power Jets Corporation, lost administrative control because of the lack of adequate working capital. But in the case of the Aerojet Corporation, there was a notable exception, in that most of the pioneers are still employed by the Corporation. A few of these pioneers are Zwicky, Zisch, Reichert, Mundt, Dorman, Ross, Young, Rogers, Gongwer, and the Millers. These men assisted the Founders in making the Aerojet Corporation a great enterprise. They are still working hard to make the Aerojet-General Corporation one of the most important industrial suppliers in all fields of astronautics.

The Aerojet Corporation has not only pioneered and excelled in the application of solid propellant rocket power, but has pursued research and development in the liquid field as well. As with solids, the Aerojet-General Corporation's liquid work was closely identified with JATO achievements.

Since the war, Aerojet has developed and produced new JATO devices, used on such planes as the *B-47* jet bomber and the Republic Aviation Corporation's *F-84* fighter-bomber. An Aerojet engine was also developed for use in an improved *Lark* missile, but the missile never materialized.

The *Regulus,* the *Terrier,* the *Loon,* and the *Sparrow* missiles have used either booster or sustainer rockets made by Aerojet. The company also has contracts to supply rockets for the *Titan* and the *Polaris* missiles. The famed sounding rocket *Aerobee* is an Aerojet development, receiving solid propellant boost and liquid propellant sustaining power from engines made by the Corporation. The *Aerobee* and the *Aerobee-Hi* missiles have become, since 1947, standard upper air research tools.

Special devices, for example, jet reverser brakes, powerpacks, turbo-starters, gas liquification systems, guidance systems, control systems, armament rockets, underwater engines, and testing atomic energy facilities, point up the broad scope of activities at the Aerojet-General Corporation. Some of the Aerojet's underwater rockets and hydroducts have propelled torpedoes (underwater missiles) at speeds in excess of 150 knots per hour.

The Reaction Motors Corporation was incorporated in December 1941, making it America's oldest rocket engine manufacturer. From the beginning, the Reaction Motors Corporation concentrated on liquid propellant developments, and, carrying through with the enthusiasm and skill of the experimenters who organized it, the Corporation rapidly became established as a going concern.

The Reaction Motors Corporation grew out of experiments conducted by the American Rocket Society during the 1930's. A number of successful rocket flights had been made, but experimenters were continually plagued by rocket engines which exploded or burned holes through the engine walls or nozzles. James Wyld, a mechanical engineer who had participated in these experiments, solved the problem by circulating fuel through the double walls of the rocket engine thrust chambers.

This rocket engine developed 100 pounds of thrust and worked so well that Wyld and two other experimenters of proven technical talent, Franklin Pierce and John Shesta, joined with Lovell Lawrence, Jr., an electronics expert of the International Business Machines Corporation, to form a rocket engine corporation. A collected "kitty" of $5,000 among the four men, and an advance from the U. S. Navy Department just after Pearl Harbor, started the corporation off on a contract to produce a JATO unit developing 1000 pounds of thrust. Within a short time, a series of engines ranging from 50 pounds to 1000 pounds of thrust had been developed. In 1943 a 3000-pound thrust JATO unit for a Navy *PBM* flying boat was ready for flight test.

More contracts followed, and the Reaction Motors Corporation began to produce 350-pound thrust, acid and aniline, rocket engines for the Navy's *Gorgon* guided bomb, and to construct a novel boost-and-cruise powerplant for the Fairchild Engine and Airplane Corporation *Lark* missile, containing 400- and 220-pound thrust chambers. Over 500 of these highly reliable *620* rocket engines were produced for the armed forces.

The corporation experimented for some time with a rocket engine having a 1500-pound thrust chamber, for use on rocket-powered rotary wing aircraft, and with pulse jet engines based on the German *V-1* design. One of the immediate results of this work was a development contract for a 6000-pound thrust rocket engine, made of 4 of the 1500-pound thrust chambers. This liquid oxygen and alcohol engine became the Reaction Motors Corporation "workhorse," and eventually powered the Navy's *Skyrocket* (D-558-2), the Bell Aircraft Corporation's *X-1, X-1A, X-1B,* and *X-1E,* and the Air Force's *XF-91* combat-type airplane made by the Republic Aviation Corporation.

In 1947, another Reaction Motors Corporation engine, a 4-chamber 8000-pound thrust unit, was ready. This engine, a "beefed up" 6000-pound unit used in Convair's *MX-774* missile, was unique in that each chamber swivelled individually for directional control of the missile. Three successful upper atmosphere missile flights were made. Two years later the largest Reaction Motors Corporation engine of all was ready, the 20,000-pound thrust, single-chamber powerplant for the *Viking* missile. The Reaction Motors Corporation also makes the 60,000-pound thrust engine for the *X-15* rocket plane.

On October 7, 1955, the Reaction Motors Corporation dedicated at Danville, New Jersey, a new $4,000,000 development, production, and administrative facility, ending about a dozen years of awkward geographical scattering of plant sites around the countryside near Rockaway, New Jersey.

In 1953 control of the Reaction Motors Corporation was sold by its founders to Rockefeller Brothers, Inc., and the Olin Mathieson Corporation. For several years Rockefeller Brothers, Inc., supplied essential financial management while the Olin Mathieson Corporation contributed its technical and production capabilities to the success of the expanding enterprise. In 1958 the Thiokol Corporation, seeking to broaden its capabilities in the rocket field by including liquid propellant rocket engines, as well as its own solid propellant engines, negotiated a merger with the Reaction Motors Corporation in a transaction by which Rockefeller Brothers, Inc., and the Olin Mathieson Corporation were relieved of their active ownership. At the present writing, the Reaction Motors Corporation is operating as a division of the now enlarged Thiokol Corporation and will presumably contribute its talents to the Thiokol Corporation's original solid propellant interests.

THE OLDER COMPANIES

The General Electric Company was one of the first American enterprises to enter into full-scale missile research, development, and manufacture, as a result of the *Hermes* missile project discussed earlier. Some of the General Electric Company's "firsts" include the first large rocket launching in this hemisphere (a *V-2*), the development and construction of the first large rocket test-firing facility in the United States, and the development of the first large-scale supersonic ramjet engine. The General Electric Company now has several major departments devoted to missile work. These departments produce ballistic missile reentry nose cones for the *Atlas* and the *Thor*. They also produce the *Vanguard* first-stage engine, guidance systems, and auxiliary power units. The General Electric Company's turbojet engines power "air-breathing" missiles, as well as manned aircraft.

Another early entry in the guided missile field, the Sperry Gyroscope Company, can point back to its 1915–1917 *Aerial Torpedoes* or *Flying Bombs,* which took off automatically, traveled to a given location, dived on a target, and exploded. One Navy model of the *Flying Bomb* could dump 1000 pounds of explosive on targets 100 miles away, a laudable achievement in those days.

More recently, the Sperry-Rand Company has been involved with a wide variety of guidance systems, stabilization systems, and control projects. Typical of recent advances in the stabilization system field is the system developed for the Chance Vought Aircraft Corporation's *Regulus* missile. The Sperry Corporation also has its own missile development project, the *Sparrow I,* sponsored by the Navy Bureau of Aeronautics. It is now manufacturing the *Sergeant* missile for the Army.

The Ryan Aeronautical Corporation has specialized in three principal missile phases, namely, rocket powerplants, surface-to-air missiles, and high-speed, recoverable, target drones. In the first category, the Corporation manufactures the complete rocket motor (designed by the Jet Propulsion Laboratory of the California Institute of Technology) for the Army's *Corporal* surface-to-surface combat missile, as well as rocket powerplants for commercial enterprises.

In the missile field, the Ryan Aeronautical Corporation has been identified not only with its own *Firebird* missile, but with major component production for such well-known vehicles as the *Aerobee* missile. The final major area of the Corporation's missile specialization, involves high speed target drones.

The North American Aviation Corporation was organized in 1928, and operated from a Dundalk, Maryland plant. By 1934, a variety of activities had been narrowed down to the manufacture and sale of airplanes. Against heavy competition, the Corporation landed an early Army Air Corps trainer-and-observation plane contract. In 1936, with a 100-man payroll, the Corporation moved to Los Angeles, California. At the present time, the company holds the record of having manufactured more airplanes than any other enterprise in the world.

Currently, the North American Aviation Corporation maintains three major divisions devoted to missiles and rockets, covering complete missile systems, guidance systems, and propulsion engines. Its Rocketdyne division is the West Coast's largest manufacturer of large liquid propellant engines. It currently supplies powerplants for *Atlas, Thor,* and *Jupiter* missiles. Its 50,000-pound thrust, liquid propellant rocket engine propels the Cook Research Laboratories' test sled, which has made over 200 runs without a major failure or replacement. The rocket engine operates on easily replenished liquid oxygen and alcohol and is designed to bring the sled to a velocity of 1500 miles per hour in 4.5 seconds, when the sled is just over a mile from the starting point.

Formerly the "Consolidated Vultee Aircraft Corporation," the Convair and Convair, Astronautics Division of the General Dynamics Corporation, located in San Diego, California, produce both the *Atlas* and the *Terrier* missiles.

Convair gained its first missile experience during the war. Convair began work on the Navy's *MX-776* missile in 1946 and successfully test-fired the first one at the White Sands Proving Ground in 1948. The missile measured 32 feet in length by 30 inches in diameter. It was designed to test the operation of advanced types of rocket vehicles, new launching techniques, handling devices, fuels, and engines. Its use was also contemplated for high-altitude research applications.

Convair also worked on the *Lark* missile, concurrently with the Fairchild Engine and Airplane Corporation on the East Coast, to develop a guided shipboard-to-air missile. The missile served as a prototype for the later developed Convair *Terrier* missile, test-fired from shipboard in 1951.

The Douglas Aircraft Company, probably best known for its *DC*-series of airplanes, is also an old hand at the missile business, having been occupied with many varieties for at least 12 years. The list of missile projects handled at one stage or another by the company sounds almost like a roll-call of the field—the *Bumper, Little John, Honest John, ROC, Nike, WAC-Corporal, Corporal E,* and the *Thor.*

The Douglas Aircraft Company entered the *Nike* missile picture in 1946 and designed airframe and launching equipment. The *Sparrow* missile project, which started off as *Hot Shot,* also had its airframe designed by the company. At the request of Army Ordnance, the *Honest John* missile went on the board in 1950, and by 1951 it was tested in White Sands.

The Douglas Aircraft Company's missile facilities have kept up with the expansion of the missile program. A new plant in Charlotte, North Carolina is now devoted to *Nike* missile production.

The Ground-to-Air Pilotless Aircraft (G.A.P.A.) Program signaled the Boeing Airplane Company's entrance into the guided missiles business. The

G.A.P.A. defense missile was highly successful. In 1951, the men responsible for the design of the missile were transferred to the Air Force's Long Range Missile Center at Patrick Air Force Base, Florida, to prepare for another missile test project, the *Bomarc*. First announced in 1953, the *Bomarc* is a delta-wing, ramjet engine, surface-to-air missile, with an internal liquid propellant rocket engine, being produced at the Boeing Airplane Company's Wichita, Kansas, facility.

The *Regulus*, a most versatile and ingenious missile, is a product of the Chance Vought Aircraft Corporation, an independent company, formerly part of United Aircraft. It started the *Regulus* missile program back in 1947. The missile took shape in 1948, and was test flown two years later at Edwards Air Force Base in California. The main philosophies behind the *Regulus* missile are versatility, economy, simplicity, and efficiency. The missile is fired from an easily installed launcher. It can be used for numerous missions, brought back, and landed.

Guided missile and rocket developments began in World War II at the Northrop Aircraft Company, which has since become identified with launching devices and high-speed rocket-powered sleds. The company incorporates the experience gained from the development of launching techniques for the *JB-10* pulse-jet missiles built during the war.

The Northrop Aircraft Company can boast of the first American rocket airplane flight—the *MX-324*. The company also had a hand in buzz bomb development work, and through its subsidiary, Radioplane Company of Van Nuys, California, became active in the pilotless target drone field. The Northrop Aircraft Company's latest claim to fame, however, is as designer and manufacturer of the United States' intercontinental cruise missile, the *Snark*. The company is also a major subcontractor on the *Hawk* missile.

The Republic Aviation Corporation has built up a world-wide reputation as the builder of the "Thunder" series of combat aircraft, including the *P-47 Thunderbolt*, the *F-84 Thunderjet*, and the *F-84F* sweptwing *Thunderstreak*. The company also designed and built a supersonic experimental interceptor, the *XF-91*, which was powered by a Reaction Motors Corporation 6000-pound thrust engine, plus a *J-47* turbojet engine. This plane was the first American combat-type fighter to exceed sonic speed. One of the company's latest projects is the low-cost, 100-mile-high, university research missile, the *Terrapin*.

The Lockheed Aircraft Corporation developed the solid propellant, re-entry research vehicle, *X-17*. It has the prime contract for the *Polaris* missile and recently received an Air Force order to place a television camera carrying reconnaissance satellite in orbit. The McDonnell Aircraft Corporation held the prime contract for the *Triton* missile, and now supplies the ramjet powerplant for the *Talos* missile. The Bendix Aviation Corporation, one of the country's leading avionic suppliers, builds the *Talos* missile at its Mishawaka, Indiana facility. The Sylvania Electric Products Company has a new Avionics and Missile Systems Laboratory. The Firestone Industrial Products Company makes the *Corporal* missile. The Utica-Bend Corporation manufactures the *Dart* missile.

The Hughes Aircraft Company is the prime contractor for the *Falcon* missile and is a leading factor in many classified missile projects. Nearly 5000 of the company's 20,000 personnel work in the Tucson, Arizona, guided missiles plant, where more than 1000 *Falcon* missiles are turned out each month.

The Bell Aircraft Corporation of Buffalo, New York, has long been identified with advanced aircraft design, including the rocket-powered *X-1, X-1A, X-1B,* and *X-2,* holders of many world records. The corporation is the prime contractor for the long-range *Rascal* (GAM 63), air-to-surface guided missile.

The Martin Company of Baltimore pioneered in upper atmosphere research rockets. Its *Viking* missile holds many single-stage missile speed and altitude records. The company also produces target-drone missiles and has the prime contract for the satellite 3-stage launching vehicle, *Vanguard.* The Martin Company has recently announced that it is doing basic research on gravity itself, the giant hand that holds us to this planet. Its Denver facility produces the Air Force's *Titan.* At Orlando, Florida, it makes the *Lacrosse* and the *Bullpup* missiles. Production of the *Matador* missile is carried on in the Baltimore plant of the Martin Company.

Work in the missile sciences began at the M. W. Kellogg Company in May 1945, when the Jet Propulsion Laboratory of the Air Technical Service Command, Army Air Force, turned over to the Kellogg Company several contracts involving captured German missiles and miscellaneous research. Many of the Kellogg Company's programs evolved into the final booster or sustainer designs of the *Nike, Honest John, Rigel, Sparrow, Meteor, Pogo, Terrier,* and the *Talos* missiles.

A subsidiary of the Grand Central Aircraft Company, the Grand Central Rocket Company was formed in August of 1954, after having operated since 1952 as the company's Rocket Division. The latter company handles solid propellant powerplants, from the basic research phase through production. It is now delivering the *Vanguard* missile third-stage rocket engines. Recently, the controlling interest has been acquired by the Tennessee Gas Transmission Company.

THE CHEMICAL COMPANIES

The Thiokol Chemical Corporation entered the rocket propellant field in 1947, nearly 20 years after its founding. Today the corporation operates a number of divisions in many states, including large rocket development facilities in Huntsville, Alabama, a rocket production plant in Marshall, Texas, a solid fuel facility in Elkton, Maryland, a liquid-polymer plant in Moss Point, Mississippi, and the world's most modern solid propellant production facility at Ogden, Utah, where the *Sergeant* missile's rocket engines are being made.   The Thiokol Corporation supplies rocket engines and boosters for a wide variety of Army, Navy, and Air Force missiles.   Its *Recruit* and *Sergeant* missile rocket engines made up the *X-17* missile. Another project, the *Big-B,* is one of the largest solid propellant rocket engines ever made.

A rundown of some of the other companies in the propellants field includes: the Buffalo Electro Chemical Company (hydrogen peroxide and dimethyl hydrazine); the Linde Air Products Company (LOX) and the Westvaco Chlor-Alkali Company (dimethyl hydrazine), both part of the Food Machinery and Chemical Corporation; the Nitrogen Division of the Allied Chemical and Dye Corporation (nitrogen tetroxide, etc.); the Pennsylvania Salt Manufacturing Company (fluorine and chlorine trifluoride); the Union Carbide and Carbon Chemical Company (fuels and oxidizers); the American Machine and Foundry Company (monopropellants, ground handling and launching gear, rockets, guided-missile systems); and the Hercules Powder Company.   The Hercules Powder Company is the parent company of the Allegany Ballistics Laboratory, an old name in solid-propellant rocket engine research, development, and manufacture.   One of its current production items is the *Terrier* missile's rocket engine.

Other missile component development companies are: the Atlantic Research Corporation engaged in solid-propellant research and development (*Vanguard's* retrorockets), combustion studies, and interior ballistics; the Western Gear Corporation with missile-actuating mechanisms and ground-control systems; the Norden-Ketay Company, developer and manufacturer of the famed Norden bombsight, with radar, gyroscope, and missile controls; the Kollsman Instrument Company with guided-missile navigation and controls devices; the Lavalle Aircraft Company with radar components; the Gyromechanisms Corporation with gyroscopes and guidance; and the Philco Corporation with guidance, control, and related systems.   The Philco Corporation also holds the *Sidewinder* missile contract and is involved in the *Falcon* missile program.   The G. M. Giannini Company is engaged in the development and manufacture of automatic and precision instruments and controls at plants on the East and West coasts.   This company was formed in 1935 to administer the patent rights connected with Enrico Fermi's radioactivity discoveries.   The Giannini Research Laboratory holds ion propulsion research contracts and recently got a specific impulse of 600 seconds from a crude ion system.   The Arthur D. Little Company is active in propellants, explosives, cryogenics, and other developments important to the rocket field.

The Ex-Cell-O Developments Company is busy with the development of rocket engines and a variety of guided missile components. The Ramo-Wooldridge Corporation is an important factor in the *Atlas, Titan,* and *Thor* missile programs, acting as systems monitor for the Air Force. The Westinghouse Electric Company has several missile guidance system projects, and Experiment, Inc., performs valuable research on missile propulsion systems. A leading inertial-guidance system and general electro-mechanical control developer is the American Bosch Arma Corporation. The General Motors Corporation's AC Sparkplug Division works in the same field. The South West Research Institute has come up with high-thrust, short-duration solid rockets for oil-well application.

In the materials field, Armour Research Foundation has made important contributions to the use of ceramics in rocket motors, and the Climax Molybdenum Corporation is doing basic research in the same area. The Reynolds Metals Company makes the *Redstone* missile's airframe. The Aerophysics Development Corporation is occupied with missile-system and rocket-propulsion problems, and Alco Products, Inc., is a producer of missile components. The Allen B. Dumont Laboratories, Inc., develops instrumentation and guidance equipment. The Cooper Development Company is a prime systems contractor for the research rockets, the *Asp* and the *Wasp.* The Diversey Engineering Company, non-existent in 1948, now does a multi-million-dollar business in the highly specialized field of missile metal machining. Havig Industries, Inc., lines solid propellant rocket motors.

The list is virtually endless and ever-growing. Companies that never had anything to do with aviation find themselves deeply involved in missiles. Devilish problems of rocketry turn out to be solvable by industrial techniques associated with civilian products, rather than weapons.

OTHER INDUSTRIES

Almost every segment of American industry is in one way or another tied up with the enormous guided missile effort. An automobile company, the Chrysler Corporation, has a missile branch and manufactures the *Redstone* and the *Jupiter* surface-to-surface missiles. The General American Transportation Corporation's Plastics Division is occupied with the development of plastic fuselages for guided missiles, resulting in smoother skins, better corrosion resistance, and so on. The B. F. Goodrich Company's Industrial Products Division, active in perfecting a high temperature insulation for the interior of rocket motors and missile booster cases, developed a semi-ceramic composition known as Pyrolock.

The rocket-powered missile is vastly different from the airplane. For example, it is more often machined, welded, and heat-treated than it is ribbed, skinned, and riveted. Often excessively costly to develop, in production it is essentially a low-cost item. Its development usually proceeds more quickly and more smoothly under small, independent, closely knit teams than when thrown to vast, complex research and engineering divisions. Many rocket and missile problems require creative rather than engineering solutions. Too often there simply is no background of data available for an "engineered" solution. As the science itself is new and constantly changing, so is the industry that supports it.

Thus it is impossible to name all the companies playing a vital role in this field. What has preceded is only a sampling, and even that is probably out of date as it is written, so rapidly is the field developing. Meanwhile, others play a vital role, too.

THE ASSOCIATED UNIVERSITY LABORATORIES

Princeton University's jet propulsion research program under the Department of Aeronautical Engineering performs basic jet propulsion studies and development. On the West coast, the 200,000-square-foot ten-million-dollar Jet Propulsion Laboratory of the California Institute of Technology continues to be a major factor in rocket design and development, particularly in the *Jupiter* missile series. The Laboratory's staff has grown to over 1000 personnel, distributed throughout aerodynamics, guided missile avionics, guided missile engineering, rockets and materials, and applied research.

Cornell University's Aeronautical Laboratories are now conducting research in high-speed aerodynamics and super-aerodynamics. They designed among others, the *Lacrosse* missile. The Physics Department of the University of Maryland has been active in the current satellite-vehicle program, as well as being a sponsoring agency for high-altitude meteorological rocketry. Its staff designed the *Terrapin* and the *Oriole* research rockets.

The Massachusetts Institute of Technology has long been in the missile field and was particularly active with the *Meteor* project. The State University of Iowa has been running the *Rockoon* project for some time, and universities in New Mexico have been closely associated with the White Sands rocket firings. Universities connected with *Aerobee* or *V-2* firings include Harvard, Michigan, Denver, Boston, Colorado, Utah, and Rhode Island. Purdue University has a Jet Propulsion Laboratory and a Rocket Laboratory, which includes four rocket test cells.

The Daniel and Florence Guggenheim Foundation announced on December 16, 1948, the establishment of jet-propulsion centers at Princeton University and at the California Institute of Technology. Their purpose was to provide post-graduate education and research in the field, with special emphasis being given to peacetime uses. One-half million dollars was allotted for a seven-year period. The principal post for each establishment is the Robert H. Goddard Professorship, associated with which are three Guggenheim Jet Propulsion Fellowships each, with stipends of two thousand dollars per fellowship.

The CalTech Center was organized and headed in 1949 by H. S. Tsien as Goddard Professor; collaborating with him were Professors F. E. Marble, S. S. Penner, and W. D. Rannie. After the resignation of Tsien in 1955, Rannie assumed the dual post of Goddard Professor and Director of the Center. At Princeton University, the directorship of the Center was the joint responsibility of Professors L. Crocco, J. V. Charyk, and M. Summerfield, the leading role being that of Crocco who became the Goddard Professor. Since 1949, about fifty graduate students in rocket and jet propulsion have won their advanced degrees as Guggenheim Fellows, and over a hundred more have been similarly trained in the Centers with the aid of financial support from other sources. Nearly all of these men have assumed leading positions in research and development in the American missile industry.

Since 1948 courses in exterior ballistics have been made available by Ohio State University to selected Air Force officers at Wright Field Graduate Center in Dayton, Ohio. With the academic year of 1949–1950 began a rocket propulsion course including elements, terminology, thermodynamics, fluid mechanics, propellants, engine stability, missile control, and multi-stage rockets, including escape rockets.

Courses on guided missiles are taught to Army officers at Fort Bliss, Texas, and at the Massachusetts Institute of Technology students may study orbital mechanics under the tutelage of Professor Sandorff. Low-temperature research is carried on in Columbus, Ohio, at Ohio State University's Cryogenic Laboratory under H. L. Johnson, notably with liquid hydrogen, and liquid hydrogen/liquid oxygen rocket engines and pump programs for the Air Materiel Command.

Located in Silver Spring, Maryland, the Applied Physics Laboratory of Johns Hopkins University was started by a group of scientists from the Department of Terrestrial Magnetism at the Carnegie Institute of Washington, D. C., in 1940, under the supervision of the National Defense Research Committee. The group, directed by M. A. Tuve, had as its original objective the investigation of problems relating to the defense of United States Navy vessels against aircraft. In March 1942, it moved to Silver Spring, where, under the aegis of the Office of Scientific Research and Development, work on such projects as gunfire control systems and proximity fuses was continued.

FIG. 88   FIRST AMERICAN ROCKET-ASSIST TAKE-OFF IN 1941

First American tests of aircraft take-off assisted by solid propellant rockets at March Field, California, August 1941. The pilot in the *Ercoupe* airplane is Air Force Captain H. A. Boushey, Jr.; on the ground right to left: F. J. Malina, Fred Miller, and an unknown Air Force mechanic. (Jet Propulsion Laboratory)

FIG. 89   *B-47* BOMBER TAKES OFF WITH AID OF *JATO* UNITS

A far cry from the *Ercoupe:* A *B-47* "Stratojet" takes off the Flight Test Center's main runway. As a part of the maximum loading tests conducted at the Air Force Flight Test Center, the "Stratojet" is equipped with special *JATO* units for added thrust. (USAF)

FIG. 90   "SHIRT-SLEEVE" EXECUTIVES, DECEMBER 1943

Aerojet President A. G. Haley and Office Manager, John Neal assembling *JATO* units during the night after a busy day in the executive offices.

FIG. 91   ROCKET-ASSIST SAILPLANE TAKES OFF

E. E. Nelson taking off in Pratt-Reed sailplane equipped with *12AS-250 Jr. JATO*, December 1948.   (Aerojet)

FIG. 92 *JATO* ROCKET MOTORS MOUNTED ON AIRPLANE

Aerojet model *14AS-1000D-4 JATO* rocket motors manufactured by the Aerojet-General Corporation, Azusa, California. This rocket motor is powered by solid propellant and provides a 1000-pound thrust for 14 seconds at 60° F. It is designed primarily as a jet-assist take-off unit to augment the power obtained from an aircraft's engines. The weight of the *14AS-1000D-4 JATO* rocket motor ready for installation is 200 pounds. The weight of the motor after the propellant charge has been expended is 115 pounds. The unit is 35⅝ inches in over-all length and 10¾₆ inches in over-all diameter. (Aerojet-General)

FIG. 93 *JATO* AIDS JET INTERCEPTOR IN TAKE-OFF

JATO gives jet interceptor, a USAF *F-84,* zero-launch capabilities. Solid rocket booster falls off shortly after craft is airborne. (USAF)

FIG. 94   FOUNDERS OF AEROJET ENGINEERING CORPORATION

Left to right: Martin Summerfield; Frank J. Malina; Theodore von Karman; Andrew G. Haley; Paul Dane; Edward S. Forman; John W. Parsons.

FIGS. 95 AND 96   Aerojet's president with his "right-hand man," Andrew, Jr (shown at right), at spade turning, Azusa, California, 1942.

FIG. 97   ROCKET ENGINE AIDS AIRPLANE IN TAKE-OFF

Airplane taking off with assistance of the *YLR63-AJ-1* liquid rocket engine. (Aerojet-General)

FIG. 98   ROCKET-POWERED TEST SLED

Rocket-powered test sleds provide researchers with a valuable tool. Spewing a white plume of smoke, the rocket-propelled decelerator roars down its track, head for the breaking area. Telemetering equipment already is sending back to the control room information on volunteer's reactions during the run. (Northrop)

FIG. 99   BELL *X-1* ROCKET-POWERED EXPERIMENTAL PLANE

The Bell *X-1* (formerly *XS-1*) rocket-powered Air Force experimental plane is shown in flight near Muroc Air Force Base, California. The *XS-1* was the first manned aircraft to exceed sonic velocity. (USAF)

FIG. 100   MODEL *1500N4C* LIQUID PROPELLANT ROCKET ENGINE

Reaction Motors Corporation 6000-pound thrust, model *1500N4C* liquid propellant rocket engine. This engine powered the Bell *X-1* in the first sonic-barrier breaking flight. Similar models of the engine have propelled the Douglas *D-558-II* (*Skyrocket*), the Bell *X-1A,* and the Republic *XF-91* to piloted flight records. (Reaction Motors)

FIG. 101   BELL *X-1B* ROCKET PLANE

The Bell *X-1B,* sister plane to the *X-1A,* which held both the speed and altitude records until beaten by the *X-2.*   (Bell)

FIG. 102   BELL *X-2* RESEARCH PLANE

The Air Force's Bell *X-2* high-speed research plane is shown at the Air Force Flight Test Center, Edwards Air Force Base, California.   The rocket-powered *X-2* was designed and built to probe the so-called thermal barrier.   Before the *X-2* was finally destroyed in a crash, it had reached over 120,000 feet in altitude and exceeded 2100 miles per hour.

FIG. 103 NAVAL AND INDUSTRIAL ROCKET LEADERS AT PATUXENT AIR STATION, OCTOBER 6–7, 1944

(1) W. Wallace Kellett, (2) Alfred Marchev, (3) Paul E. Hovgaard, (4) W. Wilbur Shaw, (5) Comdr. T. B. Clark, (6) Comdr. Paul H. Ramsey, (7) Lester D. Gardner, (8) Capt. A. P. Storrs, (9) William A. M. Burden, (10) George W. Lewis, (11) Carlton Ward, Jr., (12) Th. von Karman, (13) Arthur A. Locke, (14) Lt. George Bottjer, (15) H. M. Horner, (16) George R. Forman, (17) Allan D. Emil, (18) Howard L. Jennings, (19) W. C. Mentzer, (20) Comdr. R. M. Pray, (21) Charles S. Mac Neil, (22) Comdr. M. W. White, (23) B. R. Otto, (24) Lt. Col. D. E. Cannivan, (25) James S. Pedler, (26) Robert J. Woods, (27) Grover Loening, (28) Col. J. G. Vincent, (29) A. G. Herreshoff, (30) Walter J. Cerny, (31) Philip B. Taylor, (32) Harry E. Blythe, (33) R. H. Prewitt, (34) Bennett H. Horchler, (35) Ralph H. Upson, (36) Roger Wolfe Kahn, (37) Alan Pope, (38) Clifford C. Furnas, (39) R. E. Gillmor, (40) B. Allison Gillies, (41) Arthur T. Newell, (42) Lt. Comdr. Charles R. Wood, (43) William T. Schwendler, (45) Capt. W. G. Switzer, (46) Lt. N. W. Davenport, (47) Robert E. Ellis, (48) Leroy R. Grumman, (49) Capt. J. S. McClure, (50) George B. Wood, Jr., (51) Walter McKay, (52) Conrad F. Nagel, (53) Walter B. Clifford, (54) George W. Burgess, (55) James M. Eaton, (56) Arthur L. Parker, (57) Charles H. Colvin, (58) Rear Admr. G. F. Hussey, Jr., (59) Daniel C. Sayre, (60) James Robinson, (61) Elmer A. Sperry, Jr., (62) Lieutenant Rockefeller, (63) Bradley Jones, (64) Sherman M. Fairchild, (65) Clayton J. Brukner, (66) Myron B. Gordon, (67) Lt. F. A. Smith, Jr., (68) Lt. Comdr. Charles F. Fischer, (69) M. E. Chandler, (70) Lt. Comdr. H. B. Page, (71) Leslie A. Baldwin, (72) William S. Hough, (73) Rex B. Beisel, (75) J. E. Rheim, (76) Roy C. Sylvander, (77) Andrew G. Haley, (78) R. T. Goodwin, (79) John R. Weske, (80) John D. Akerman, (81) Edward P. Warner, (82) Delbert M. Little, (83) R. Paul Harrington, (84) Lt. Comdr. Paul A. Holmberg, (85) Stacy Jones, (86) Carl de Ganahl, (87) S. H. Wilde, (88) Millard E. Bowlus, (89) R. Dixon Speas, (90) Capt. J. A. Callagham, (91) Otto E. Kirchner, (92) S. K. Hoffman, (93) George W. Brady, (94) E. H. Heinemann, (95) Erle Martin, (96) W. J. McGoldrick, (97) L. E. Root, (98) C. W. Meyers, (99) Allan B. Murray, (100) D. F. Bachle, (101) Lt. Comdr. W. E. Garity, (102) Lt. Comdr. J. C. Clark, Jr., (103) Lt. Jean Mayer, (104) Lt. H. A. Turner, (105) Lt. J. W. King, (106) Lt. W. E. Bates, (107) Capt. I. W. Hobbs, (108) Lt. Comdr. R. J. Teich, (109) Lt. E. J. von Briesen, (112) Comdr. E. J. O'Donnell, (113) George B. Post, (114) Arnold M. Kuethe, (115) William A. Mechesney, (116) Andrew J. Fairbanks, (117) B. J. Vierling, (118) Robert R. Dexter, (119) Hugh L. Dryden, (120) L. Welch Pogue, (121) Guy L. Bryan, (122) Wilbur C. Nelson, (123) Malcolm P. Ferguson, (124) H. A. Sutton, (125) John C. Miller, (126) R. H. Lasche.

ROCKETS OF TOMORROW WILL COME BECAUSE ROCKET MEN OF
TODAY ARE THINKING ABOUT THEM . . . HERE ARE A FEW OF
THESE MEN

Fig. 104 Left to right: Major Gen. John B. Medaris, U. S. Army Ordnance
Missile Command, D. D. Coffin, V.P. and Mgr. Missile Systems Div., Raytheon,
Lt. Gen. Arthur G. Trudeau, Chief of Army Research & Dev., C. F. Adams,
President, Raytheon Mfg. Co.

Fig. 105 Internal problem at the Martin Company: With aid of cutaway
model, Engineer Donald Markarian and N. Elliott Felt, Jr., Operations Manager, work out a first-stage structural problem.

Fig. 106 (*Left*) Dr. Dean E. Wooldridge, President of The Ramo-Wooldridge Corporation. Fig. 107 (*Right*) Dr. Simon Ramo, President, Space Technology Laboratories (a Division of The Ramo-Wooldridge Corporation).

Fig. 108 (*Left*) Dr. H. W. Ritchey, Vice President and Technical Director of the Rocket Division, Thiokol Chemical Corporation and winner of the C. N. Hickman Award of the American Rocket Society. Fig. 109 (*Right*) Dr. William H. Pickering, Director of the California Institute of Technology Jet Propulsion Laboratory, is shown with instrumented end of satellite.

Fig. 110 Discussing future rocket propulsion possibilities at Rocketdyne, North American Aviation, are S. K. Hoffman, general manager; T. F. Dixon, chief engineer; and George Sutton, manager of Advance Design.

Fig. 111　Dr. Wernher von Braun, Dr. R. E. Porter, General Electric Co., Col. C. D. Hudson, USA, Commanding Officer Redstone Arsenal.

FIG. 112　"SKULL" SESSION AT CONVAIR, ASTRONAUTICS DIVISION

Left to right: J. L. Bowers, assistant chief engineer, design; Dr. Hans R. Friedrich, assistant chief engineer, development; Krafft A. Ehricke, technical assistant to the chief engineer; J. R. Dempsey, vice president of Convair and manager of Convair, Astronautics; William H. Patterson, assistant to the manager, and Mortimer Rosenbaum, chief engineer.

FIG. 113   PRESENTATION OF ARS ASTRONAUTICS AWARD

Andrew G. Haley, then President of the American Rocket Society, hands Dr. Wernher von Braun the citation for winning the ARS Astronautics Award.

Fig. 114   Dr. Joseph Kaplan, Chairman of the United States Committee of the International Geophysical Year.

Fig. 115 Pictured at a recent planning conference for the Terrier-Tartar missile are the top executives of Convair (Pomona), a Division of General Dynamics Corporation. *Seated left to right:* R. C. Loomis, Assistant Division Manager—Operations: C. F. Horne, Vice President and Division Manager; C. D. Perrine, Assistant Division Manager—Engineering and Chief Engineer; G. E. Sylvester, Assistant Chief Engineer—Product Engineering. *Standing left to right:* K. M. Smith, Manager of Long Range Planning, and E. R. Peterson, Assistant Chief Engineer—Advance Engineering.

Fig. 116 Boeing Board of Directors. *Left to right:* James E. Prince, vice president—administration; Paul Pigott, director; W. E. Beall, senior vice president; E. C. Wells, vice president—engineering; J. O. Yeasting, vice president—finance; William G. Reed, director; Dietrich Schmitz, director; William M. Allen, president; C. L. Egtvedt, chairman; F. P. Laudan, vice president—manufacturing; J. E. Schaefer, vice chairman; D. A. Forward, director; Darrah Corbet, director; Artemus L. Gates, director.

Fig. 117 (*Left*) Grayson Merrill, general manager, Fairchild Guided Missiles Division with a model of the OSPREY Long Range Surveillance Drone which is under development for the U. S. Army. Fig. 118 (*Right*) Dr. Louis G. Dunn, Executive Vice President and General Manager, Space Technology Laboratories (a Division of The Ramo-Wooldridge Corporation).

Fig. 119 Men like Captain W. D. Hammond, Range Safety Officer at Cape Canaveral, Florida, play important roles in our missile and space exploration programs. The two big dials before him tell where the missile is in its trajectory (left, marked "pro") and its azimuth (deduction of flight) at all times. His fingers are poised to throw the "fuel cut-off" and "destruct" switches at an instant's notice, destroying the "bird" in flight, should it veer off course and become a danger to friendly territory. (USAF)

FIG. 120   *THOR-ABLE* ROCKET

This is the Air Force's *Thor-Able* rocket being readied for launching.   Note
the cloud of oxygen escaping from the vent valve.   This is the first two stages
of the Air Force's Moon rocket.   Instead of the test reentry nose cone you see
here, a small third stage motor is added to give it Lunar flight capabilities.

The Bureau of Ordnance, United States Navy, requested the Applied Physics Laboratory to undertake guided-missile defense work in 1944, and the following year awarded a broad research and development contract under the code name of the *Bumblebee* Project. The University of Virginia joined the program early in 1945, to make tests aimed at developing rocket-launched, ramjet-powered guided missiles for the supersonic speed regime. Ten other universities and fourteen industrial enterprises collaborated with the Applied Physics Laboratory on launching, propulsion, aerodynamics, radar, control, telemetering, and warhead design, as well as ground and flight testing. A ramjet engine test area was constructed at Forest Grove Station by the Standard Oil Development Corporation. Later, the Applied Physics Laboratory constructed, with Convair and the Department of the Navy, a large test facility at Dainger Field, Texas, now known as the Ordnance Aerophysics Laboratory. The Applied Physics Laboratory also designed the *Talos* missile.

The great industry now developing the rocket engines, missile airframes, guidance systems, and many other components of the final article is closely supported by government bases, installations, test centers, and research facilities. Capsule information on some of the more important government-run or government-supported facilities demonstrates the breadth of the United States' effort.

THE REDSTONE ARSENAL

The Redstone Arsenal, sometimes called the "Rocket City," extends over 40,000 acres of land formerly occupied by two Army bases and is the center where some of the most advanced missile projects in the United States are developed. Here, since 1949, top military rocket experts developed such weapons as a new, 2-inch, folding-fin, air-to-air rocket; propaganda (leaflet)-carrying rockets; improved "bazookas" and *Honest John* missiles. Under Wernher von Braun at the Army Ballistic Missile Agency, a group of 120 top German rocket experts have developed and perfected to the production stage the *Redstone*, the *Jupiter*, the *Jupiter-C* series and other missiles.

THE PICATINNY ARSENAL

Picatinny Arsenal, at one time a supplier for Washington's Continental Army, is today a large, well-staffed facility operated by Army Ordnance. Located in Northern New Jersey, just west of Dover, it stretches over 5000 acres and includes 1200 buildings. Famous for its World War II "bazooka" developments, its rocket work has involved many later projects, including a 4.5-inch, folding-fin artillery missile (*M-8*) and a 3.5-inch antitank "bazooka" weapon of improved design and effectiveness. The Arsenal has been active in the assist-takeoff field. The *Snake,* a mine-field-clearing rocket-propelled device, is a Picatinny oddity.

THE NATIONAL ADVISORY COMMITTEE FOR AERONAUTICS

Set up by Congress in 1915 ". . . to study . . . the problems of flight with a view to their practical solution," the NACA has built up a large array of laboratories and testing stations to do practical work of its own and also supports the activities of colleges and scientific institutions. The committeee of fifteen men is appointed by the President and consists of representatives from the military air arms, Civil Aeronautics, the Weather Bureau, Bureau of Standards, Smithsonian Institution, and others.

This top committee is served by a network of technical subcommittees which recommend programs, coordinate them, and act as information agencies. The Director of Research controls the following three main research centers from Washington: the Langley Aeronautical Laboratory, Langley Field, Virginia (established in 1918), which studies aerodynamics, stability, control, flutter, vibration, and other phenomena with an array of 30 wind tunnels; the Ames Aeronautical Laboratory at the Navy's Moffet Field, San Francisco (established in 1940), which studies high-speed aerodynamics with large, fast wind tunnels, one of which measures 40 by 80 feet; and the Lewis Flight Propulsion Laboratory at the Cleveland, Ohio, Airport (established in 1942), which conducts research and tests of rocket and ramjet engines, often under simulated conditions.

Actual testing takes place at the High-Speed Research Station of the Edwards Air Force Base, Mojave Desert, for piloted aircraft. Free-flying rockets and other transonic and supersonic devices are examined at the Pilotless Aircraft Research Station at Wallop Island near Chincoteague, Virginia, established in 1945 and operated in conjunction with the Langley Laboratory.

The NACA is slated to play a much larger role in rocketry and astronautics in the immediate future as a result of legislation enacted by the Congress and approved by the President in 1958. A new civilian agency with broad powers to carry out research and development in the space flight field as well as in airborne flight has been created, the National Aeronautics and Space Administration (NASA), which will absorb all of the facilities and personnel of the present NACA. Unlike the present NACA which was confined mainly to laboratory research, the new NASA has the authority to undertake the development of experimental vehicles and engage in space research with them. Thus, NASA can contract for and utilize vehicles like the *Atlas* without the warhead. This enlarged role of the NACA (now NASA) will make it a very important factor in the United States program for the exploration of space.

THE WHITE SANDS PROVING GROUND (WSPG)

Originally established on July 9, 1945, in the confines of the National Monument bearing the same name, White Sands formally was known as the Naval Ordnance Missile Test Facility (NOMTF). The *V-2* missiles were fired from the range soon after the war, while the Air Force conducted missile launching and bombing runs out of near-by Holloman Air Force Base. The first rocket tested at the base was a *Tiny Tim*, on September 26, 1945. As the tempo of both installations increased, overlapping schedules caused increasing difficulties in the congested area occupied by the two stations. The Defense Department designated the area as an integrated range in August 1952, with arrangements for all three services to have access.

Under this arrangement the Proving Ground was operated by Army Ordnance, with Air Force and Naval officers on the Commanding General's staff. The overall operation of the base performs two broad missions—testing ordnance missiles (since it is an Ordnance facility) and coordinating the tests made by other services.

THE AIR FORCE MISSILE TEST CENTER

The establishment of the Air Force Missile Test Center resulted from a decision of the Joint Chiefs of Staff in 1945, based on a survey of the capabilities of the ranges then existing. Holloman Air Force Base and the White Sands Facility combined offered only 135 miles and the Navy ranges at Inyokern and Point Mugu could not be economically lengthened to more than 150 miles.

A Committee on Long Range Proving Grounds, established in 1946, unanimously recommended Cape Canaveral, Florida, on June 20, 1947, after a comprehensive survey of possible sites. Here the range extended southeast and could be lengthened nearly half-way around the world on a great-circle route without danger to private interests. This land was cheap, isolated, and in an almost consistently good climate, while islands in the Bahamas and the Antilles offered the possibility of a fairly long chain of sites for observation stations.

The Navy's Banana River Air Station was given over to the Air Force in the summer of 1948, and on October 1, 1949, was activated on the basis of joint operation by the three services. It was assigned to the Air Force in June 1951, but joint operation and accessibility continued. Although still not complete, the two-hundred-million-dollar range has been in continuous operation since the first flight on July 24, 1950, of a *V-2/WAC-Corporal Bumper* missile, for distance evaluation.

The Center builds no missiles, but trains troops in their use and provides and controls the range for the testing of missiles by contractors. Island stations are located on the Grand Bahamas, Eleuthera Island, San Salvador, Mayaguana Island, Grand Turk Island, and all the way to Ascension Island, over 3000 miles away.

Patrick Air Force Base, headquarters center, lies about 14 miles east of the City of Cocoa, Florida, and about 50 miles east of Orlando, and covers about 1922 acres of government land. A submarine cable connects the base with most of the outlying islands.

THE HOLLOMAN AIR DEVELOPMENT CENTER

The Holloman Air Development Center was formerly established in 1942 as the Alamogordo Army Air Field, and after some use for atomic bomb testing it was converted to test a variety of rocket devices. The first launching took place in 1947, and in August 1952 the Center was integrated with the adjacent White Sands Proving Ground to create a master facility equally available to all services.

THE EDWARDS AIR FORCE BASE—MUROC DRY LAKE

The Edwards Air Force Base is located in Kern County, California, about 60 miles northeast of Los Angeles. Here a series of planes, including the Northrop Aircraft Corporation's *MX-324* rocket-powered flying wing and the Bell Aircraft Corporation's *X-1, X-2* rocket planes, and others, have been and are being tested. Ground instrumentation and test cells to support rocket engine work are available. Propellant servicing, preflight pressure, igniter and electrical checks are performed here. Powered flight tests are carried on, usually with *B-29* carrier airplanes as the first stage, to conserve propellants for use at higher altitudes.

THE EXPERIMENTAL ROCKET ENGINE TEST STATION (ERETS)

The Experimental Rocket Engine Test Station facility was established in the Mojave Desert 31 miles from Edwards Air Force Base in 1951. The test stands, instrumentation, and other equipment were designed and built by the Aerojet-General Corporation. A variety of large static thrust test stands, ranging up to capacities of a half-million pounds of thrust, and towering over 100 feet into the air, are available. The station has offices, shops, maintenance, and housing facilities, and is nearly self-sufficient. A similar facility exists at Fort Crowder, Missouri, also designed by the Aerojet-General Corporation, and operated by the Rocketdyne Division of the North American Aviation Company.

THE ARNOLD ENGINEERING DEVELOPMENT CENTER (AEDC)

Named after the late General H. H. Arnold, this center was the result of a study made by Von Karman in 1944 to establish a facility to test all kinds of supersonic aircraft, engines, guidance systems, and guided missiles under simulated free-flight conditions. The Center, constructed in 1949, contains numerous supersonic and hypersonic wind tunnels. It is operated for the Air Force by Aro, Inc., near Tullahoma, Tennessee, a location chosen for its plentiful Tennessee Valley Authority power.

THE NAVAL AIR ROCKET TEST STATION

This facility is located at the former Naval Ammunition Depot, Lake Denmark, New Jersey, about 25 miles northwest of Newark and adjacent to the Army's Picatinny Arsenal.

The test station was originally organized at the Naval Aeronautical Rocket Laboratory to develop methods for testing liquid-propellant rocket engines, ignition delay measurements for hypergolic substances, additive and corrosion research test stand designs, and the evaluation of liquid versus solid propellants for given applications. It was modernized early in 1950 and placed under the supervision of the Bureau of Aeronautics for the evaluation of whole rocket engines, components, and propellants. It thus performs a mission corresponding to that of the Philadelphia Aeronautical Engineering Laboratory for reciprocating engines, and the Aeronautical Turbine Laboratory in Trenton, New Jersey, for turbojet engines.

The first commander of the Naval Air Rocket Test Station was Captain R. Jackson. The technical staff assisting him included Commanders D. A. Seiler, R. C. Truax, and scientists B. N. Abramson and J. Clerk.

THE U. S. NAVAL ORDNANCE TEST STATION—INYOKERN

The U. S. Naval Ordnance Test Station was established in 1943 by the Navy, for projects conducted in its behalf by the California Institute of Technology. It is located in the Mojave Desert, about 150 miles northeast of Los Angeles. Inyokern, dramatically expanded in the war years, now covers an area measuring 25 by 50 miles, and employs over 12,000 persons. It has the mission of developing and testing Naval rockets, missiles, and aviation ordnance. Special rocket and ballistic research ranges are available.

The Michelson Research Laboratory, a key facility at the station, conducts research in basic and applied aerophysics, electronics, metallurgy, propulsion, and guidance systems. It has a materials testing laboratory, a heat-treating and foundry unit, a machine shop, weather testing and altitude chambers, and rocket launching equipment.

Administratively the station is divided roughly into the Explosives, Experimental Operations, and Research Departments—the last of which is further subdivided into the Physics, Chemistry, Mathematics, Applied Science, and Ballistics Departments. Research on underwater ordnance is also carried on here.

THE POINT MUGU MISSILE RANGE

The United States Navy Missile Test Range at Point Mugu is located about 50 miles northwest of Los Angeles, on the California coast. It has been in operation since October 1946, as a temporary test center. It comprises a 7500-acre tract, with laboratories and full equipment for testing the flight characteristics of radio-controlled missiles. Recently, it was designated to become part of a long-range ballistic missile firing range in the Pacific.

THE UNITED STATES NAVAL ORDNANCE TEST STATION—CHINA LAKE

Located 160 miles northeast of Los Angeles, the China Lake facility (one of a system; others are at Pasadena, Long Beach, and San Clemente Island) was established in 1943 for rocket and guided missile testing. A research track called *SNORT* (*Supersonic Naval Ordnance Research Track*) provides a bridge between the wind tunnel and free-flight testing. In many respects it resembles the test sled installation used by Colonel Stapp for deceleration measurements at the Holloman Air Development Center. Armament rockets, such as *Tiny Tim, Mighty Mouse,* and *Ram,* are target-tested at China Lake.

In retrospect the results of corporate acquisitions and mergers over the years have been reasonably helpful and encouraging to the industry. An example in point is Aerojet-General Corporation which, under the ownership control of W. O'Neil and his family, and under the direct leadership of Dan A. Kimball, A. H. Rude and W. E. Zisch, has maintained a high degree of alertness and wide success in all the ramified fields of astronautics.

North American, General Dynamics, The Martin Company and Thiokol Corporation have also been alert and progressive with the result that the rocket industry is highly competitive and healthy in every respect.

Space limitations do not permit a further discussion of the great contributions of the old-line companies and of the many smaller but vastly important companies such as Atlantic Research Corporation, Experiment, Inc.; G. M. Giannini Co., Inc., and so on, each of which has maintained its complete independence.

9

Other Rocket Countries

Sputnik made most of the countries of the world space conscious. Those nations that had rocket programs in progress suddenly looked on the large rocket with renewed interest—both as a means to space flight and as a weapon. In Western Europe, countries that had been preparing to defend themselves against more or less conventionally executed nuclear warfare suddenly saw themselves under the guns, to to speak, of Soviet ballistic rockets. Russia realized the great propaganda value of their epochal achievement, and made the most of it.

Tentatively, this effort seems to have backfired for the Soviets, for it brought to the major Western Countries a realization that they had to allow large missiles (1500-mile IRBMs) to be based on their territory. It also interested them in missile production for defense. They realized too that, for the most part, it would have to be a cooperative effort, for the establishment of a large missile program would cost more than most countries could afford. But, whatever the future holds in this respect, some countries, through their work with relatively small rockets, are managing to provide themselves with a good foundation in the elements of modern rocketry.

POSTWAR ROCKETRY IN BRITAIN

After the United States and Russia, Britain is the leading developer and producer of guided missiles. As early as October 1945, England test-fired two captured *V-2* rockets, but unfortunately nothing came out of the firings but a few reports. The wealth of German information was temporarily ignored. The little that was done between 1945 and 1949 took place in government laboratories, in dark secrecy. Coordination with industry was negligible. By 1950, however, the government seems to have been galvanized into intense activity, with a broad and comprehensive missile program.

The major organizing factor in British rocketry has been the Royal Aircraft Establishment (RAE), founded in 1918. The descendant of a series of similar bureaus dating back to the nineteenth century, it advises the Royal Air Force on flight problems relating to aerodynamics, propulsion, structures, and metallurgy. It is responsible for designing autopilots, navigational instruments, pressurization equipment, bombsights, radar, fire controls, and guided missile systems.

Rocket propulsion development is carried on at Wescott, Buckinghamshire, and missile tests are conducted at the Royal Air Force Guided Weapons Trials Wing at Aberporth, South Wales. Final testing of Britain's missiles takes place at the proving grounds located at Woomera, South Australia (north of Port Augusta) on a range extending some 1200 miles northwest into the Indian Ocean. Other ranges are being completed at North Coates, Lincolnshire, and at South Uist, Outer Hebrides.

The Society of British Aircraft Constructors (SBAC) has announced that 400 British companies are engaged in missile development and supporting work.

Most notable of the companies manufacturing missiles are: Bristol Aircraft Ltd., the English Electric Co., de Havilland Propeller Ltd., A. V. Roe, Fairey Aviation, and Vickers-Armstrong.* Bristol Aircraft has four plants concentrating their efforts on missile work. Ferranti, manufacturers of guidance equipment, which is associating with Bristol Aircraft on one of its projects, has two plants giving support to the missile program.

Thus, until recently, the main British research effort has been in antiaircraft rockets, JATO, and generally short-range tactical missiles which can be used for close support.

What Britain vitally needs, and what it has concentrated on, are a well-tried, reliable series of air-defense missiles, and quick-climbing, rocket-powered interceptor airplanes. Britain has developed also a few upper atmosphere research rockets. Lately, she has started work on a 2500-mile range ballistic missile known as the *Black Knight*.

An immediate-post-war British missile, the liquid propellant *T. R.* air-launched research rocket made by the Royal Aircraft Establishment and Vickers, was used primarily for aerodynamic research. It measured 11 feet long, 18 inches in diameter, and achieved a maximum velocity of 900 miles per hour.

---

* Others include: E. K. Cole & Co. Ltd. (*Fireflash* radar), E. M. I. Engineering Development Ltd., The General Electric Co., Ltd., Sir George Godfrey and Partners, Imperial Chemical Industries, McMichael Radio Ltd., Metropolitan Vickers Ltd., The Sperry Gyroscope Co. Ltd., The John Thompson Conveyor Co. Ltd.—all *Sea Slug* ancillaries.

Rolls-Royce Ltd. (Rocketdyne License), Bristol Aeroplane Co. Ltd., Avica Equipment Ltd., The British Thompson Houston Co. Ltd., S. G. Brown Ltd., Burnley Aircraft Products Ltd., Delaney Gallay Ltd., Diamond H. Switches Ltd., Dowe Instruments Ltd., Elliott Brothers (London) Ltd., Goodmans Industries Ltd., Graseby Instruments Ltd., High Pressure Components Ltd., Hymatic Engineering Co. Ltd., I. V. Pressure Controllers Ltd., Kelvin and Hughes Ltd., King Aircraft Corp. Ltd., Laporte Chemicals Ltd., Lion Electronic Developments Ltd., Muirhead and Co. Ltd., W. Bryan Savage Ltd., Smiths Aircraft Instruments Ltd., Solartron Electronic Group Ltd., Teddington Aircraft Controls Ltd., Vactric (Control Equipment) Ltd., Venner Ltd., W. Vinter Ltd., Western Manufacturing (Reading) Ltd.

The *A. W. A.* Test Vehicle, developed by Armstrong Whitworth Limited in 1950, the wingless, 15-foot, Mach 2, unguided Bristol Company twin-ram-jet test vehicle *JTV-1* designed by the Royal Aircraft Establishment and the *Dart LXCTV-2099* are all aerodynamic research vehicles. The *Dart* missile uses a plastic propellant, is only 5 feet long, and is reported to reach a speed of Mach 1.7. Launched from a ramp with three 5-inch boosters which give it 50-g acceleration, the missile has no sustaining rocket engine. At an altitude of about 20,000 feet, airburst occurs, separating the nose from the body. A nose cone "fans out" and the vehicle descends at a rather slow speed. Acceptable instrument recovery is therefore possible. The *Dart* missile was developed from a *Longshot* prototype missile.

In the surface-to-air category, the *Lop-Gap* and the *RTV-1* (Rocket Test Vehicle) are two of the earliest known British missiles, dating from 1948. The Royal Aircraft Establishment developed both of them, aided on the *RTV-1* missile by the cooperation of Fairey Aircraft. Both are liquid-propellant missiles. The *Lop-Gap* missile is about 14 feet long and travels at a speed of approximately 1000 miles per hour. The *RTV-1* missile is 22 feet long with its booster, and is reported to have attained a speed of over 2000 miles per hour.

The Fairey-Royal Aircraft Establishment's solid propellant *Stooge* missile, perhaps the first post-war missile in the surface-to-air category, weighed less than 750 pounds and had a top speed rarely greater than 350 miles per hour. It was ramp-launched and command-guided. This was one of Britain's earliest guided missiles.

First operational British air-to-air missile, the Fairey Aircraft *Fireflash*, dates back to World War II. It has no sustainer engine, but uses wraparound boosters to accelerate it to maximum velocity. At high altitude the boosters separate from the main body, and the vehicle coasts to its target. It is homed by the launching plane. It is now a training weapon for the fighter command.

A more modern air-to-air weapon is the de Havilland Propeller Company's *Firestreak* missile. Using a single, solid propellant rocket engine internally mounted, this missile is infrared homing and is reputed to be one of the most effective missiles of its kind.

Another air-to-air missile on which little information has been released is Vickers-Armstrongs' *Red Dean*. It reportedly has been cancelled.

In the ground-to-air category, Britain has three impressive entries: the *Bloodhound*, the *Thunderbird*, and the *Sea Slug*. The *Bloodhound* missile is manufactured by Bristol Aeroplane Company and grew out of that company's work with ramjet test vehicles. Ferranti Ltd. supplies the guidance system, while two Bristol *Thor* ramjet engines provide its sustainer power. It is boosted to its 1500-foot-per-second ramjet ignition velocity by four wraparound solid propellant boosters. The *Thor* engine is reported capable of delivering 15,000 pounds of thrust at a speed of Mach 2 at sea level.

The *Thunderbird* missile is an English Electric Company product and is a radar beam-rider. In true British tradition it gets initial boost from four wraparound solid propellant boosters. Marconi Ltd. supplies the guidance system. The *Thunderbird* missile has been variously reported as using both a solid and a liquid propellant rocket engine sustainer. The liquid propellant motor is a Napier *NRE-17 RTP*.

The Royal Navy's bid in the surface-to-air field is the *Sea Slug* missile. Designed by the Navy, it is being manufactured by Armstrong Whitworth Ltd., with the General Electric Company supplying the guidance system, and Sperry Gyroscope Ltd. providing the control system. The *Sea Slug* missile, like its cousins, uses wraparound solid propellant boosters. The original liquid rocket engine sustainer is being replaced by solid propellant rocket engines for ease of handling.

There are reports that Britain's A. V. Roe Ltd. is working on an air-to-surface missile patterned after the United States and the Bell Aircraft Corporation's *Rascal* missile, but nothing has been released. The British call this kind of weapon a "stand-off" bomb.

In the surface-to-surface category, de Havilland Ltd. is reportedly working on a 2000-mile range IRBM with Rolls Royce Ltd. supplying the rocket engine. The Ministry of Supply has established a Ballistic Missile Division for overseeing this work. Presumably this organization also has cognizance over any space flight plans Britain may have.

Meanwhile, because of requirements for extremely rapid manned interceptors, Britain has pushed a VTO (Vertical Take-Off) program. The most important project in this field is an 11-foot Fairey VTO test vehicle, sponsored by the Ministry of Supply. This craft continues the development of the German *Natter* rocket plane.

The Fairey model is ramp-launched by two 600-pound-thrust, solid propellant rocket engine boosters. Sustained flight is possible by a liquid propellant, twin-chamber, 1800-pound-thrust *Beta-I* rocket engine. Launching acceleration and the path leading to interception is determined by radar, while autopilot control moves the upper chamber, thus deflecting the thrust line to correct the path. The American *MX-774* and the *Viking* missiles have used this general principle very successfully. Other British rocket plane projects were short-lived.

The best-known British rocket engine is probably the Armstrong-Siddley *AS Sn.1, Snarler*. Weighing 215 pounds, it delivers 2000 pounds of thrust from its liquid oxygen and methyl alcohol (with water) propellants. Design of this engine started in 1946. The present model was tested in 1950 in a Hawker *P. 1702* fighter plane. It obtains driving power for its propellant pumps from an accessory drive off the main engine, a Rolls Royce Nene Turbojet. The influence of the Walther 509 engine, and to a lesser extent the V-2 engine, is visible in this motor.

The *Sprite* rocket engine was developed by the de Havilland Engine Company as a JATO unit. Measuring 84 inches in length by 20 inches in diameter (maximum), it weighs 350 pounds empty and 925 pounds full. It can be mounted inside wings, fuselages, or nacelles, or externally in streamlined pods. Tankage, part of the unit package, provides for 39 gallons of hydrogen peroxide and 2.5 gallons of sodium or calcium permanganate, delivered to the thrust chamber by compressed air at 3000-pounds-per-square-inch pressure. An interesting feature of this rocket engine is a provision for a "die-away" thrust, which permits thrust to decrease from the maximum needed at start of take-off.

The basis of a *Super Sprite* rocket engine is believed to have been applied by the de Havilland Company to produce the *Spectre,* a liquid propellant rocket engine designed for tremendous thrust at very high altitudes, for surge speed in combat.

Other rocket engines about which little is reliably known are the *Alpha* (RAE) and the *Beta I* and *II.* The *Alpha* rocket engine was used in the RAE (Royal Aircraft Establishment)-Vickers *Rocket Model,* a venerable transonic aerodynamic research vehicle, reportedly propelled at a speed of Mach 1.38 in level flight during the summer of 1948.

The *Beta II* rocket engine apparently replaced the *Alpha* in the *Rocket Model.* It delivers 900 pounds of thrust for 58 seconds from a single chamber fed by compressed-air-pressurized propellants consisting of 30 percent hydrazine hydrate and 57 percent methyl alcohol with 13 percent water.

FRENCH POST-WAR MISSILE DEVELOPMENTS

The French rocket development program carried on during World War II by Barre and his colleagues chiefly was concerned with a rocket called the *EA-41.* The first actual French liquid propellant rocket, operating on gasoline-ether and liquid oxygen, was unguided and fin-stabilized. The rocket engine was cooled by the gasoline-ether propellant, itself precooled by its proximity to the liquid oxygen. While only static tests were made during the war, a free firing test was made at Toulon as soon as France was declared liberated.

At the close of hostilities France, like Britain, did not fare well in the procurement of German scientists. But France did get Eugen Sänger and his wife Irene Sänger-Bredt of antipodal bomber and ramjet engine fame. Austria's Zborowski came and has since formed a new firm called Bureau Technique Zborowski. Some of the major tasks being undertaken there are the development of a BTZ army infantry rocket, ramjet engine-powered

Lutin (range is 3 miles, velocity 280 miles per hour, weight 33 pounds, warhead 9 pounds), a surface-to-surface *Ogre-1*, and another missile with a liquid propellant rocket engine booster and ramjet engine sustainer. Just what the Sängers did for the French Air Force has not been released, but ramjet and rocket engine developments naturally are presumed.

France's main emphasis appears to be on research rockets and multipurpose missile development. France's *Veronique* upper atmosphere research vehicle is the largest missile to be produced in free Europe since the war. It was developed and built by the Ballistic and Aerodynamic Research Laboratories (Vernon), which forms part of the Directorate of Armament Research and Fabrication.

A number of tests have been made with the missile in Colomb-Bechar in North Africa, and the peak altitude reached to date is 84 miles. The French have a firing program for their easily transportable *Veroniques* during the International Geophysical Year. Corbeau, Pilz, and other key engineers have been working on the missile for some five years.

The National Office for Aeronautical Studies and Research (O.N.E.R.A.) of Chatillon has an *OPD.320* experimental rocket which can carry 100 pounds or so of parachute-recoverable instruments. A *CT.10* guided target plane is made by S.N.C.A. du Nord (also of Chatillon). An improved *CT.20* guided target plane has been announced and can be recovered by parachute. The *Brequet 910* is an unpowered missile used for research work. The Société d'Etudes et Constructions Aéronautiques uses *ECA 20* and *ECA 26* test vehicles in connection with its guidance studies.

The mysterious *EOLE-51* was an experimental, fin-stabilized, unguided rocket studied by the Directorate of Armament Research and Fabrication. Two launchings were made in 1952. It ran on alcohol and liquid oxygen propellants and was sheet-metal constructed. The study has since been abandoned.

Like the United States, France gained some experience with *V-1* missile types. The *Arsenal 5.501*, dating from 1948, was a pulse-jet target drone which took off under the boost of two rockets. It had a range of about 200 miles and was recovered by parachute.

In the field of combat rockets and guided missiles, the accent is on flexibility of role. All told, the records show the French have worked, or are working, on a total of no fewer than 45 missiles. Most of France's missiles are *Terrier*-size or smaller. None has a range of over 125 miles. Only about a dozen are known to have Mach 1-plus speed capabilities. Few missiles are produced in any number, most of them being considered as development vehicles.

In the small-ordnance-missile field, a number of French developments are known. The SNECMAS *S.S. 10* antitank rocket is fired from Potez tanks. A versatile missile, begun in 1952, it has also been adapted for surface-to-air and for air-to-air use. It is wire-controlled much like the German *X-4* missile, and spins slowly while flying. The *S.S. 10* missile has been tested with the Dassault 315 *Flamant* airplane. The *S.S. 11* is an improved *S.S. 10* missile.

The *Matra (M-04)* missile is a product of the Société Nationale de Constructions Aéronautiques du Sud-Est and the Société Générale de Mecanique, Aviation, Traction (Matra). It is reported to be a two-thirds scale model of ground-to-air and air-to-air missiles under development, and is powered by an S.E.P.R. rocket engine delivering 2750 pounds of thrust (for 14 seconds) on liquid propellants. The *Matra* missile is all metal with a Duralumin skin. It stands a shade over 15 feet high and weighs 1020 pounds loaded, 770 pounds empty. Air launch tests have been made in the Sahara Desert since 1952, and complete instrumentation permits the recording of data at ground stations. In a flight test at Colomb-Bechar, a top speed of 1118 miles per hour was attained.

A recently announced missile development is the SNCA du Sud-Est *1522* air-to-surface and air-to-air missile. No details are available. A Sud-Est *1524* missile has been tested at Colomb-Bechar in North Africa and has successfully destroyed target airplanes. The Société d'Etudes et Constructions Aéronautiques is also working with a research missile, mainly as a test vehicle for guidance systems. The recently organized Etablissements Jean Turck is also in the missile business in France, and is currently developing guidance systems and other missile components. The Société Japy of Arcueil makes launchers for French surface-to-air and other guided missiles.

The French have not neglected the rocket airplane field. The SNCASO *Trident* SO-9000 interceptor airplane is fitted out with three tail-mounted, inboard, *S.E.P.R. 461* liquid propellant, rocket engines and with two wingtip-mounted ramjet engines. The 3-chamber rocket engine, designed to provide the *main* power of the interceptor, has been extensively tested in the 6026 *Espadron* airplane. Model *SEPR 51* rocket engine was used in this application. With only a fraction of total available power used, supersonic speeds were registered in level flight and in climb.

The *Trident* interceptor airplane was first rocket flight-tested on September 4, 1954, but just how far above the speed of Mach 1 it has traveled is not known. Charles Goujon was the pilot. Earlier the plane reportedly flew only on its jets, and first took off on March 2, 1953, with Jacques Guignard as pilot. The S.E.P.R. rocket engine operates on nitric acid and furaline, a hypergolic mixture. S.E.P.R. liquid propellant, rocket engines are made at the Société d'Etude de la Propulsion par Traction (founded in

1944). The group also makes solid propellant rocket engines for airplanes and missiles.

POST-WAR ROCKETRY IN OTHER COUNTRIES

If the amount of information available is any index, Switzerland (an old specialist in antiaircraft weapons) leads the minor national effort in rocketry, followed by Italy, Canada, Australia, Scandinavia, Holland, Japan, and Argentina, though not necessarily in this order.

Most Swiss rockets are developed and produced by the Oerlikon Company of Zurich. Among them are a basic 3.17-inch powder rocket, 2 feet long, carrying a 2.2-pound contact-detonating warhead, and a 550-pound, beam-riding rocket propelled by nitric acid and paraffin. The smaller rocket can be used as either a surface-to-air or an air-to-air vehicle. The larger one measures 16.5 feet long and can carry its 44-pound warhead at a speed of 2460 miles per hour to reach an altitude of 66,000 feet. It is a mobile-launched beam-rider. Part of a complex radar-controlled weapon system, this guided rocket uses a proximity fuse.

One Swiss proximity fuse is driven by a turbine immersed in the rocket's exhaust. The power derived is applied to a miniature radar set which measures distance to target and at the proper time explodes the warhead.

Oerlikon has a *Type 54* surface-to-air missile which is 19.73 feet long and has a maximum diameter of 1.34 feet. Flight control is maintained by a combination of aerodynamic control and thrust deflection. It has four swept, cruciform wings and four sweptback tail surfaces. Operating on kerosene and white fuming nitric acid, it can reach an altitude of 47,500 feet on 220 pounds of thrust for 30 seconds.

In Spain, Hispano-Suiza has a 3.15-inch rocket that is used for just about everything—air-to-air, air-to-surface, and surface-to-air. It is solid propelled, produces 1200 pounds of thrust, and attains a speed of 2000 miles per hour. Weighing 22 pounds (with a 2.2-pound warhead), it measures 3.5 feet long, and is quite similar to the Oerlikon solid propellant rocket.

Italy produced no significant rockets in World War II, but there is evidence of awakening interest. A military Rockets and Missiles Committee and a Center for the Study of Reaction Propulsion have been established, and a new Air Force rocket range has been announced. The firm Contraves Italiana is working on high-altitude surface-to-air missiles, one of which was shown at an international air meeting in Geneva in 1955. This company also manufactures Oerlikon rockets under a Swiss license.

The *Orione* rocket, a product of Polverfici Giovanni Stacchini of Rome, is available in 2.25- and 3.4-inch calibers and may be used for both anti-aircraft and land combat. A (Aurelio) Robotti *AR.3* rocket was shown at the Salone della Tecnica in Turin recently, and an *AR.4* rocket is known to exist. An experimental rocket of the Stablimenti Meccanici Reuniti Whitehead Moto Fides has also been exhibited. The firm Italjet, a subsidiary of the Aerojet-General Corporation, is making 14-AS-1000 JATO units and "bazooka"-type rockets.

In Canada, the *Velvet Glove* air-to-air missile, slated for use on the *CF-100* airplane, is being manufactured for the Defense Research Board at Valcartier, Quebec, and at Cold Lake, Alberta. It is supersonic, and has already been fired from both *CF-100* and *F-86* aircraft. Other missiles are reportedly under development by Avro Canada, and the Canadian Army is supporting a surface-to-surface missile project. The de Havilland organization undoubtedly will soon emerge with highly important projects which are now probably under way.

In Scandinavia, Sweden has at least six types of missiles under development or in production, including antitank, air-to-surface, air-to-air, and surface-to-air. Both SAAB and Bofors are working on missiles and a missile-development coordinating agency (Robotvapenbyran) has been established. SAAB fighters including the *J-35* Delta model, are now equipped with air-to-air rockets. One must never discount Sweden.

The Japanese have two very small liquid-propellant experimental rockets under development at the University of Tokyo. One of them, called the *Pencil* rocket, measures 5 inches long and has been clocked at 382 miles per hour at horizontal firings at Tokyo's Supersonic Aviation Engineering Institute. A smaller rocket measuring 3 inches long, called the *Baby*, is also under development. Japan also has a *Kappa* series of rockets she is using for International Geophysical Year research firings. The *Kappa-3* rocket achieves a speed of Mach 3.7 and an altitude of 20 miles. The *Kappa-5* rockets go up to an altitude of 80 miles. Japan is preparing to go into production in the next few years on both air-to-air and ground-to-air rocket weapons. Japan will soon be a world leader in rocketry.

Holland is working on a common missile program with Norway. Argentina is reported to have been making some rocket engine tests, and an *A-3F* antitank missile is under development.

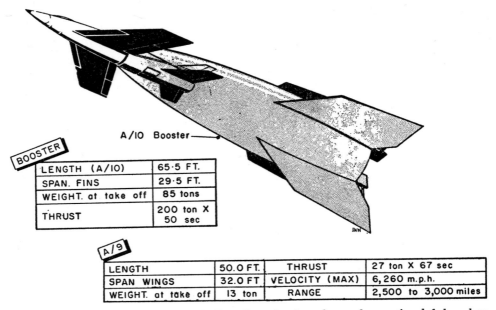

BOOSTER

LENGTH (A/10)	65·5 FT.
SPAN. FINS	29·5 FT.
WEIGHT. at take off	85 tons
THRUST	200 ton X 50 sec

A/10 Booster

A/9

LENGTH	50.0 FT.	THRUST	27 ton X 67 sec
SPAN WINGS	32.0 FT	VELOCITY (MAX)	6,260 m.p.h.
WEIGHT. at take off	13 ton	RANGE	2,500 to 3,000 miles

The Russian skip-bomber is believed to be based on the antipodal bomber concept of Dr. Eugen Sänger (1935) and the German *A-9, A-10* winged rocket. This was a winged *V-2* with a special booster. The *A-9* has the following specifications: length, 50.0 ft.; span wings, 32.0 ft.; weight at take-off, 13-tons; thrust, 27 ton x 67 seconds; velocity (max.), 6260 miles per hour; range, 2500 to 3000 miles. Similar figures for the *A-10* were: length, 65.5 ft.; weight at takeoff, 85 tons; thrust, 200 ton x 50 seconds.

TRAJECTORY OF RUSSIAN SKIP BOMBER

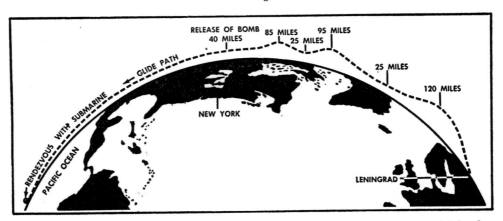

This diagram shows proposed trajectory of rocket-boost bomber which the Russians now have under development. (*Missiles and Rockets*)

FIG. 121 BRITISH TEST MISSILE

A vertical take-off test vehicle developed by Britain's Fairey Company. (Gatland)

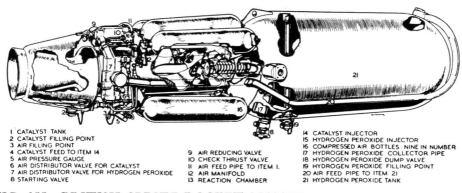

1 CATALYST TANK
2 CATALYST FILLING POINT
3 AIR FILLING POINT
4 CATALYST FEED TO ITEM 14
5 AIR PRESSURE GAUGE
6 AIR DISTRIBUTOR VALVE FOR CATALYST
7 AIR DISTRIBUTOR VALVE FOR HYDROGEN PEROXIDE
8 STARTING VALVE

9 AIR REDUCING VALVE
10 CHECK THRUST VALVE
11 AIR FEED PIPE TO ITEM 1.
12 AIR MANIFOLD
13 REACTION CHAMBER

14 CATALYST INJECTOR
15 HYDROGEN PEROXIDE INJECTOR
16 COMPRESSED AIR BOTTLES NINE IN NUMBER
17 HYDROGEN PEROXIDE COLLECTOR PIPE
18 HYDROGEN PEROXIDE DUMP VALVE
19 HYDROGEN PEROXIDE FILLING POINT
20 AIR FEED PIPE TO ITEM 21
21 HYDROGEN PEROXIDE TANK

FIG. 122 BRITISH *SPRITE* ROCKET MOTOR

A cutaway view showing the various parts of the *sprite* rocket motor.

FIG. 123 *SUPER SPRITE* ROCKET MOTOR ON TEST BED

The de Havilland *Super Sprite* rocket motor, designed for assisting the take-off of large military aircraft, is seen here on the test bed at the de Havilland Engine Company's development center at Hatfield. The *Super Sprite*, designed to be jettisoned by parachute after take-off, delivers 4200 pounds of static thrust. Total duration is 40 seconds. (de Havilland)

FIG. 124   BRITISH MISSILE TAKES OFF

A British guided missile being fired. This probably represents an early stage in the development of a ground-to-air missile being produced by a large industrial organization playing a leading part in this field. Firing from Aberporth, South Wales, are eight solid rockets boosting the missile initially. (Gatland)

FIG. 125   BRITISH RAMJET MISSILE IN FLIGHT

A guided ramjet missile accelerating after launching assisted by eight solid rocket boosters.   (Gatland)

FIG. 126 BRITISH RAMJET MISSILE SHEDS FOUR ROCKET
          BOOSTERS

The four twin boost motors fall away and the ramjet missile carries on under
its own power at a speed of about 2000 miles per hour. (Gatland)

FIG. 127 FRENCH *SS-10* ANTI-TANK MISSILE

Father of the *Dart* missile, the optically guided, wire-controlled French *SS-10*, is a highly mobile anti-tank missile. (Secrétariat d'Etat à l'Air)

FIG. 128 FRENCH HELICOPTER ROCKET LAUNCHER

FIG. 129 FRENCH *CT-10* MISSILE

The French *CT-10* is a development of the German *V-1*. (Secrétariat d'Etat à l'Air)

FIG. 130   FRENCH *TRIDENT II* INTERCEPTOR PLANE

Trident II (S.O. 9050) built by Ovest Aviation.   Tail view of military interceptor version of *Trident I* research aircraft.   Note two rocket chambers compared with three motors in research prototype.   Superior performance is claimed for this version.

FIG. 131   FRENCH *TRIDENT I* RESEARCH PLANE IN FLIGHT

Trident I (S.O. 900) built by Ovest Aviation shown in flight.   Performance revealed in 1955: Mach 1.6 at altitude 53,000 ft; supersonic in climb; total rocket thrust 9000 pounds.   Supplementary power is available from turbojet engines on wingtips.

FIG. 132 SWISS *TYPE-54 OERLIKON* MISSILE TAKES OFF

Fire one! A Swiss *Type 54 Oerlikon* missile two seconds after the ignition of the 2200-pound thrust, liquid propellant rocket engine. (Missiles and Rockets)

FIG. 133 JAPANESE *BABY* MISSILE IN LAUNCHER

Postwar Japanese rocketry has been pretty much restricted to upper air research vehicles such as this *Baby* missile.

FIG. 134   JAPANESE *KAPPA* RESEARCH ROCKET

The launcher of the *Kappa* rocket is at the same time a carrier.   *Kappa* is Japan's major research rocket for International Geophysical Year firings.

FIG. 135   *SPUTNIK III*

A replica of *Sputnik III* on display at the USSR General Agricultural and
Industrial Exhibition in Moscow, June 1958.

FIG. 136   BERTH FOR "LAIKA'S" SPACE JOURNEY

Andrew G. Haley beside replica of capsule which carried the ill-fated dog,
"Laika," on her journey into outer space in *Sputnik II.*

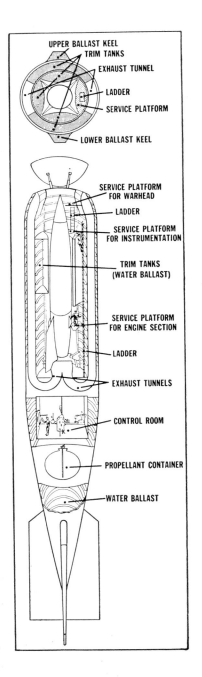

UPPER BALLAST KEEL
TRIM TANKS
EXHAUST TUNNEL
LADDER
SERVICE PLATFORM
LOWER BALLAST KEEL

SERVICE PLATFORM
FOR WARHEAD
LADDER
SERVICE PLATFORM
FOR INSTRUMENTATION
TRIM TANKS
(WATER BALLAST)
SERVICE PLATFORM
FOR ENGINE SECTION
LADDER
EXHAUST TUNNELS
CONTROL ROOM
PROPELLANT CONTAINER
WATER BALLAST

FIG. 137 SUBMARINE LAUNCHED MISSILE

Underwater launching platform for *V-2*, developed at the end of World War II. The system was never activated, but the Soviets are believed to have developed similar weapons systems.

FIG. 138   THE FRENCH ASTRONAUTICAL PIONEERS (PARIS, 1927)

From left to right, sitting: Robert Esnault-Pelterie and André Louis-Hirsch; *standing:* Henri Chrétien (inventor of Cinemascope), J. H. Rosny aîné (writer, President of the Académie Goncourt), A. Lambert (astronomer, Paris Observatory) Jean Perrin (Nobel Prize), R. Soreau (President of French Civil Engineers), General Ferrié (Head of French Army Signal Corps, Member of the Institute), Jos. Béthenod (Founder of Compagnie Générale de T.S.F.), E. Fichot (President of French Astronomic Society), Em. Bélot (Astronomer).

FIG. 139   SECOND IAF CONGRESS, LONDON, 1951

Seated left to right: Haley, ARS; Sänger-Bredt, GfW; Oberth, GfW; Sänger, GfW; Loeser, GfW; *Standing, left to right:* Stemmer, Cleaver, Mur, Sawyer, Tabanera, Carter, Hecht, Smith, Koelle, Hjertstrand, Clarke, Durant, Smith, Shepherd.

FIG. 140   FIFTH IAF CONGRESS, INNSBRUCK, 1954

A. G. Haley, Hugh Dryden, Theodore von Karman, F. L. Neher.

FIG. 141   EIGHTH IAF CONGRESS, BARCELONA, 1957

Left to right: V. A. Egorov, USSR; L. V. Kurnosova, USSR; Alla Massevitch, USSR; Gerald C. Gross, Vice Chairman, ARS Delegation; A. G. Haley, Chairman, U. S. Delegation; Ross Fleisig, AAS Delegation.

FIG. 142 SEVENTH IAF CONGRESS, ROME, 1956

Left to right: Dr. Theodore von Karman (USA), Dr. S. Gerathewohl (USA), A. G. Haley (USA), F. C. Durant (USA), Dr. L. Bevilacqua (Brazil), Dr. J. Kooy (Netherlands), Prof. Leonid Sedov (USSR).

Fig. 143   Mr. Mitsuo Harada, founder of the Japan Astronautical Society, is a science commentator and writer.   The society's membership includes an imposing percentage of Japanese university professors.

Fig. 144   Professor Fritz Zwicky, brilliant student of Einstein, Director of Research for several years at Aerojet, and author of the morphological study of rocketry.

FIG. 145   SEVENTH INTERNATIONAL ASTRONAUTICAL CONGRESS
           IN ROME, 1956

USA-USSR tête-à-tête: A. G. Haley and L. I. Sedov at the VIIth IAF Congress
in Rome.

Fig. 146   Pope Pius XII, surrounded by General G. Arturo Crocco, Dr. Eugen
Sänger, Dr. Irene Sänger-Bredt, Mrs. T. M. Tabanera, Mr. J. A. Stemmer, and
many others, talking to A. G. Haley.   At this same audience were Dr. Leonid
Sedov, USSR, Dr. Theodore von Karman, and many others who are not in this
picture.

Fig. 147 ARS delegate A. G. Haley, Mrs. L. R. Shepherd, Dr. L. R. Shepherd, president of the IAF (1957), Mrs. R. McMilland and Val Cleaver, former chairman of the BIS, at the *Fontana di Trevi* in Rome, at the VIIth IAF Congress.

224

10

The World Gets Together

In September, 1956, the International Astronautical Federation met in Rome for its seventh annual congress. It was an occasion for words of secular advice to all mankind from Pope Pius XII. "Do not delay examining the general problems which the invasion into interplanetary space will present," he said. The Pope addressed a group of international scientists who needed no such advice themselves, for they were acutely aware through their work in rocketry and astronautics of the imperative need for international cooperation to establish a code of law for space as quickly as possible. But at that time, despite the fact that the United States and the Soviet Union had announced plans to launch satellites during the coming International Geophysical Year, the world at large remained unaware of the problems which, with the launching of the first satellites, would affect the security of all peoples.

The admonition by a world leader not to delay was, therefore, welcomed warmly by this small band of scientists who, in relative obscurity for seven years, had been laying foundations for international cooperation for the approaching age of space. Six years previously, at the second IAF congress in London, this international group made the first organized attempt to promote world cooperation among rocket and astronautics workers. A symposium was conducted publicly by the delegates who discussed many aspects and problems of interplanetary flight. Astronautical exhibits were displayed. These were the organized beginnings, naturally ahead of the time when mankind generally would be prepared to grasp the prospect of man in space. Hermann Oberth, perhaps the greatest of the rocket pioneers, already had warned his colleagues that "one of the most important tasks confronting modern space research is the comprehensive education of mankind on our Earth and the complete recasting of the firmly rooted Western idea that space travel is merely utopian adventure."

Cooperation among the nations in any aspect of rocketry did not exist before the twentieth century and developments of any substance did not occur until the 1930's. Indeed, cooperation among nations in any important activity is a significant attainment, for "softening the harsh outlines of sovereignty, like smoothing the surface of granite, is a long process." International law always has, as Fenwick has noted, "lagged far behind the newer phases of international relations brought about by the social and commercial intercourse of modern times."

One of the earliest achievements in genuine cooperation was the establishment, in 1865, of the International Telegraphic Union, twenty years after the invention of the electric telegraph. At that time there was no corresponding political union in Europe or elsewhere in the world. Two years later another step forward in international cooperation was taken. By a convention signed in 1867, Austria, Belgium, France, Great Britain, Italy, the Netherlands, Spain, Sweden, and the United States agreed to administer and maintain the lighthouse at Cape Spartel, on the Atlantic coast of Morocco.

Twelve years later the International Meteorological Organization, whose roots go back to 1853 when ship owners throughout the world exchanged meteorological observations over the oceans, was established by 19 nations at a meeting in Rome. In 1882–83 the First International Polar Year was introduced and 50 years later (1932–33) the Second International Polar Year. These established meteorological, magnetic, and auroral stations in both polar regions which contributed greatly to knowledge of the earth's magnetism and of the ionosphere and they were preludes to the recent International Geophysical Year.

But, as we know today, all these were faltering footsteps when measured against the stupendous impact of events in the first half of the twentieth century. For in the fifty years after 1900 the world advanced farther scientifically than in the previous 2000 years combined, and the prospect today is that in the next twenty-five years the world will advance farther scientifically than it has in the previous fifty.

While international cooperation, in any appreciable form, is a development of the past thirty to forty years, nevertheless, in that short period, the world has advanced also in the new social science of cooperation professionally through private societies. Just as the development of sea transportation over 2000 years always has been, by its intrinsic nature, an international enterprise, the development of flight into space is, and will always be, by its essence, international in all its effects. Almost as quickly as rocketeers and astronauts aspired to advance the science of space flight in all its aspects, they aspired also to achieve this noble purpose on the basis of law through international cooperation.

Attaining international cooperation in the fields of rocketry and especially astronautics must be the ultimate object so long as man adheres to the principle that it is desirable to have government under law, including peaceful conquest of the universe. Incidentally, perhaps the greatest achievement of the announcements of forthcoming satellite flights, July 29, 1955, from Washington and April 15, 1955, from Moscow, was that neither engendered threats of war.

During the first three decades of the twentieth century the great rocket pioneers earnestly undertook theoretical formulations of rocket and astronautical projects and philosophies. Hermann Oberth of Rumania, Konstantin Ziolkovsky of Russia, Hermann Noordung of Austria, Walter Hohmann of Germany, Robert Esnault-Pelterie of France, Robert H. Goddard of the United States, and other eminent engineers, scientists, and industrial experimenters, published basic studies that led to the great mass of literature and to the extensive experimentation which, bursting forth in 1930, underlie our present-day rocket knowledge.

Before 1930 pioneers exchanged letters and sometimes visited one another. Ziolkovsky remained in seclusion in Russia where he wrote *Space Investigations by Means of Propulsive Space Ships* (1914) and *A Rocket Into Cosmic Space* (1924). Because he understood only Russian he was unacquainted with the West; and the Western pioneers not understanding Russian, were not acquainted with Ziolkovsky. Goddard, himself, who by 1926 had made the world's first successful liquid propellant rocket, then was extremely prudent about disseminating information.

One of the splendid pronouncements of this era was the statement contained in a letter by Oberth to Goddard in 1922. With respect to space flight, he said, ". . . I think that only by common work of the scholars of all nations can be solved this great problem."

In lighter vein, international cooperation of a friendly competitive sort could be detected in the 1930's—if one looked hard enough. Gerhard Zucker, owner of a mail-rocket franchise from the German Post Office, went to Scotland for a friendly mail-shooting contest between the two countries. Unfortunately a series of mishaps cancelled the contest before a winner could be determined. Mail rockets were enjoying a vogue at the time, one which did not subside completely until some ten years later. An international "mail-shoot" took place in 1936 at the Rio Grande between the two towns of McAllen, Texas, and Reynosa, Mexico. Several shots were fired each way and everyone enjoyed themselves.

Around 1900 a wealthy society matron in Paris, a Madame Guzman, announced an award of 100,000 francs, the "Prix Guzman," to go to the first person to establish interplanetary communication. The optimism of the time is indicated by the stipulation that Mars, being too near at hand, would not be included in the competition. Needless to add, the prize was never claimed.

In this form of international cooperation the first serious gesture was the establishment in 1929 by Robert Esnault-Pelterie and a banker, Andre Hirsch, of the "REP-Hirsch Prize." This award consisted of the payment of 5000 francs to the author or experimenter who had done the most to further the idea of space travel in a given year, and was administered by the Société Astronomique de France. This prize was awarded between 1929 and 1936, with the exception of three years when it was considered that no worth-while contribution had been made.

Hermann Oberth received a double award, 10,000 francs, in 1929 for his book *Road to Space Travel*. In 1930 and 1933 Pierre Montague received the prizes for papers on gaseous mixtures utilizable in the propulsion of rockets. In 1933, A. Sternfeld received an additional prize of 2000 francs for a paper, "Invitation to Cosmonautics." Louis Damblac received a "Prize of encouragement" of 2000 francs for a paper on proving ground tests. Alfred Africano and the American Rocket Society were honored in 1936 with the prize for design of a high-altitude rocket. Malina received the final award before World War II, but the medal was actually delivered to him by Andre Hirsch on August 25, 1958, at the Amsterdam Congress of the International Astronautical Federation.

The Hermann Oberth Medal was established after the war and today is administered under the aegis of the International Astronautical Federation. In 1954 it was awarded to J. Strughold for his work in the field of space medicine. In a further postwar gesture of international recognition, Ananoff presented A. V. Cleaver of the British Interplanetary Society with a medal from the Aero-Club de France for his organizational work on the Second International Astronautical Congress in London, 1951.

At the Fourth International Astronautical Congress in Zurich the Gunter Loeser Memorial Medal was established, to be awarded annually on the basis of competition. The medal honors one of the founders of the International Astronautical Federation who was killed when a helicopter, in which he was carrying out meteorological observations in Nebraska, crashed. The first such award is to be presented to the author of the best paper on "The Economics of Space Flight."

Germany's DGRR for some time has kept an "Ehrenbuch der Astronautik," a roll of honor of astronautics, which now contains the names of Oberth, Ananoff, Esnault-Pelterie, Von Pirquet, Pendray, and Cleaver, representing Germany, Austria, France, United States and Great Britain, respectively.

In 1952, through the efforts of Ananoff, and with the backing of the Groupement Astronautique Française and the Aero-Club de France, a special astronautical medal was awarded posthumously to Ziolkovsky and was received by Russian officials of the Paris embassy. This medal was sent to Russia and placed on exhibit in Ziolkovsky's native town of Kaluga.

The American Rocket Society Astronautics Award was approved in 1954 by the ARS Board of Directors. It was proposed and endowed by A. G. Haley. The memorabilia consists of a bronze and gold leaf trophy designed by F. J. Malina and cast in Paris, and a bronze medal to be awarded annually, also designed by Malina, the die being made in Paris. This endowment is for 101 years. Dr. Theodore von Karman was awarded the medal in 1954.

The first common forum for astronauts in all nations was established in Germany in 1927—the Society for Space Travel (VfR). Russians may dispute this statement, as announcement was made in 1926 of a "World Center for All Inventors and Scientists" which was somehow integrated with reaction power research societies in Moscow and Leningrad. No evidence is available, however, that this was more than a short-lived paper project. In any event, the German society grew rapidly. Five hundred members from Germany, Austria, Russia, and France joined the first year. Similar societies sprang up in other countries. In those days, membership in such societies did not improve one's professional standing, and much effort of the societies was devoted to proving to the public that astronautics was a science which could be pursued by sane men.

In the United States, meanwhile, the present American Rocket Society was growing. In 1930 the first bulletin of the Society appeared, containing an article on the "Universal Background of Interplanetary Flight." For many years this early ARS publication carried a column on "News from Abroad" suggesting strong interest in international astronautical affairs. France's great pioneer astronaut, Robert Esnault-Pelterie, presented to the Society an autographed copy of his historic *L'Astronautique,* and on January 15, 1931, arrived in New York. Two thousand people turned out at an ARS meeting to hear him speak, although, at the last minute, illness detained him in his New York hotel and G. Edward Pendray of the ARS had to read his speech.

In 1933 Philip Cleator founded the British Interplanetary Society (BIS) which immediately became an influential force in astronautics. A year later he traveled to Germany to find that the VfR "was no more." He wrote that the Raketenflugplatz "appeared derelict," meaning that the Army had taken over German rocketry.

After years of private studies, and with the establishment of national rocket societies, it was only natural following World War II that the rocket technicians of the world should associate formally in an international organization. Interplanetary flight will cost huge sums, and many, such as the late Gunter Loeser, hold that "this huge task cannot be performed by a single country." In the late 1940's, Germany's GfW circulated a resolution for close international cooperation among the world's astronautical societies, and in June 1949 the GfW and the British Interplanetary Society formally proposed that an international congress on astronautics be held. A. Ananoff of France made elaborate preparations for the Congress with the close cooperation of H. Gartmann of Germany and A. V. Cleaver of the BIS. While contributions of Gartmann and Cleaver to the world organization were tremendous, in fairness to Ananoff it must be recorded that he organized the first congress of 1950 almost singlehandedly.

The First International Astronautical Congress convened in Paris on September 30, 1950, with representatives of France, Germany, Austria, Great Britain, Denmark, Spain, and Argentina present. The United States did not participate. Some of the most interested scientists, such as Oberth, were prevented from attending because of visa trouble. A. Ananoff was elected president of the Congress and H. Mineur was named honorary president. Madame Gabrielle Camille Flammarion and Madame de Vendeuvre were named vice presidents. A. V. Cleaver held the chair for the important October 2 session when the general nature of the federation was agreed upon. Eight resolutions were adopted, the substance of which was that an international organization should be formed for the study and development of interplanetary flight. The organization was to be inaugurated at the next Congress, prior to which the various societies would send in proposals for a constitution, voting procedure, membership, and so on; these would be studied by the British Interplanetary Society and coordinated by it and by a temporary committee headed by Sänger of Austria.

No technical sessions were held, but the First Congress was a significant step in the history of rocketry. Science had crossed national boundaries. The mission of the proposed new organization was clear: convert the rocket from an engine of war to a peaceful vehicle of interplanetary exploration.

The primary importance of the Second International Astronautical Congress, held in London in September 1951, was the general interest that was aroused in the artificial satellite vehicle. The exchange of scientific knowledge at the meetings in Caxton Hall from September 3 to 8 was the first organized attempt to promote world cooperation for satellite development among rocket and astronautic workers.

The original societies were represented, as was the United States, by the American Rocket Society, the Reaction Research Society, the Pacific Rocket Society, and the Detroit Rocket Society. Dutch and Canadian societies were then known to exist, but they did not participate in the Congress.

The Congress was established as the International Astronautical Federation (IAF). A secretariat was authorized in Switzerland. E. Sänger was elected president. Gunter Loeser of GfW and Andrew G. Haley of ARS were elected vice presidents, and Joseph A. Stemmer was named secretary.

The BIS had done much to prepare the tentative draft of the constitution, and during this Congress the all-important question of voting was studied. It had been recommended at Paris that each nation have one vote, and with the two German societies merged, it was feared that the United States would dominate voting with five votes. The Paris provision of the year previous for one vote per nation was established as the voting arrangement.

Vice president Haley began the task of obtaining membership for the IAF in the International Council of Scientific Unions.

The Third International Astronautical Congress in Stuttgart in September, 1952, heard Hermann Oberth discuss "Private Research in Astronautics," a paper which might well keynote all Congresses. He outlined many space problems which should be investigated with the aid of astronautical societies (rather than by large-scale, government-subsidized, classified research) and which thereafter would form the basis of world cooperation.

E. Sänger was re-elected president, and A. G. Haley was re-elected vice president. L. R. Shepherd of the BIS was elected vice president, and J. A. Stemmer was re-elected secretary.

The Constitution of the International Astronautical Federation which had been drafted during the previous year by the Loeser-Haley committee was adopted. The principle of one vote per nation, regardless of the size of the country or the number of its rockets or astronautical societies, which was advocated strongly by the American Rocket Society delegation at London, was approved. It was decided that the ARS would be the voting member from the United States.

At the Fourth International Astronautical Congress in Zurich in August, 1953, societies from ten nations were represented and three new members were admitted: the Philadelphia Astronautical Society, the South African Interplanetary Society, and the Yugoslavian Astronautical Society. Japan and Israel sent observers and new societies in Spain and Egypt were reported in formative stages.

It was evident throughout the Fourth Congress that the IAF was becoming a potent factor in international efforts for scientific cooperation. Through the efforts of the Federation, for example, the United States Air Force gave permission for the Swiss scientist, Professor Eugster, to insert 400-gram packages of nuclear track plates in high-altitude, constant-level balloons.

Recognizing the need for year-round means of international dissemination of information, this Congress appointed Hecht, Sänger, Casiraghi, Shepherd, and Ordway as a committee to set up a quarterly publication, *Astronautica Acta*. The need for such a publication was evident since members meet only once a year, and in some instances even the annual meeting could not be attended by members located in distant lands.

The problem of obtaining recognition from world scientific organizations was given considerable attention and emphasis.

Durant was elected president. Haley was elected vice president, Hecht was elected second vice president, and Stemmer was re-elected secretary.

The Fifth International Astronautical Congress met at Innsbruck, Austria, with the opening session August 2, 1954, held in the Great Hall of the University of Innsbruck.

The American Astronautical Society, the Spanish Astronautical Society, the Egyptian Astronautical Society, the Japanese Astronautical Society, and the Brazilian Interplanetary Society were admitted to membership. For the first time since 1952, France sent a large delegation, but the Frenchmen did not seek formal accreditation. Russia again failed to send observers. The Croatian Society for Natural Sciences, Astronautical Section, sent an observer.

With increased membership and other encouraging signs of further international cooperation, the delegates approved publication of *Astronautica Acta* by Springer-Verlag, the German publishing house, with editorial functions remaining with the IAF. The news section was dropped from *Astronautica Acta* and instead a special bulletin containing news was set up for publication by the Secretariat in Zurich.

An international astronautical research institute was again considered, but no action was taken. Frederick C. Durant was re-elected president, and Teofilo M. Tabanera of Argentina and E. Buch Andersen of Denmark were elected vice presidents. J. A. Stemmer was re-elected secretary.

Three days after the United States announced its plans to launch a small satellite during the International Geophysical Year (1957–58) the Sixth International Astronautical Congress convened in Copenhagen. Two months earlier, in April, 1955, the Russians had announced the organization of "The Interdepartmental Commission for Interplanetary Communications."

Of particular interest at this Congress was the attendance in person of a two-man delegation from the Yugoslavia Rocket Society, Messieurs Ajvaz and Sivcev. These engineers attended the meetings faithfully. During the course of the second day of the plenary session, K. Ogorodnikov and L. I. Sedov, Russian academicians, also appeared and attended the business and technical sessions of the Congress. The Russians necessarily attended as observers because no rocket society from Russia had applied for membership.

The Constitution was amended to permit the adherence of corresponding members—educational and other institutions, which could not qualify as "societies"—but careful limitations were placed upon such adherence, the main safeguard being that any institution applying from a particular nation must have the approval of the Voting Member Society of such nation.

All the officers were re-elected, and Darrell H. Romick, as acting chief delegate of the ARS, again nominated L. R. Shepherd of BIS.

The Seventh Annual Congress, mentioned at the start of this chapter, was remarkable in many ways. Over 450 experts in the natural and social sciences attended the meetings in the Eternal City. Approximately 50 papers were presented. The organizational effort was outstanding, including excellent conference facilities, efficient use of simultaneous translation (into four languages), and a beneficial camaraderie in the Secretariat.

Three new national societies were elected, making a total of 21 voting members: Committee on Astronautics, Academy of Sciences (Russia); Polskie Towarzystwo Astronautyczne (Poland); and Société Française d'Astronautique (France).

The most felicitous occasion of the Congress was the special audience with Pope Pius XII. In reviewing the history and contributions of the International Astronautical Federation, the Pope noted particularly the leading role played by the Federation in bringing about the proposed launching of the artificial earth satellite. He pointed out that God did not intend to limit man's knowledge to the earth alone. Rather He offers to the human mind the whole creation so that man may see through it and "thus may understand always more profoundly the infinite grandeur of his Creator."

But, the Pope added:

"Without delving into details, I might say, Gentlemen, that plans of such a range entail intellectual and moral aspects which cannot be ignored; they require a certain conception of the world, its meaning, its end. . . . The most advanced explorations into space will only serve to bring a new reason for disunion if they are not effected along with a deeper moral intention and a more conscious attitude of devotion in the higher interests of mankind."

Administratively, the most important achievement of the Congress was the unanimous adoption of amendments to the IAF Constitution. These amendments increased the authorized number of vice presidents of the Federation from three to five, and established new procedures for nominating and electing IAF officers.

For 1956–1957 the Congress chose L. R. Shepherd as president and Frederick C. Durant, Teofilo Tabanera, Paul J. Bergeron, A. Sedov, and Julio Marial as vice presidents.

The program by which the IAF would act as a consultative international nongovernmental organization to United Nations Educational, Scientific and Cultural Organization upon the planning, organization, and execution of a program relating to space flight and astronautics in general was presented by A. G. Haley who was elected official IAF representative to, and who attended, the New Delhi Conference of UNESCO in November, 1955.

Formal recognition of the IAF as a consultative Non-Governmental Organization (NGO) of UNESCO has been achieved.

Once space travel becomes a reality—in fact, almost from the first occurrence of manned space flight—a number of thorny international legal problems are bound to arise. Among others, these include flight over sovereign territory (how high does sovereignty exist); radio channel allocation throughout a wide range of frequencies; satellite navigational control; weather monitoring.

It is desirable that the machinery for sorting out these problems exist before they occur, rather than have to be jerry-rigged afterwards. It also seems desirable to set up this machinery in already recognized, established international bodies. This was the reason for the considerable effort during the past few years to link the International Astronautical Federation with the United Nations Educational, Scientific and Cultural Organization.

Events now moved at an exhilarating pace. October 4, 1957, while IAF delegates were converging on Barcelona for the Eighth Congress, the Soviets announced successful launching of the first Sputnik, Alpha I. Only brief information about Sputnik was contained in the Barcelona papers, and Spanish censorship prevented distribution of newspapers from other countries. The reporters asked good questions, but primitive ones at first. On the first day, IAF scientists commented somewhat as follows:

How many stages? Most probably three.

The thrust of each stage? Many answers, but general agreement to total thrust in the order of 270,000 lb.

Burning duration and acceleration of each stage? About 2 minutes for first stage to about 4500 miles per hour. Burning duration thereafter was considered too conjectural, but the second stage must have brought the satellite to about 12,000 miles per hour and the final stage to the order of 18,000 miles per hour.

How long would the beep last? Hard to estimate, but on the basis of conjecture that Doppler, or DOVAP, equipment was being used, from four to seven weeks.

Most of the conjecture was fairly well cleared up by the end of the Congress, especially when a brief description of the launching vehicle by Y. A. Pobedonostsev, taken from an article in *Sovietskaya Aviatsia,* was circulated. The few details given confirmed the guesses mentioned above.

In view of the legal complications and involvements bound to arise as the result of ventures into space above the earth's atmosphere, A. G. Haley, who was elected president for the ensuing year, suggested the creation of a committee "to define the regions of jurisdiction of air law, and of space law." By common consent, John Cobb Cooper, general counsel of the International Air Transport Association and world-renowned international lawyer, was named chairman of the committee, which was designated the "Cooper Committee."

IAF Secretary, Joseph A. Stemmer, raised questions concerning the legality and propriety of actions taken during the preceding Congresses—a matter which is of real and legitimate concern to Mr. Stemmer because of his duty to conform the actions of the Federation to appropriate Swiss law.

The British Delegation, under the leadership of L. R. Shepherd, L. J. Carter, and the new Chairman of the British Interplanetary Society, K. W. Gatland, formally moved for the creation of a committee to correct thoroughly and revise the Constitution of the Federation. The basic British proposal was enlarged somewhat by the action of the delegates in adding thereto an opportunity for the consideration by the committee of entirely new additions to the Constitution.

The Committee appointed included A. G. Haley, Chairman, U.S.A.; Fritz Gerlach, Germany; Alla Massevitch, USSR; Georges Delval, France; L. J. Carter, England; and J. A. Stemmer, Switzerland.

A. G. Haley was elected president of the IAF for the ensuing year; vice presidents elected were A. Hjertstrand, Sweden; J. M. J. Kooy, Holland; Leonid I. Sedov, USSR; L. R. Shepherd, Great Britain; T. M. Tabanera, Argentina; K. Zarankiewicz, Poland. J. A. Stemmer was re-elected secretary.

Since World War II, many significant missions have been accomplished by individuals in the cause of international cooperation in astronautics. The journeys of Cleaver and Ordway to Paris for the First Astronautical Congress; and of Durant, Elliott, Sawyer, and Haley to the Second Congress; the "missionary" anabases of Sänger and Loeser through Germany to Paris after Stuttgart, and of Von Karman and Haley from Paris to Zurich to Milan and from Brussels to Innsbruck during the Fourth and Fifth Congresses; the world forays of Singer and Alperin; the "proselyting" missions of Stehling to Canada and of Tabanera to Brazil, Chile, Peru, and Colombia; Haley to Mexico, France, and Cuba and in 1958 on several occasions throughout Eastern and Western Europe, including lecture visits to universities at Moscow, Leningrad, Prague, Warsaw and Belgrade; the attendance at, preparation of, or delivery of papers at the several International Congresses by Romick, Gompertz, Ordway, Canney, Brannon, Gross, Klemperer, Petersen, Bergaust, Singer, Newell, Tousey, Von Braun, Spitzer, Sawyer, Cornog, Van der Wal, Schaefer, Ehricke, Rosen, Snodgrass, Stehling, Truax, Zaehringer, Stuhlinger, Strughold, Satin, Grosch, Elliott, Pierce, Vaeth, Dornberger, Merrill, Rannie, Dryden, Alperin, and many others—just to mention those within the periphery of our special acquaintances—have contributed a composite impetus to international cooperation of immeasurable importance.

Many of the major nations of the world today have rocket and astronautical societies belonging to the IAF, including Argentina, Spain, Italy, Greece, China, Bulgaria, Czechoslovakia, Israel, Great Britain, Denmark, Egypt, Germany, Japan, the Netherlands, Norway, Austria, Switzerland, Sweden, South Africa, Brazil, Yugoslavia, and the United States. The journals and other publications of the societies are interchanged, membership is open to all qualified persons without regard to national barriers, correspondence is freely interchanged, and personal visits are becoming more and more frequent.

On the higher international level, we have the United Nations itself. No one is wise enough to describe the course of the eventual evolution of space government, but, for the moment at least, the most eligible agency would appear to be the United Nations and its subsidiary affiliates. Basic investigations in the realm of the natural sciences would logically fall under the jurisdiction of UNESCO. The tremendous demand for radio spectrum in connection with the exploration of space and the colonization of other planets would certainly require the International Telecommunications Union to make adequate provisions therefor.

Until recently, there has been some reluctance, almost approaching hostility, to the consideration of plans for regulation of radio frequencies for use in space travel. In November 1956, the author traveled to Warsaw, Poland, to propose joint activity between the International Radio Consultative Committee (CCIR) and the International Astronautical Federation. He proposed that the CCIR undertake a review of the requirements of space travel for radio frequencies and promised the cooperation of the IAF in this endeavor. The CCIR did not agree to the joint effort at that time.

Slowly, but surely, the international nature of space travel regulation is being recognized. The administrative groups of some of the private international scientific organizations look at astronautics with a certain amount of timid horror, but these groups are being shocked into interest by robust and learned members who recognize in astronautics one of the truly great challenges of civilization.

In the years immediately ahead much more can and will be done by these bodies to further astronautics throughout the world. In the past several years the writer has had opportunity to travel to many places throughout the world and to observe the remarkable work done by these international organizations. They have already achieved the greatest degree of international cooperation the world has seen, largely because people today are inclined to give their technicians greater freedom than they permit their statesmen.

Yet all this is only the beginning. The science of astronautics is ready to serve mankind if political organization can keep pace.

During the CCIR meeting, July–August 1958, in Geneva, a proposal for the allocation of radio frequencies for astronautical services was presented and it is expected that these proposals will be given further consideration and action during the CCIR Plenary Session in Los Angeles and at the Administrative Radio Conference which will convene in Geneva in August

1959. These proposals, which are of fundamental importance, are set forth in Appendix 2 of this book.

The IXth Annual Congress of the International Astronautical Federation convened in Amsterdam on August 25 and adjourned on August 30, 1958. Scientists and other interested persons from thirty-one nations attended the sessions. Eighty papers were read at the Congress and twenty-five were on the main theme of the Congress, namely, "Propulsion Systems and Propellants," and the remainder were on other aspects of astronautics. A Colloquium on Space Law was held at Rolzaal-Binnenhof, The Hague. This Colloquium was presided over by Andrew G. Haley, Chairman, with the following Chairmen: Robert Homburg (Paris); Luiz de Gonzaga Bevilacqua (Brazil); Michel Smirnoff (Yugoslavia); de Rode-Verschool (Holland); Fritz Gerlach (Germany) and Welf Heinrich, Prince of Hanover (Germany).

At the Colloquium a resolution was adopted by those present, and later ratified at a Plenary Session of the IAF, which reads:

"1. That the legal problems involved by the development of Astronautics be settled through a new international Convention;

2. That within the framework of the Federation there be created a Permanent Legal Committee, open to lawyers of the various Societies or groups affiliated with the Federation, and whose members be entrusted with the study of all the problems of the law of space to be included in the Convention mentioned in Resolution No. 1.

3. That the above resolutions be communicated to the Secretary General of the United Nations who should be assured of the desire of the Federation of cooperating in any initiative to be taken in the field of Astronautics by the United Nations."

Haley was re-elected President and elected as Vice Presidents were: L. I. Sedov (USSR); T. M. Tabanera (Argentina); Paul Bergeron (France); Eugen Sänger (Germany); L. R. Shepherd (United Kingdom); and K. Zarankiewicz (Poland). J. A. Stemmer (Switzerland) was re-elected to the office of Secretary.

11

A Red Star in the Heavens

Persistent **P. S.** (Post Sputnik) questions in the United States were:
"How much of a lead in rocketry do the Russians have?"
Another was:
"When will we catch up?"
A considered answer to the first question:
"On the average, six months to a year."
And to the second:
"If we make the right decisions, in five years. If not, never."
This was America's dilemma, and with 1958 off to a hectic start, the
problem seemed on the way to solution. Meanwhile, many people remained
shocked at the forced realization that in this field, at least, the Soviets had
outstripped one of the greatest technological nations of all time. Official
and unofficial estimates of just where the Russians were, and how they got
there, varied from the sublime to the ridiculous. One thing emerged as
certain—they had gotten the jump on the United States. Study of available
data reveals both how much and why: the facts which were disclosed by
observation, plus careful study of Soviet technical papers, confirm a high
degree of Russian competence in rocketry.

That they can place ever larger and more complex satellites in orbit is a
proven fact. These Sputniks also confirm sufficient missile and rocket knowhow to enable the Russians to build intercontinental ballistic missiles.
Soviet statements that Russia has in fact successfully tested intercontinental
ballistic missiles were later confirmed by reports of United States Air Force
radar monitors on the Turkish Black Sea coast.

Our summary of Russian achievement lists 13 missiles, of which eight are
operational, three are in production, and two are being tested, as of the
Spring of 1958. In the first group are the *M-100A,* a standard **USSR**
air-to-air missile with a range of 5 miles; the *T-8,* a solid propellant surface-
to-air missile "in use for several years," with a 20-mile range; the *M-2,* a 25-
foot-long, 20-mile range antiaircraft missile "similar to the *Nike Ajax* missile,

but larger"; the *T-5B*, a 30-foot long, 2.3-foot-diameter, tactical "free-flight artillery rocket, much like the United States' *Honest John* missile," with a range of 25 miles; the *T-7A*, a 25-foot long, 2.5-foot-diameter, short-range (50 miles) ballistic missile with a 17,600-pound-thrust, solid propellant engine; the *Comet III*, a 15-foot-long air-to-surface missile, solid-propelled to a range of 100 miles—radar guided; the *T-1*, a 400–600 mile range ballistic missile, 50 feet long, 5.5 feet in diameter, powered by a 77,000-pound-thrust, liquid propellant rocket—"Improved version of the German *V-2*"; the *T-2*, an 1800-mile-range ballistic missile, 100 feet long with a 15-foot diameter using a 254,000-pound thrust *M-103* liquid propellant first stage and a 77,000-pound thrust liquid propellant second stage.

In production (but not yet fully operational) are the *Comet I*, a solid propellant, 100-mile range ballistic missile capable of being launched from submerged submarines; the *Comet II*, the same as the *Comet I* except that it has a range of 600 miles; and the *T-4*, the same as the *T-1* except that it has wings and can extend its range through gliding to 1000 miles.

In test are the *T-3* intercontinental ballistic missile, reported as having a 5000-mile range and a length of 125 feet (in "final test"); and the 12,000-mile-range skip-bomber (after the Sänger-Bredt antipodal bomber design of the mid-1930's) with an 820,000-pound thrust liquid propellant rocket engine booster. It is described as a manned bomber capable of operating at altitudes up to 160 miles (in "flight test" status).

Other, more detailed reports list even more rockets to the Soviets' credit, some growing out of German technology, others of obvious original Soviet design. Among these is the *T-3A*, a 3-to-4-stage vehicle designed for satellite launching and capable of placing up to a ton of payload in an orbit ranging between 125 and 1000 miles of altitude. Another persistent report talks of a moon rocket being constructed with a first stage of 20 clustered rockets, each with a thrust of 254,000 pounds—over 5,000,000 pounds total thrust. This would be the vehicle with which the Russians plan to land their small roving, unmanned "tankettes" to explore and report back on moon surface conditions. From its size, it would also seem practicable to consider it as a major part of any rocket system for placing a man on the moon.

Nothing seems to have been done by the Russians with the research vehicles they captured from Germany, other than to study them. Surface-to-air missiles, however, underwent immediate and intensive programs designed to develop, improve, and supply the armed forces. *Taifun* missiles, perhaps the first in service, were installed for antiaircraft defense on at least two ships, the *Sovietski* and *Sovietoki Soynuz* aircraft carriers, and possibly on a battleship of the *Sovietski Loyuz* class. These may be the *Molotov* rockets that have been reported for shipboard defense. *Rheintochter* and *Schmetter-*

ling missiles are reportedly in service with the Red Army, and may be in quantity production in Kiev and Irkutsk.

The *Wasserfalls* were apparently rushed through development, and batteries of these missiles were set up around Moscow and Leningrad as early as 1952. A 1000 to 20,000-pound improved version of the *Wasserfall* has been reported. A manned vertical take-off rocket-powered airplane which lands tail first by means of drogue chuted and braking rockets is rumored—possibly an outgrowth of the *DFS-346* rocket plane. The air-to-air rocket *R-4M* has been improved. The warhead has greater destructive power and now weighs 15.8 ounces, 1.8 ounces less than formerly.

Russian studies of the *V-1* flying bomb have resulted in a missile something like the American *Matador,* but larger, and capable of attaining a speed of about 700 miles per hour. The pulsejet engine has been discarded in favor of the turbojet engine which the Russians have developed to a high level. Ranges up to 1500 miles are possible. A large number of experimental launchings of these missiles have taken place near Taimyr, from land ramps and submarines. A possible launching rate of 40 missiles per hour per ramp has been reported.

In recent years, however, many of the German-type missiles have been replaced by vehicles of more original Russian design—for example, the *Comets I* and *II* are now capable of being launched from submerged submarines.

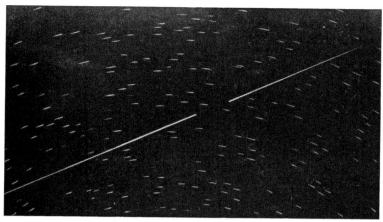

FIG. 148   SOVIET EARTH SATELLITES

A photograph of the carrier rocket taken by K. Koseleva, an astronomer at Pulkovo, by means of a short-focus astrograph at dawn on October 10, 1957. Owing to the daily rotation of the Earth, the stars in the photograph are seen as short, white dashes. The trail of the carrier rocket is a straight line. The interruption in the rocket trail was made to determine the moment of flight.

FIG. 149   RUSSIAN SPACE DOG AT ALTITUDE OF 210 KILOMETERS

A dog in a hermetically sealed canister installed on a test rocket. The photograph was taken automatically by a film camera on the rocket.

FIG. 150 SPACE MONKEY RETURNS TO EARTH AFTER FLIGHT

A technician removes a space-soaring monkey from the nose compartment of the Aerojet-General Corporation's *MX-1011 Aerobee* guided missile No. 19 after historic flight into the stratosphere at Holloman Air Force Base, New Mexico, on September 20, 1951. (USAF)

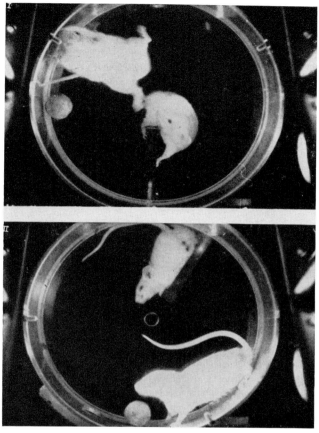

FIG. 151   MICE FLOAT WITHOUT GRAVITY IN SPACE

Single scenes from a motion picture of two mice in a two-section rotating drum in an *Aerobee III* missile, 1952. The first photograph, made shortly after separation of the rocket nose from the rest of the rocket, and two minutes of zero-gravity, shows how the mouse in the rear drum can grasp the sides of his platform to maintain his equilibrium, while the mouse in the front compartment is floating in air during this zero-gravity period. Note that the ball is suspended in air, away from the sides of the drum. The conclusion from this experiment and these photographs is that gravity sense is lost if there is no way of keeping in one place. In other words, mammals who are able to hold on to something can orient themselves and in no way be affected by the zero-gravity period. The second photograph, which was taken a few seconds after parachute opening when the deceleration applied to the nose cone by the drag parachute approximates one *G*, shows the mouse in the front compartment standing poised and normally oriented as he follows the drum movement. In contrast with the first photograph, the rubber ball is now supported by the drum. The mouse in the rear compartment prepares to jump off the small shelf with normal agility. (USAF)

FIG. 152　SPACE SUIT UNDER TEST IN THE LABORATORY

Inside the new high-altitude chamber developed for the USAF's Air Research and Development Command, Neils Jensen shows how he can handle a wrench, while wearing the pressure suit that protects him at a simulated altitude 95 miles above the earth's surface. Jensen is a scientist from Litton Industries, Inc., the contractor who designed the chamber for ARDC's Air Force Office of Scientific Research. (USAF)

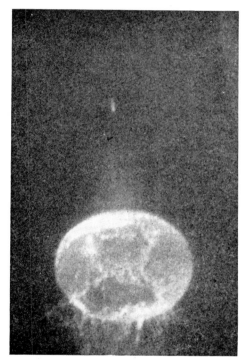

FIG. 153 PROJECT FARSIDE

Launched from a huge polyethylene balloon at 100,000 feet of altitude, the four rocket stages burned out and dropped away successively—each adding to the acceleration of the next stage. The final stage then "coasted" nearly 3000 miles. It remained in the vacuum of space about 75 minutes, sending back important new information by radio.

FIG. 154   NOSE CONE UNDER REENTRY TEMPERATURE TEST

The terrific heat that a missile nose cone is subjected to upon reentry into the earth's atmosphere is demonstrated in the above laboratory demonstration. These nose cones could not withstand the high temperatures.

FIG. 155   REENTRY NOSE CONE TEST CHAMBER

This is the test chamber used to test the endurance of missile nose cones to the conditions present upon reentry into the earth's atmosphere.

FIG. 156 EXPLORER

Here, the U. S. Army's *Juno-I* (*Jupiter-C*) *Explorer* launching vehicle lifts off in billowing smoke and falling ice. Except for the first stage rocket (here lettered UE), this is nearly identical to the *Juno-II* moon vehicle. *Juno-II,* instead of a *Redstone* first stage, uses the bigger, more powerful *Jupiter*. Upper spin stages are the same, however.

247

FIG. 157   MOON ROCKET

The gantry tower has been rolled back and on Test 1529, the Air Force's Moon rocket stands alone. Note the three sets of umbilical cords connected to each of the vehicle's three main stages. These carry external power and instructions to the bird prior to launch, and disconnect only at the moment of firing.

FIG. 158 LANDING ON THE MOON

At end of surface-to-surface flight from earth to moon, this is how nuclear-powered space liner would land on the satellite. Using light thrust to counter lunar gravity, the rocket is "backed down" until the gondola touches the surface. Then the power plant is landed nearly 1000 feet away at the limit of the connecting cables, for protection of personnel from radiation hazards. Crewmen use microwave radio to communicate with earth, pictured upper right as it would appear from surface of the moon. The vehicle could carry a 15,000-pound payload to moon, with sufficient fuel to take off and return to a position just outside the earth's atmosphere. Crew would transfer to a reentry glider to complete the round trip. (Courtesy Krafft A. Ehricke, Convair, Astronautics)

FIG. 159 NUCLEAR ROCKET MISSILE OF THE FUTURE

This is an artist's concept of a nuclear rocket missile. Theoretically capable of hundred-fold increases over the payloads of today's missiles, nuclear rocket vehicles may make interplanetary travel possible with single rather than multi-stages. In concept, the engine would use energy of nuclear fission to convert a working fluid into propulsive gases—much as heat from an electric plate turns water into steam. (Rocketdyne)

FIG. 160   CREW PROTECTION FROM THE RADIATION OF A
                 NUCLEAR ROCKET

Krafft A. Ehricke's moon rocket would hang the payload (here, manned 1000
feet below its nuclear power plant), after having been boosted out into space by
the chemical rocket in the background.   This configuration, Ehricke says, could
deliver 22,000 pounds on the Moon.

FIG. 161   NUCLEAR-POWERED INTERPLANETARY VEHICLE

Liquid hydrogen carried in the tanks at right would be heated by a nuclear reactor and then expanded through the rocket nozzle at the far right, thus producing the necessary thrust to propel the ship through space.   A crew of at least 8 persons could be carried in the cabin at left, some 300 feet from the source of nuclear radiation.   The hydrogen tanks are so arranged that the fuel serves as a shield between the nuclear reactor and the crew compartment.   In the above picture the vehicle has entered an orbit around its target planet and a small chemically-powered rocket or "satelloid" (left center), which formerly attached to the mother vehicle, has been dispatched on an exploratory mission into the planet's atmosphere.   A remote-controlled television robot is being maneuvered about the rear of the ship for inspection and servicing of the propulsion units. Use of the robot eliminates the need for sending humans to that portion of the ship endangered by nuclear radiation.   At an ideal velocity of 90,000 feet per second, this vehicle could undertake several fast missions within the inner solar system.   It could make a journey to Mars and back (including exploration around Mars) in less than a year.   It would not take off from the surface of the earth but would be launched from an earth satellite orbit.   (Courtesy Krafft A. Ehricke, Convair Astronautics)

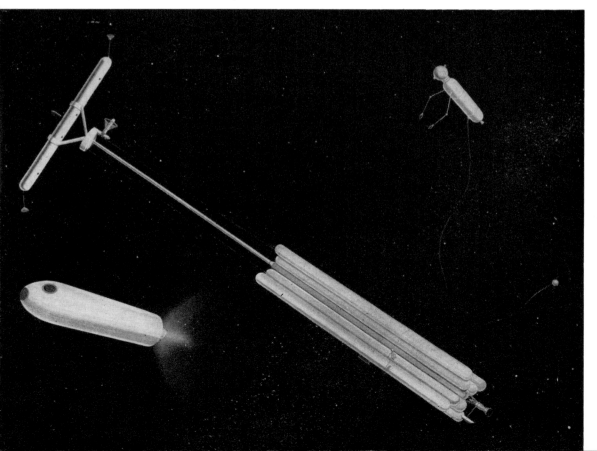

FIG. 162 SOLAR-POWERED SPACE SHIP

Sunlight captured by the large plastic sphere at right is used to heat liquid hydrogen carried in the three tanks at the center of the structure. The gaseous hydrogen is expelled through two rockets between the sphere and the tanks. One half of the sphere—the half facing the sun—is transparent. The other half is coated with silver or aluminum to form a mirror-like surface which collects solar radiation and concentrates it on a heat exchanger along the focal line of the reflector. A crew gondola with attached radar antennas is shown at the opposite end of the vehicle. The ship is constructed so the radiation-collecting surface always faces the sun regardless of the direction of thrust. The light weight of the plastic sphere would give the ship an advantage over comparable chemical rockets as the latter would need heavy supplies of oxygen—in addition to hydrogen fuel—to make combustion possible. Solar-powered spaceships, due to their lightness and their low thrust capabilities, would be best fitted for space operation between orbits. The ships would be constructed at and launched from an orbital satellite. (Krafft A. Ehriche, Convair, Astronautics)

FIG. 163   SATURN IN BLUE LIGHT

This is a 200-inch photograph taken at the Mount Wilson and Palomar Observatories.

FIG. 164   JUPITER IN BLUE LIGHT, SHOWING LARGE RED SPOT

This is a 200-inch photograph showing the satellite Ganymede and its shade on Jupiter (above), taken at the Mount Wilson and Palomar Observatories.

FIG. 165   SPIRAL NEBULA IN *COMA BERENICES,* SEEN EDGE ON

This is a 200-inch photograph taken on an unfiltered red sensitive plate at the Mount Wilson and Palomar Observatories.

FIG. 166   HORSEHEAD NEBULA IN *ORION* SOUTH OF *ZETA ORIONIS*

This is a 200-inch photograph taken in red light at the Mount Wilson and Palomar Observatories.

FIG. 167   SPIRAL NEBULA IN *VIRGO*, SEEN EDGE ON

This is a 200-inch photograph taken at the Mount Wilson and Palomar Observatories.

Russia lists few research rockets. The reason behind this is that, from the beginning, she has used military hardware for research purposes, changing mainly payload (warhead), staging, burning times, etc., for accomplishing different missions. This is the same principle applied by the United States Army Ballistic Missile Agency in its *Jupiter-C* series of reentry-research and satellite-launching vehicles. It is also the principle that permitted the Lockheed Aircraft Corporation to develop the highly successful *X-17* reentry test rocket for the United States Air Force. In the construction of the *Jupiter-C* missile the Army used a military, liquid-propelled *Redstone* missile for a first stage and clustered solid-propelled *Recruit* missiles or *Scale Sergeant* missiles, for varying numbers of successive stages, depending on the requirements of the particular mission. Similarly, the *X-17* rocket plane used a *Sergeant* missile for the first stage, three *Recruit* missiles for the second stage, and a single *Recruit* missile for the third and final stage—all "off-the-shelf" military hardware. Another example of this "economy" approach is the United States Air Force's balloon-launched *Far Side* rocket, consisting of four stages of clustered, readily available, small, solid propellant rockets.

The Russians are known to have used this "building block" approach to rocketry on more occasions than one. Reports have reached the West, for example, that for one specific research purpose they have even clustered the unbalanced *T-1* and *T-2* missiles' first-stage liquid propellant rocket engines together. Their moon rocket, of course, must be an approach to the ultimate in this sort of thing, apparently utilizing the military *T-2* missile's first-stage rocket engine.

Since the war, there is strong evidence that the Russians may have made considerable progress in the development of various forms of high-energy propellant systems. A Russian report, for example, claims to have solved the problem of storing free chemical radicals. Also, it seems likely that they have already made successful flights of rockets using liquid ozone as an oxidizer for boron slurries.

It is important to remember that the Russians have worked steadily on a high priority basis since 1945 to develop the science and technology of large, strategic rocketry. The Russians have been sold on the practicability of space flight for over half a century and three years ago gave it the highest priority. The West, on the other hand, began serious work on large rockets only three or four years ago, and is only just now beginning to realize the full significance of space flight.

Early in 1955, the Soviet Union established within the Academy of Sciences the Commission for Interplanetary Travel, a body of 27 of Russia's top scientists. Their job was to organize a progressive space flight program, to identify its problems, and to see that they were solved. A measure of their success in doing this is found in their satellite-launching record to date.

The Soviet Academy of Sciences is an elite organization composed of hundreds of scientists, assisted by practical experts and technicians. Membership in the Academy brings a special stipend and great professional prestige. In essence it is the centralized body of control for all Soviet science. The interests of the Academy range from pure science through engine design and medieval history. In 1952 it had 40 commissions and committees, 14 museums, 4 observatories, 57 institutes, 38 research stations, and 15 laboratories. Through these and other agencies it directs the work of thousands of scientists and technicians throughout the Soviet Union. Policy and direction flow from the Council of Ministers through the Chief Scientific Secretary, appointed by the Communist Party. The current secretary is A. V. Topchiev. The president of the Academy is a respected organic chemist, A. N. Nesmeyanov.

The formal name for the Interplanetary Travel Commission is: The Commission for the Coordination and Control of Scientific-Theoretical Work in the Field of Organization and Accomplishment of Interplanetary Communication of the Astronomical Council of the Academy of Sciences of the USSR. The fundamental task of the Commission is ". . . to assist in every way the development of scientific-theoretical and practical work in the Soviet Union concerning questions of studying cosmic space and the accomplishment of astronautics."

The responsibilities and powers of the Astronautics Commission are specific and extensive. The Commission is charged with:

1) "Taking actions which secure the active participation of academic and branch scientific-research establishments in work for the investigation of cosmic space."

2) "Organization of work on drawing up problem plans and programs of scientific investigations on the fundamental trends of astronautics."

3) "Broad attraction of scientific-research establishments, of universities and individual investigators to the solution of problems to secure the realization of flight into cosmic space."

4) "Coordination of scientific activities of individual research institutions on the problems of astronautics."

5) "Popularization of the tasks and achievements in the field of astronautics."

In addition, the Commission shall:

6) "Review the plans and reports of the 'scientific research institutes which work on the program controlled by the Commission.' "

7) "Sponsor scientific conferences on astronautical problems."

8) "Serve as the award committee in stimulating the submission of scientific work in competition for the triennial K. E. Ziolkovsky Gold Medal, established in 1954."

9) "Maintain, through the Foreign Section, contact with the scientific organizations in foreign countries which are concerned with high-altitude research and space flight."

The Chairman of the Commission on Astronautics is Academician L. I. Sedov. Sedov is a distinguished physicist who has been known for his works in analytical mechanics and gas dynamics.

A comprehensive idea of the extent and location of Soviet astronautical work may be gained from the following breakdown of the five major scientific divisions of the Academy of Sciences, worked up by William P. Lear:

PHYSICS-MATHEMATICAL SCIENCES

1) Physical Institute (Moscow)
   Conducts research in atomic fission, cosmic rays, physical optics, spectroscopy, radio physics, propagation of electromagnetic waves, radar, acoustics, theoretical physics.
2) Physical-Technical Institute (Leningrad)
   Conducts research in semiconductors, electronics, polymers, physics of nuclei, properties of solids, dielectrics, synthetic rubber, etc.
3) Institute of Crystallography (Moscow)
   Pursues a number of practical problems, for example, the use of different crystals such as dielectrics in oscillating circuits which have special features in selectivity, resonance, etc.
4) Mathematical Institute (Moscow)
5) Institute of Geophysics (Moscow)
   Studies the origin of the earth, seismology, earth's electric and magnetic fields, winds, cyclones, tides, ocean currents, etc. The institute has numerous laboratories and stations scattered all over the territory of the USSR.
6) Institute of Seismology (Moscow)
   A kind of subsidiary organization of the Institute of Geophysics.
7) Hydrophysical Laboratory (Moscow)
   Another ramification of the Institute of Geophysics; studies ocean currents, winds, spectroscopy of ocean noise, means of reducing ocean waves by means of films of oil, propagation of oceanic disturbances in depth, etc.
8) Astronomical Observatory (Pulpovo)
   Observation.
9) Institute of Theoretical Astronomy (Leningrad)
   Conducts research in perturbations, astronomical tables and purely theoretical work in celestial mechanics on the basis of data collected by the Astronomical Observatory.
10) Committee on Meteors
    Subsidiary of the Institute of Theoretical Astronomy.
11) Laboratory of Astronomical Instruments
12) Laboratory of Radio-Physics and Radio Technique (Moscow)
    Studies short waves, ultrashort waves, nonlinear oscillations, etc.

13) Spectroscopic Laboratory (Moscow)
14) Acoustical Laboratory (Moscow)
15) Committee on Cosmic Rays (Moscow)
16) Committee on History of Physics-Mathematical Sciences
17) Committee on the Development of Physical Methods in Geophysical Research
18) Committee on Astrophysics
19) Committee on Geodesy
     Studies maps, profiles of the sea, soundings, etc.

TECHNICAL SCIENCES

1) Institute of Energy (Moscow)
   Studies the terrestrial electric field, lightning, production of gas, etc.
2) Institute of Fuels
3) Institute of Metallurgy (Moscow)
4) Institute of Mining (Moscow)
5) Institute of Machine Construction (Moscow)
   Conducts research in the theory and construction of machines (jointly with the Institute of Metallurgy)
6) Institute of Mechanics (Moscow)
   Conducts research in stability, gyroscopes, dampers, plasticity, shells, aerodynamics, supersonics, propellers, jet, etc.
7) Institute of Automatics and Telemechanics (Moscow)
   Studies control problems (particularly nonlinear ones), autopilots, etc.
8) Committee on Communications (Moscow)
   Studies problems in steam, diesel and electric locomotives, automatic blocking systems for railroads, traffic control, etc.
9) Committee on Waterways
   Studies construction of canals, waterways, etc.
10) Committee on Radio Communications
    Studies the use of short and ultrashort wave propagation, taking into account the nature of the earth's surface, presence of iron ores, etc.
11) Committee on Welding and Electrothermal Devices.
    Studies welding techniques, stresses in structures, etc.
12) Committee on Standardization.

In addition the Soviet Union maintains a strong interest in and provides support to a number of East European research and development installations at Rechlin (a former German Air Force facility), at Kaliningrad (formerly Koenigsberg, East Prussia), Peenemünde (rebuilt under Professor Artakianov), a Polish site (Heidelager) to supplement Peenemünde, the Lehesten Rocket Motor Facility, the Walther Rocket Propulsion Works in Prague, the Rabe Rocket Institute, and the BMW Factory in Berlin. The Lehesten facility may have been deactivated and moved to Russia.

Also, we know that when the Russians overran eastern Germany they captured Peenemünde, and other sites, while obtaining Nordhausen and various other missile facilities from the Allied group by agreement. In doing this, they inherited a fairly representative slice of the German missile technology.

Recently, the Russians have made a number of official claims for the future. For example, they say they soon will launch a television relay station satellite to a 22,000-mile-high, one-day orbit, so that it will remain stationary over one point on the earth's surface. They are known to be building a manned orbital satellite with re-entry capabilities. They have said that they will send a man to the moon within five years, and to Mars and Venus before 1970. The rest of the world now has no alternative, but to assume they are serious. One thing is certain—they have certainly demonstrated their ability to date. They have established an organization capable of concentrating maximum effort on any project of this nature that they may choose.

The Russians realize the potential economic and military advantages accruing to the nation that first masters outer space. It can only be assumed that the Soviet Union is not only working towards vehicles to place Russian military personnel in the cosmic void, but also to put in their hands the weapons that they will need for warfare in this unfamiliar environment. It is a fantastic era that is upon us. Russia realizes this. It is imperative that other countries do too.

12

After Today—Infinity

The future of rocketry lies in the minds and affairs of men and in the endless reaches of countless galaxies. As men learn to use this new mode of travel and communication, new worlds will open up for scientific exploration and philosophic thought, for economic exploitation, and eventually for expanded human habitation. It is practically impossible to forecast, except in broad generalities, the great changes that will inevitably take place in our lives—material, social, and philosophic—but rocket scientists and thoughtful men of many nations have been reflecting on these questions more and more deeply as the pace of rocketry has quickened. Our survey of the growth of rocketry logically leads us now into this brief chapter, a speculative look into the future.

The Milky Way contains roughly 40,000,000,000 individual stars. Many stars are like our sun. Its diameter is some 100,000 light years; its thickness at the center, maybe 10,000 light years. A light year is a measure of distance and is about 5,865,696,000,000 miles. With presently known theories we can build rockets that will traverse the Milky Way and go on and on to other galaxies, many times farther away.

At the present, in the physical sciences, we are leaving the age of classical mechanics and moving into an era where Albert Einstein's great accomplishment, the General Theory of Relativity, will become common knowledge in high schools. It is an age in which speed will be measured (like the Mach number) in terms of theoretical maximum—i.e., the speed of light. It is an age in which a million miles will be a negligible navigational error; when men will age at different rates, depending on where they are; when man will be hard-put to remain as large as his environment.

Barring self-inflicted oblivion in the interim, this age is less than a century away, for the rate of scientific progress is accelerating tremendously. As the science of men changes, so must the ways of men change. For it is in the social, legal, moral, ethical, and other human considerations, as well as the physical aspect of our environment, that we are approaching one of the greatest upheavals in the entire history of mankind. Most of us, unfortunately, cannot or do not think in terms that go beyond the traditional confining limits of our own comfortable environment. This is the basic danger —that we as individuals will not develop with the world around us. Whereas the great scientific discovery translated into a vehicle (such as a rocket) may be the synthesis of many minds, the individual comprehension and appreciation of what it means must be the thoughtful conclusion of a single mind for it to be of any value at all.

This new age will not suddenly appear, delivered as it were on a silver platter. On the contrary, it will be the end result of many unrelated, often-unsuspected, hard-fought trials and hard-won accomplishments. The state of fumbling confusion (and near panic) that now grips a world divided is both normal to, and symbolic of, the state of rapid change now taking place in the world. It will be so for some years to come. Let us take it step by step from the present age of the primitive "blast-off" rocket through the age when manned space flight is as easy and as common as motoring is today— and a whole lot safer.

The United States and Russia are now engaged in a more or less conventional race for space, with Russia momentarily leading. Behind the scenes in both countries, continuing efforts are being made to develop more sophisticated forms of propulsion and travel. Here again, odds are that the Soviet Union has made more progress than the United States. However, with the right decisions, it seems likely that the United States can recapture the lead on both counts.

Conventionally, both East and West are trying to perfect their long-range chemical rockets. These are the Intercontinental and Intermediate Range Ballistic Missiles—ICBMs and IRBMs. Simultaneously, they are, bit by bit, moving out into space. *Sputnik I* was launched on October 4, 1957; *Sputnik II,* about 5 weeks later, *Sputnik III,* 8 months later. The United States has its satellites aloft and shows signs of catching up with some of Russia's later, more sophisticated earth-circling vehicles.

Following on the time scale, within the next few years, are television camera-carrying satellites, solar battery-powered satellites, manned satellites, instrument-carrying moon rockets—first circling or crash-impacting, then landing—and perhaps manned moon rockets . . . all within the period prior to 1965. Russia, with her present lead, will certainly accomplish most of these things. Odds are that the United States will catch up in this period.

Importantly, America has established a national civilian space flight agency (NASA), with broad powers and a generous budget. Although this was done by the Government, more because of the embarrassing pressure of public opinion than because of any firm conviction that it was necessary, it is still a significant move in the right direction. Before long, that **very** organization will prove dramatically the reason for its existence. Meanwhile, the Soviet Union has had a top-level Commission for Interplanetary Travel for several years.

The bid for man's first maneuverable flight into space is being made equally by the United States and Russia. The United States has the Air Force's North American *X-15* rocket plane which may ultimately reach an altitude of 200 miles in its later modifications. It is a study vehicle designed to test out methods of switching from jet-reaction to aerodynamic controls. It will also provide much valuable data on the survival needs of man in space and on the techniques of re-entering the earth's atmosphere. The Russians are making their bid with a rocket-boosted skip bomber—the *T-4A* designed originally in the mid-1930's by Eugen Sänger. This vehicle appears to be already in the preliminary flight test stage. Both of these vehicles, the *X-15* rocket plane and the *T-4A,* will probably reach and exceed the limits of the earth's atmosphere during the years 1959–60.

Also in this period, instrumented rockets will probe the far side of the moon. They may even land and set up remote control monitoring stations. Again, the first moon rockets will probably belong to Russia, because the Russians have already made a big start in that direction. However, at this stage the United States should be well on the way to catching up.

In the years 1961–62, efforts will be made to place a man in a three-day orbit from which he will return by a system of complex metal parachutes. It's an even toss-up whether the United States or Russia does this first. The logical next step will be to place (or to construct) a large, permanent, manned satellite in space. This would be on the order of the Wernher von Braun concept of the orbiting, rotating wheel.

Meanwhile, somewhere along the line, reconnaissance satellites carrying television cameras, recorders, and retransmitters will be launched. Estimated time for the first American attempt is during the years 1960–61. The Russians may try it earlier—or not at all because of the poor resolution of television cameras and the fuzzing effect of the atmosphere. However, Russia has said that she will launch a television relay satellite to a one-day, stationary (over the earth) orbit at an altitude of 22,000 miles in the "near future." This would enable Moscow and other Russian cities to transmit television programs to nearly half the world, including Asia, Southeast Asia, the Middle East, all of Africa and West Europe. Such a satellite would be a marvel of design and engineering accomplishment, for it would have to have a continuous, constant source of power; extremely reliable television receivers and relay transmitters (nobody could get up to repair them); and very precise launching and orbiting ability—otherwise it would not remain at one point above the earth's surface.

There will be other conventional rocket accomplishments during the next few years—each one of them startling at the time. These will include instrumented rockets fired farther and farther out into space until at last Mars and Venus are orbited. A comparatively easy shot would then be to fire an instrumented probe into the sun's gravitational field to take physical readings of the immediate environment of space around the glowing orb—until the intense heat melted the rocket. This would be one of several likely projects during the first International Astrophysical Year (IAY), say, along about the mid-1960's. The International Astrophysical Year would be to the solar system what the recent International Geophysical Year is to earth.

For all of the accomplishments of chemical rockets, they are indeed primitive compared with what lies ahead. Today, the chemical rocket is everything in rocketry. Tomorrow, it will be an obsolete system. Chemical rockets take too much fuel, which they consume too rapidly, for really practical space flight. True, they will first place man in space, but before long they will be replaced by other systems, based largely on electrically driven jets deriving their energy from nuclear transformations or solar radiation.

Some work in this direction is being carried out now—for example, this country's multi-million-dollar nuclear aircraft propulsion system project. As a propulsion system in itself, it is probably a large waste of money. It concentrates on a primitive form of nuclear power (compared to fusion) and faces immense shielding and heat transfer problems. However, should it be successful, the very fact of getting a nuclear powerplant aloft will be important.

Present American research on nuclear aircraft propulsion deals with atomic fission—the breaking apart of the atom, which is similar to a controlled atom bomb. This fission plant could just as readily be made to produce electrical power. Then, there is controlled fusion—the tamed H-bomb. America, Britain, and Russia are working on this principle. The Russians are known to be advanced in this field, though perhaps they lag the British.

A primitive concept of the nuclear rocket would use either a fission or a fusion heat source to heat gases carried on board, which in turn would be ejected like a chemical rocket's exhaust. A vehicle powered in this manner would have its range limited by the weight and volume of condensed gas it could carry on board, just as the chemical rockets in use today, those employing as propellants some of the more exotic reactants, such as fluorine, hydrogen, boron, lithium, or even free radicals.

The basic disadvantage of the chemical rocket is that the energies available from even the most reactive chemical or free-radical combinations are not much greater than the typical and well-known heat of combustion of fluorine and hydrogen. In other words, in the field of chemical reactions there appears to be an energy ceiling that is, unfortunately, too low for effective space flight. A further disadvantage that would become very critical if the chemical energy ceiling could be overcome is the fact that the combustion rocket is really a heat rocket, and the hot gases generate pressure in all directions which must be contained by solid walls. That is, ordinary heat energy is applied against the walls of the combustion chamber, as well as in the useful, longitudinal fore-and-aft direction. All the energy consumed in pushing against the side walls is wasted. Not only is it wasted, but it causes trouble in that the heat thus transferred must be carried away. In space, this is very difficult, since there is no cooling air available and radioactive coolers would be heavy.

The first step in electrical propulsion utilizes ions—electrically charged particles of matter. These can be accelerated either electrostatically or electromagnetically to great velocities. Here Newton's Third Law of Motion applies, just as in a chemical rocket, except that the thrust is exerted against the electrical or magnetic apparatus that accelerates the particles of matter. It is purely and simply, a momentum transfer—from the accelerated particles to the vehicle. It's a kind of magnetic ramjet engine.

Again, it seems certain that all three of the major rocket building countries are working on ion propulsion. In America, specific impulses of over 1000 seconds have been achieved with primitive ion propulsion systems in the laboratory. This compares to an impulse of from 250 to 275 seconds for the best chemical rocket available today.

One group of space flight scientists would not use chemical rockets at all, but since ion propulsion produces thrusts of less than one G (though for long periods of time) it would be unsuitable for orbiting the earth preliminary to actual escape. However, it is possible with present theory to build a system of turbojet and ramjet powerplants with which near orbital velocity could be achieved within the upper limits of the earth's atmosphere. As the vehicle increased in altitude from 500,000 to 1,000,000 feet—and as its speed increased to, say, 18,000 miles per hour—it would reach the working limits of its "air-breathing" ramjet engines. However, under these near-orbiting conditions, the atmosphere would be almost 100 percent ionized. Then, powerful magnetic coils would be excited, accelerating both the free ions of space and ionized material carried on board. The chemical ramjet engines would stop operating entirely, and the rocket ship would be operating on ion propulsion exclusively.

For high-altitude space voyages, the ion rocket would have to carry nearly 100 percent of its working material, but in the "immediate environment" of earth, say, an altitude up to 40,000 miles, there is quite a high natural ion density (a thousand or more ions per cubic centimeter). While these could not provide all the working fluid, they would aid materially in conserving fuel carried on board. Such a magnetic-powered rocket ship should be spaceborne within ten years and may well be called a magnetic ramjet. Ion propulsion should provide fairly practical means for traveling to most points in the solar system and back.

One of the more speculative forms of reaction engine is the photon rocket. While the ion rocket is known in theory and can also be constructed, the photon rocket is known in theory only. It utilizes energy in its purest form, using light rays to provide thrust. Its thrust would be minute, but would be available for incredibly long periods of time. It would be suitable, for example, to consider a voyage to Alpha Centauri, some three-and-a-half light years away. We may see photon rockets being tested in the laboratories around the turn of this century.

By then, however, we will have large manned space stations orbiting the earth. There will be one or more permanent bases on the moon, and a manned expedition will be on its way to Mars and Venus.

However, before then, a discovery even more significant than the development of atomic energy or the re-discovery of the rocket will happen. This will be the discovery of a way to utilize free space energy—magnetic, electrical, or gravitational. The solar battery is such a device, but for the moment it has very limited use. Navigational trajectories to nearby planets will take full advantage of their gravitational pull.

Some say, however, that man is on the verge of a highly sophisticated discovery. Moscow talks of gravity-free planes. A number of companies and government laboratories in the United States are conducting anti-gravity research. Simultaneously, man's study of the basic nature of matter is probing deeper and deeper into nature's secrets. There is nothing specific, but working with it and noting the mounting energies applied in that direction, one can sense the pulsing beat of history in the making. It is possible that the enigma of gravity will be solved within the next 50 years—perhaps sooner. With this solution will come means of "absorbing" the vast "free" energies that permeate all of space.

Science is a wonderful and unpredictable thing. We set out on a search for one thing and discover another. If we are lucky, we appreciate that discovery when it first appears. How many times, however, have secrets been revealed to man, only to be ignored. The discovery of the beautiful aniline dyes that brighten our life today, remember, stem from a chance reaction in a research program to make a better explosive. So it is in all science; often it is more important to recognize the importance of an event than actually to cause the event.

So man's science will reveal more and more of nature's secrets, propelling him to and from worlds and realms as yet unknown. The next fifty years will go down in history as the age of discovery. Let us hope that it does not also go down in history as the age of man's greatest destruction of himself and the things he has wrought. This is the reason why it is as vital to be concerned with the advancement of man's ability to get along with his fellow man as it is to promote the advancement of science.

A new era of science and sociology is now dawning. Concepts that have been absolute since the beginning of human history must now be carefully appraised. The fence that has confined us in the yard we call "earth" is now being pulled down. Our relationships with ourselves take on entirely new terms of reference. The earth is no longer the limit of our boundaries, but merely a point in vast space. There may be other intelligent beings on other planets whose countenances bear little resemblance to our own. As we prepare our rockets to carry us into space, we must also prepare our minds to carry us forward into the future.

Perhaps a quick way to indicate present vistas of rocketry of the future is simply to give the names of the lecturers and the titles of their papers delivered at the Amsterdam Congress of the IAF in 1958. Here are some of the papers presented on propulsive systems of the future:

T. von Karman: *Magneto fluid dynamics in relation to space flight problems.* E. Sänger: *Sources of radiation for photonic rockets.* J. Ackeret: *The use of gasturbines for rocket propulsion in space.* L. R. Shepherd: *Electrical propulsion systems for space flight.* B. Lewis and B. Karlovitz: *Space propulsion by interstellar gas.* J. Vandenkerckhove: *Notes on the optimum design of solid propellant powerplants for missiles systems engineering.* W. Peschka: *On utilization of atomic hydrogen as fuel for liquid fuel rockets.* M. Serruys: *Contribution of thermodynamics to the evaluation of possibilities or performance of rockets.* K. Knothe: *Relativistic treatment of rocket kinematics and propulsion.* H. J. Huth: *Electric power for space flight.* I. Sänger-Bredt: *Working fluids for rockets heated by non-conventional chemical energy.* W. H. Bostick: *Plasma motors: The propulsion of plasma by magnetic means.* E. Ostinelli: *Limit performances of space ships employing fission power of uranium nuclei or fusion power of deuterium nuclei.* J. Hilsenrath: *Thermodynamic properties of highly ionized gases.* D. Altman: *Chemical propulsion in the new space age.* H. Bednarczyk: *Acceleration of conducting particles by magnetic fields.* F. Winterberg: *The attainment of exhaust velocities up to 20,000 m/s by means of isothermic expansion in nuclear rockets.* O. K. Rice: *The recombination of atoms and other energy-exchange reactions.* L. G. Napolitano: *Magneto fluid dynamics of two interacting streams.* J. H. Houtman: *Efficiency and ram-rocket start of self-tanking multi-coupled rocket.* E. Stuhlinger: *Advanced propulsion systems for space vehicles.* J. J. Barre: *Physiothermic autopropulsion units-radioactive process of heat transfer permitting acceleration of mass particles.* R. John, R. Schweiger, J. Vos, M. E. Malin: *Electric arc plasma generators applied to propulsion.* A. B. Mickelwait: *Analytical and numerical studies of three-dimensional trajectories to the moon.* P. S. Lykoudis: *On a class of compressible laminar boundary layers with pressure gradient for an electrically conducting fluid in the presence of a magnetic field.*

13

The Working Societies

The requirements of narration have necessitated numerous lengthy references, from Chapter 3 through the remaining text, to the American Rocket Society, the British Interplanetary Society, the USSR organizations, and to the German societies from the VfR to the current DGRR. This chapter is intended to summarize the objectives of all astronautical societies.

The close relationship between the development of the astronautical sciences and their accessory societies is unusual. In no other major discipline does one find a similar situation. Astronomy, geology, biology, mathematics, and physics progressed for centuries without their scholars and investigators forming special groups.

Despite a fairly long, if erratic, history, little sustained expansion of the astronautical sciences occurred except through the cadre of rocket and astronautical societies. We must accept that the astronautical sciences are essentially twentieth-century sciences, or at least that their significant development as basic sciences belongs to this century.

The tight interlocking of rocket and astronautical activities to practical experimentation and serious theoretical work has strengthened greatly the rocket-astronautical position of today. Close cooperation of societies with industry, government, and academic institutions has paid dividends. Even in countries with definite conformist tendencies, the influence of the rocket-astronautical society has been, and is being, felt; and this often has been the sole rapport between what is going on in the field and the public.

While a few of these societies, in periods of distress (generally financial), have been driven to some form of sensationalism, it is correct to say that this aspect has been greatly minimized. This development is especially significant when one considers the emotional appeal of space flight. The societies, as a whole, have exerted a moderating influence by separating science from science fiction and fact from the comic strips.

The societies range in size from less than a hundred to many thousands of members. In almost all cases, work is done by a few enthusiasts, especially during periods of growth. Yet the few that virtually sustain their societies have what is almost a messianic zeal, and their enthusiasm has done much towards bringing about the respectability that rocketry and astronautics enjoy today. Working with the academic detachment of the astronomer, and with the practicality of the mechanic, these new scientists, through their societies, form an intellectual vanguard of space exploration.

UNITED STATES

American Rocket Society. The name of the American Rocket Society is synonymous with the development of the science of rocketry in the United States. Founded as the American Interplanetary Society in New York in the spring of 1930, the Society in its earliest days was little more than a forum for those with visionary ideas about sending vehicles into space. Of its founders only three, Clyde Fitch, Dr. William Limkin and David Lasser, had any training in the sciences. Its first mission, therefore, was to promote interest in the field of astronautics. To do this a mimeographed publication was issued under the direction of C. W. Van Devander, a member of the Society and a professional writer. The "Bulletin," as this first publication was called, was in the beginning devoted to theoretical considerations of space flight and rocket design.

As with any young organization eager to attract attention, the Society, in the first few years of its existence, undertook several successful promotional programs. Newspaper notice was achieved at the outset through a ceremony at the Museum of Natural History in New York on April 30, 1930. The ceremony consisted of the presentation to the Society of a copy of *The Discovery of a New World,* one of the first space travel books, by Sir Hubert Wilkins a descendant of the author, John Wilkins, Bishop of Chester. The event was prominently displayed in the press.

In January of 1931 another event acquired even greater publicity for the young Society. It was learned that Esnault-Pelterie, the noted French aeronautical designer and rocket theorist, was coming to the United States. The Society invited him to address a meeting and he accepted. Having hoped to fill the five-hundred seat auditorium of the Museum of Natural History, the Society's members were astounded when twenty-five hundred people turned up to hear the lecture. Although Esnault-Pelterie was "indisposed" and could not attend, his paper was read to the throng.

Thus by the time the Society was a year old it had become fairly well known and had begun to attract new members, many of whom were eminent engineers and scientists. Early in 1931 G. Edward Pendray and his wife, Lee Gregory Pendray, made a trip to Europe and were well received in Berlin by the Verein für Raumschiffart (Society for Space Travel), which was actively conducting rocket experiments. An era of rocket experimentation then ensued. The tales and "folklore" of this period are so interesting, and often so amusing, as to warrant a book in themselves.

The Society's publication, the name of which had been changed to "Astronautics," at this time began to print technical articles on such matters as fuel sources, construction methods, motor cooling and rocket design, thus departing from its earlier theoretical format. As other rocket groups were formed across the country "Astronautics" became a clearing house for scientific and technical ideas in the whole field of rocketry.

By 1936, the Society had begun to achieve recognition from the world's rocket groups. The REP-Hirsch prize awarded by the French Astronomic Society, was presented to Alfred Africano, an ARS member, for the design of a high-altitude rocket. The prestige attaching to this award is indicated by the fact that the prize was first awarded to Hermann Oberth, the great German rocket pioneer. As noted in Chapter 3, F. J. Malina also received this award.

Extensive study and testing of rocket motors continued in the period after 1936. A significant accomplishment was the design and construction by James H. Wyld of a highly efficient fuel cooled rocket. The design was so effective that immediately after static firing in December 1938 the motor was cool enough to touch. Wyld then set about to build a rocket to be propelled by his new motor, but the advent of World War II caused him to break off his work on this project.

The war inhibited the rapid growth and development of the Society, as defense requirements left few members time to continue with their Society work. The members of the ARS did, however, contribute mightily to the war effort by putting their rocket knowhow to work at solving problems presented by the military services. The Wyld rocket showed promise as a means of assisting the takeoff of Navy flying boats. After an expression of interest by the Navy, ARS members Wyld, Shesta, Pierce and an engineer, Lovell Lawrence, formed, in New Jersey, Reaction Motors, Inc., a corporation for the design and construction of such rockets.

As has been narrated in Chapter 8, the second great rocket company, Aerojet Engineering Corporation, was founded contemporaneously with Reaction Motors. Several of the founders were members of the ARS, but Von Karman and Haley were not. It is quite impossible in this chapter to provide a detailed account of the Society activities and growth during the past two decades. It is also quite impossible to give credit to any one person or any one achievement without giving equal credit to hundreds of other untiring and highly successful Society leaders.

Today the American Rocket Society numbers more than 10,000 scientists, engineers, technicians and interested members of the public. The Society publishes *Jet Propulsion*, a monthly magazine devoted to the advancement of the field of jet propulsion through the dissemination of original papers disclosing new knowledge or new developments. The term "jet propulsion," as used by the publication, embraces all engines that develop thrust by rearward discharge of a jet through a nozzle or duct, and thus includes air-consuming engines and underwater systems as well as rockets. The publication is considered in the world of the astronautics community as being the most competent periodical in its field. The circulation is well in excess of 12,000.

The Society also publishes a monthly magazine, *Astronautics*, which is devoted to the dissemination of current information and to the publication of excellent, but not entirely technical, articles in the field of social and natural sciences related to astronautics. Its circulation is in excess of 20,000.

The Society has flourishing Sections in regional areas of the country. Some are named for cities, some are named for States, and some are named for geographical regions, as follows: Alabama, Antelope Valley, Arizona, Central Colorado, Central Texas, Chicago, Cleveland-Akron, Columbus, Connecticut Valley, Dayton, Florida, Fort Wayne, Holloman, Indiana, Maryland, National Capital, New England, New Mexico-West Texas, New York, Niagara Frontier, North Texas, Northeastern New York, Northern California, Pacific Northwest, Philadelphia, Princeton Group, Sacramento, St. Joseph Valley, St. Louis, San Diego, Southern California, Southern Ohio, Twin Cities, University Park, Valley Forge; and Student Chapters in the Academy of Aeronautics, University of Michigan, Georgia Institute of Technology, New York University, Parks College (Saint Louis University), Polytechnic Institute of Brooklyn and Stevens Institute of Technology.

Since its inception in 1930 the ARS has been served by presidents David Lasser, 1930–1932; G. Edward Pendray, 1932 and 1934–1936; Nathan Schachner, 1932–1933; Laurence Manning, 1933–1934; John Shesta, 1936–1937; Alfred P. Africano, 1937–1940; H. Franklin Pierce, 1940–1942; Roy Healy, 1942–1943 and 1947; Cedric Giles, 1943–1944; James H. Wyld, 1944–1946; Lovell Lawrence, Jr., 1946; Charles A. Villiers, 1948; William L. Gore, 1949–1950; H. R. J. Grosch, 1951; C. W. Chillson, 1952; F. C. Durant, III, 1953; Andrew G. Haley, 1954; R. W. Porter, 1955; Noah S. Davis, 1956; R. C. Truax, 1957; George B. Sutton, 1958; J. P. Stapp, 1959.

American Astronautical Society. In November 1953 thirty-five persons attended a meeting at the American Museum of Natural History of New York City in answer to a letter of H. J. Behm and J. R. Rosenquist. Each recipient of the letter had come to organize an astronautical society of national scope in this country, and by the time the meeting had terminated an organization committee was selected to draft a constitution and work out other details leading to incorporation. On 22 January 1954 the constitution was accepted and the society organized. A month later The American Astronautical Society was incorporated in the state of New York.

In 1955 the activities of the society increased rapidly, with the result that the AAS became nationally known. The *Journal of Astronautics* was improved. Lecture programs featured such eminent scientists as Dr. J. R. Pierce, Johann Klein and J. G. Vaeth.

The AAS is a scientific organization dedicated to the development of the astronautical sciences. The society cooperates closely with national and international astronautical, rocket, astronomical, engineering and other organizations. Several levels of membership are maintained, the grades depending upon the scientific experience and qualifications of the applicant. An affiliate category allows all those interested in astronautics to become identified with the society.

National Rocket Club. The youngest of the American rocket organizations is the National Rocket Club, Washington, D. C. This is the nation's first non-technical organization for individuals interested in the advancement of the United States' missile and space exploration programs. The National Rocket Club was founded by Erik Bergaust, rocket and astronautics author-editor, former founder and president of the Norwegian Astronautical Association, and former president of the Washington section of the American Rocket Society.

Other Societies. Other American societies have had varying fortunes. Some joined the American Rocket Society as sections (The American Rocket Society Club of Purdue University became the "Indiana Section" and the Niagara Frontier Rocket Society became the "Niagara Frontier Section"). Some joined a recent innovation in American societies in this field, the American Astronautical Federation. Some nine or ten small local societies, not including the American Astronautical Society (already a national organization), belong to it.

Some AAF members, notably those of Yale, M.I.T., and Cleveland, perform rocket experiments. The Federation is not interested in international affairs and is not a member of the International Astronautical Federation. Some, like the Cornell (University) Rocket Society, apparently survive through a cohesion resembling school spirit, and do perform some instructive experiments. Others, such as the United States Rocket Society (Glenn Ellyn, Illinois), publish mimeographed journals. Still others fall apart gradually through loss of interest.

GREAT BRITAIN

In early October of 1933 three or four persons met at the home of P. E. Cleator to discuss plans for the formation of a group devoted to the study of astronautics. It was agreed at this informal gathering that the organization would be called the British Interplanetary Society, that Mr. Cleator should be its president, and that its first meeting would be held in Liverpool on Friday, the 13th day of that month. The date did not prove to be inauspicious, for within ten weeks the Society's membership soared to fifteen.

One of the first acts of the new Society was publication of the *Journal of the British Interplanetary Society*. In addition to the primary mission of scientific education, the purposes of the Journal were twofold: to keep contact with the current membership and to attract prospective adherents. The financing of this new Journal was first undertaken by its editor, P. E. Cleator. When it appeared that there were insufficient funds, the second and third issues were supported by a friend of the Society, John Moores.

In conjunction with its efforts to publicize the purposes and interests of the Society, a series of lectures was planned at once. Since its inception the BIS has maintained a lecture program of unexcelled integrity and interest.

The hearty few who formed the Society in 1933 intended to undertake a fruitful program of rocket designing and testing, along with their theoretical studies of astronautics. These ambitions were soon to run aground on the shoals of an obsolete statute and official indifference.

Any testing of rockets in Britain in the 1930's was subject to the provisions of the Explosives Act of 1875. An application to the Home Office was answered, in 1936, by a statement to the effect that liquid fuel experiments were clearly made illegal by the Explosives Act, but that if a suitable testing range could be found which was approved by the police authorities, if the design of the rocket satisfied the advisers of the Secretary of State and if they considered the firing of the rocket to be reasonably safe, and if all other provisions of law were satisfied, the Society could test a powder rocket. Since powder rockets had been obsolete for more than a decade, this statement effectively ended the Society's hopes that testing could be undertaken without an attempt to amend the statute. A promise by an M.P. to raise a question in Parliament on this matter failed of fulfilment. Thus the plan for experiments with hardware never was realized.

An earlier solicitation by the Society of the interest of the Government in the development of reaction motors was answered in 1934 with what has become a classic statement of bureaucratic myopia. The reply, under the seal of the Under Secretary of State, read:

> We follow with interest any work that is being done in other countries on jet propulsion, but scientific investigation into the possibilities has given no indication that this method can be a serious competitor to the airscrew-engine combination. We do not consider we should be justified in spending any time or money on it ourselves.

In 1936 the publication of P. E. Cleator's *Rockets Through Space* brought the idea of interplanetary communication before a much wider audience than was then available to the *Journal*. The book led to a brief discussion of the subject on the BBC and both led to increased membership. Still the idea of space flight was met with incredulity in some quarters.

From its inception the Society was eager to associate itself with similar groups abroad. In January of 1934, BIS President Cleator went to Berlin to visit rocket experimenters. While in Berlin, Mr. Cleator was introduced to Dr. Otto Steinitz, Esnault-Pelterie of France, Guido von Pirquet of Austria, G. Edward Pendray of the USA and Dr. Jakow Perlmann and Professor Nicholas Rynin of the USSR, all of whom became members of the Society. This pattern of international contact has been expanded in recent years. Today the Society maintains communication with the world community through its own offices and through its membership in the International Astronautical Federation.

At present the British Interplanetary Society, still true to its original goals of space navigation, is a well-established organization with a large membership. While its efforts before the war to draw the attention of the British Government to the importance of jet propulsion and rocketry were unsuccessful, events during the war proved the soundness of its views. When the government was ready to undertake jet and rocket programs, it found a body of men ready and able to do the job—the membership of the British Interplanetary Society.

As in the case of the ARS, to mention here all the great and immortal names of the BIS is not practical. The few exceptions which follow are made on the most capricious basis—that of old friendship and personal idea exchanges. Already mentioned is the immortal Cleator, who was forced to abandon the presidency of the BIS because he was too efficient and thereby a thorn in the side of the Secretariat and he found real satisfaction in the fact that he was succeeded by his friend, Professor A. M. Low.

The author of this book admires Professor Low with the same sort of feeling he has for Sir Frank Whittle, Lovell Lawrence, and a number of others with whom he has shared similar experiences. In correspondence before his death, Professor Low told of many of his achievements and failures. He was indeed proud that he was the second president of the BIS and that he succeeded Cleator. He once remarked, "I held this position for many years at a time when my scientific friends used to advise me not to lend my name to so absurd a project." His devotion to rocketry, Cleator observed, had a jeremiad touch because, in the face of the opinion of the war experts that rockets from the continent to England were impossible, the very first arrived not far "from my laboratory when I was on leave from the army." He continued, "It shook my house quite badly but the public at the time thought that it was only a bomb-damaged bursting gas main! When I heard that the crater showed signs of freezing I naturally thought of liquid oxygen and guessed the truth." On another occasion, a rocket arrived not very far from where the BIS was holding a meeting!

Professor Low designed the world's first guided rocket to be steered either by a wire method or by wireless. The patent application is extremely interesting because it contains the words ". . . so that its direction of flight may be controlled for the purpose of enabling the rocket to pursue a hostile airman." One can easily share with Low his famous statement that his chief dislikes were "prejudices, noise and the pretence that science knows all."

One cannot, it seems, think of the BIS without also thinking of Dr. L. R. Shepherd who has been its chairman on many occasions as well as vice president and president of the International Astronautical Federation. And there is always that veritable launching pad of British astronautics, Len Carter, the stalwart secretary of the BIS. Then there are those great astronauts whom we meet at the IAF Congresses—Val Cleaver, Kenneth W. Gatland, A. E. Slater, G. V. E. Thompson, John Humphries. There is also the world-famous and beloved writer, A. C. Clarke, and the talented artist and engineer, R. A. Smith, both former chairmen of the BIS.

For sixteen years the BIS has published the *Journal of the British Interplanetary Society* which has contained much of the best literature on astronautics. This publication is now edited by G. V. E. Thompson. The BIS also publishes *Space Flight,* the first "popular" magazine to appear under the highly disciplined sponsorship of a learned society. The editor, Patrick Moore, is a fellow of the Royal Astronomical Society and a talented writer.

THE SOVIET UNION

It is extremely difficult to tie in the written and spoken words of Russian astronautical scientists with evidence of private society activity. Historically, there has been no known sustained effort at the nongovernmental society level in the Soviet Union, in spite of the fact that the country has produced a rich literature, fictional and technical, dealing with rocketry and space travel.

In the 1920's a short-lived student space flight group had been reported, which, late in 1929, was followed by a more sophisticated organization called the Gruppa Isutcheniya Reaklivnovo Dvisheniya, or Reaction Motion Investigation Group. Pioneer astronauts Rynin and Perelman were in charge of sections of the group in Leningrad and Moscow. This, too, was in reality a student society, being attached to the Leningrad Institute of Transportation and the Moscow Institute of Aerodynamics. The group was short-lived. One, Fortikoff, tried to reorganize the Moscow section in 1930 or 1931 without success.

The only other pre-war knowledge of organized astronautical development comes from the Society for Aviation and Chemical Warfare. Within the general period 1920–1935, there is evidence of both interest and activity in astronautics from the society, which subsequently gave rise to a Study Group for Reaction Propulsion. It is reported that the present Moscow Aero Club is its offspring. In 1954 a small American astronautical society in Philadelphia corresponded with a Soviet Astronautical Group attached to the Aero Club.

On January 13, 1954, a new release from the Astronautics Section of the Chkalov Aero Club (apparently an official space flight organization in the USSR) stated that the idea of interplanetary travel soon will be realized. A month later, the section avowed that space flight must serve peaceful purposes. Five special committees on astronomy-astrophysics, rocket technology, interplanetary navigation, human biology and guidance-control, were established at the same time. And in June 1954 a satellite vehicle symposium was scheduled for that fall.

The official USSR group, the Commission on Interplanetary Communications of the Astronautical Council of the Academy of Science, has been discussed in Chapter 11.

GERMANY

The first rocket society in the world, Verein für Raumschiffart, was founded in June 1927, in Breslau, for the purpose of enlisting popular support in the development of rocketry and to perform actual experiments with rockets. The presidency was accepted by Johannes Winkler, who agreed to publish a monthly journal, *The Rocket*. The society did so until December 1929, when the membership numbered nearly 900, including nearly all of the world's rocket pioneers. Winkler left a few months before this to work with the Junkers Aircraft Company, and Hermann Oberth took over the presidency.

Practical experimentation on rocket motors began, followed later by the launching of a number of nose-driven liquid-propellant vehicles of primitive design. Further income was derived from public showing of test runs. Press coverage continued to be lively and essentially favorable. In April, 1931, Major Hanns-Wollff Dickhuth-Harrach became president of the society.

The first successful flight of a liquid-propellant rocket at this facility took place in May 1931, two months after a similar flight of a rocket by Winkler at Dessau which was the first such in Europe. Important theoretical contributions were made by Professor Oberth, though he and the society were embarrassed by the failure of a flying model of a "moon rocket" made in connection with a German movie, "Girl in the Moon."

General political and economic pressures abroad in Germany in 1932 began to bring a decline in the society. Personal frictions, injudicious publicity, and some legal difficulties led in the end to the seizure of the society records by the Gestapo and the drafting of key personnel into civil service positions where they could be observed. The society collapsed in 1933.

So much has been written in Chapters 3 and 4, and indeed throughout this book, concerning the German societies and their membership, that additional comment would be repetitive. The current statistics on astronautics, including the societies, periodicals and industry of Germany, follow:

German Society for Rocket Engineering and Space Travel (Deutsche Gesellschaft für Raketentechnik ünd Raumfahrt). Stuttgart-Zuffenhausen, Neuensteiner Street 19. (Member of IAF.) President, E. Sänger. Officers, F. Gerlach, K. Grupp, W. Georgii, E. Robger, K. Eisele, H. Goeckel, F. L. Neher, D. E. Koelle. Number of members, 1500.

German work Community for Rocket Engineering (Deutsche Arbeitsgemeinschaft für Raketentechnik e.V., Bremen). Erlenstreet 6, Bremen. (Member of IAF.) Officers, A. F. Staats, F. Schade, H. Langkrär, R. Haber, R. Schoepfer, K. Haupt, Dr. R. Büchner. Number of members, about 300.

German Museum for Rockets and Space Travel (Deutsches Raketen und Raumfahrtmuseum e.V., Stuttgart). Reinsburger Street 54, Stuttgart. (Member of IAF.) Director, A. Fritz. Officers, A. Michely, M. Benndorf. Number of members, about 100.

Publications

DVL—News (DVL—Nachrichten). Communications of the German Experimental Institute for Aeronautics. Managing editor, O. Gdanice, Mülheim/Ruhr.

The World of Flight (Flugwelt). Monthly journal for the whole field of astronautics, official organ of the Federal Association of the German Aviation Industry. World of Flight Publishing House, Wiesbaden.

Research Series (Forschungsreihe). Publication of the former Northwest German Society for World Space Research. Managing editor, H. Kaiser; publisher, German Work Community for Rocket Engineering, Bremen.

Aviation Engineering (Luftfahrttechnik). Organ of the Society of German Engineers, VDI Publishing House, Düsseldorf.

Communications from the Institute for Research in the Physics of Jet Propulsion (Mitteilungen aus dem Forschungsinstitut für Physikder Strahlantriebe). Editors, Eugen Sänger and Irene Sänger-Bredt; Publishing

House Aviation Engineering, E. V. Olnhausen, Stuttgart, and Publishing House R. Oldenbourg, München.

Physics Sheets (Physikalische Blätter). Editor, E. Brüche; managing editor, E. Moritz; Physics Publishing House, Mosbach/Baden.

Rocket Letter (Raketenbrief). Communication sheet of the German Work Community for Rocket Engineering. Bremen Publisher, Schween, Bremen.

Rocket Engineering and Space Travel Research (Raketentechnik und Raumfahrtforschung). Issued by the German Society for Rocket Engineering and Space Travel, printed by H. Henkel, Stuttgart-Zuffenhausen; organ of all German-speaking rocket and space travel associations.

World Space Travel (Weltraumfahrt). Editor, H. Gartmann; Umschau-Publisher, Frankfurt. Also an authoritative organ and excellently edited.

Journal for Aviation Sciences (Zeitschrift für Flugwissenschaften). Organ of the Scientific Society for Aviation. Vieweg Publisher, Braunschweig.

Here, briefly, is a rundown on some of the leading German institutions concerned with astronautics, their work, plans and personnel. It is, in effect, a capsule of astronautics in Germany today:

Institute for Research in the Physics of Jet Propulsion (Forschungsinstitut für Physik der Strahlantriebe e.V., Stuttgart-Flughafen). Directors, E. Sänger and I. Sänger-Bredt. Number of people, 30. Specific items: Mechanics of jet propulsion, especially economic rocket-assisted takeoff units; chemical ramjets and rockets; nuclear jet propulsion systems; physics of chemical and nuclear combustion processes, including the effects of mixture preparation and nonequilibrium phenomena; gas radiation, especially that of combustion gases and plasmas; physics of wall effects, especially heat transfer in boundary layers, as well as gas-kinetic and optical boundary layer phenomena.

Institute for Applied Gas Dynamics at the German Experimental Institute for Aeronautics (Institut für Angewandte Gasdynamik an der Deutschen Versuchsanstalt für Luftfahrt, Aachen). Director, A. Naumann. Number of people, about 37. Specific items: Transonic flow; supersonic flow; oblique shock diffusers for supersonic ramjet engines.

Institute for Jet Propulsion Works of the German Research Institute for Aeronautics (Institut für Strahltriebwerke der Deutschen Forschungsanstalt für Luftfahrt, Braunschweig). Director, O. Lutz. Number of people, 14. Specific items: Thermodynamics of chemical reaction; combustion chamber studies; high temperature materials; mixing problems; jet noise.

FRANCE

In France no clearly marked path leading from simple beginnings to efficient organizations representing the rocket and astronautical sciences can be found. One is rather confronted with a series of stops and starts, spurts of activity followed by periods of stagnation. The nation produced pioneer thinkers of extremely high caliber, such as Robert Esnault-Pelterie, who helped to provide the basis upon which the science of astronautics now stands and who composed works that will eternally enrich world scientific literature. Yet France has not been able to sustain an astronautical movement at the society level despite many and varied attempts. Brilliance in thought and action too often became blended with apathy and "political" bickering.

From the beginnings, French astronautics was dependent on the policies and philosophies of large, relatively stable scientific organizations whose opinions and operations were well established by time. Even if a pioneer science like astronautics could demonstrate a measure of respectability to the older societies under whose wing it had settled, it could not always be compatible with their well-tried ideas and notions of the nature of things. The capable support of Ananoff, Bing, Mineur, Esciangon and others was not enough. French astronautics was never free.

If one considers the French Astronomical Society's Astronautics Committee as an astronautical organization, one must go back to 1927 to seek out the beginnings. The mission of this committee, according to Hirsch, was to distribute a prize as a reward for the best theoretical or experimental work leading to the realization of interplanetary flight. Members of this committee, which administered the prize (set up by Hirsch and Esnault-Pelterie) included Flicot, Perrin, Deslandres, Urbain, Gaumont, Lambert, Rosny and Chrétien. Later, in 1938, an Astronautics Section was officially established within the astronomical society, which had its first meeting on 9 May, 1938. As it turned out this was to be one of the last, for the conservative astronomers did not feel that astronautics aided the prestige of their society, and had the section dissolved.

Eight years passed before Alexandre Ananoff and René Monier were able to create an astronautical section within an organization known as the Association of French University Aero Club. As president, Ananoff was aided by Marc Carre, the general secretary and editor of *L'Astroned,* Jacques Depardieu, director of public relations, and Theo Welter, treasurer. All were supported by an imposing list of technical advisors, four fine journals were published, the section's aims were pursued, but the end came in 1947.

In September of the same year French astronautics became identified with the French Aeronautical Club, and membership was able to jump over 200. Various schemes were hatched to arouse interest in rockets, one of which involved postal rockets. In 1950 this French astronautical group, as it was known, staged the world's first International Astronautical Congress in Paris. From this grew the International Astronautical Federation. Despite this great achievement and the work of Ananoff and others, internal problems with the Aero Club arose, a renewed *Astroned* ceased to appear, so that in 1952 France was again without any astronautical society and so remained for three years. French observers (Ananoff, Vassy, Cauchie, Corbeau and others) unofficially represented the country at IAF congresses with no society behind them. At the present time, however, the French Astronautical Society is an active organization.

The new French Astronautical Society was organized in 1957 under the leadership of General Paul J. Bergeron and with the active cooperation of M. Lacombe (vice president), M. Olivier-Martin (vice president), Georges Delval (secretary-general), M. Larguier (technical secretary), M. J. J. Barré, M. Rohner (administrative secretary), M. Couten, M. d'Eaubonne, Colonel R. Genty, M. Robert Homburg, M. Lecarne, M. Michaud, M. E. Vassy, M. Verdier, Dr. J. Pérés, Prof. E. Brun, Prof. M. Janet, Prof. M. Malavard, M. P. Muller, M. H. Gutton, M. Willaume Rolland, Prof. Theodore Rainard, Prof. U. Martin and M. Robert Roux. With this hearty corps of excellent scientists, the Society has made rapid progress. *Bulletin d'Astronautique* (7, Avenue Raymond Poincaré, Paris 16e) was issued in 1957 and contained a featured article on propulsion by the distinguished Jean Corbeau of the French armament establishment. In the fall of 1958 the French Society enlarged *Astronautique* and it is now one of the most distinguished journals available to the interested scientists. The Society now numbers about 300 members.

ARGENTINA

The Argentine Interplanetary Society was formed in 1949 and since that time there has been a slight change in the name, from Society to Association (Asociación Argentina Interplanetaria). The actual founders were Professor Teofilo M. Tabanera, José Ovidio Martinez, Francisco von Proschek, and others. The Society has in excess of 500 members, 30% of which are university graduates, 25% university students and the rest interested persons. No account of the AAI would be complete without a tribute to the charming and competent Hermione Balado, who is now Mrs. Tabanera.

The AAI is a charter member of the IAF and Professor Tabanera is also an "immortal" who attended the 1950 founding congress of the IAF in Paris. He also has been vice president of the IAF for the longest period of time of anyone, namely, five years, and he has been chairman of most of the important committees. The AAI publishes an excellent astronautical review, *Revista de la Asociación Argentina Interplanetaria*.

In 1957, the AAI unanimously voted to bestow the Tabanera Trophy on the person doing the best theoretical or practical work in space travel.

The contestants for the trophy need not be members of the AAI, as the selection will be made from all of South America.

The Institute of Astronautics Center, National University of Cuyo, Mendoza, Argentina, has been in existence for five years.   It was founded by Dr. I. Fernando Cruz, former Rector of the University, and until his return to Germany it was directed by Dr. Walter Georgii.   The present Rector is Dr. Luis C. Caggiano.   The work of the Institute is conducted by a committee composed of Professor Teofilo Tabanera, Carlos Picandet and Alberto Herrero.   The Center forms part of the Department of Scientific Research at the University, and cooperates closely with the faculties of nuclear physics, aerophysics, astronomy, mathematics and medicine.

AUSTRIA

The early Wissenschaftliche Gesellschaft für Hohenforschung existed from 1928 to 1938, the war ending all activities.   This group was reorganized into the Österreichische Gesellschaft für Weltraumforschung (ÖGfW) in 1950, at Innsbruck, Austria, the founders being Hans-Joachim Rückert and Professor Ferdinand Cap.   The latter was the first president. Count Guido von Pirquet is honorary president.   Technical information is published by the Society in *Mitteilungen,* at irregular intervals.   An official organ of the Society is *Weltraumfahrt.*   The present membership is approximately 200.   The activities of the ÖGfW consist of public lectures on astronautics, lecture series, publication of scientific articles, and public information meetings.   Professor Friedrich Hecht, president of the ÖGfW from 1951–1958, is now editor-in-chief of *Astronautica Acta,* the official organ of the IAF.   The 1958 Council of the ÖGfW comprises Prof. (Mrs.) Erika Cremer (president); Dr. Friedrich Waliczek; Hermann Redlich; Erich Dolezal (secretary); Rudolf Nowak (treasurer); Ing. K. Redlich (2nd treasurer).

BELGIUM

An Astronautical Section has recently been formed within the Belgian Association of Aeronautical Engineers and Scientists, of which Professor Fraeijs de Veubeke is president.   An eminent Belgian scientist, Jean Vandenkerckhove, has championed the organization of such a group.

BRAZIL

The Interplanetary Society of Brazil was organized in 1945 and has grown from an original membership of 32 to its present 100.   Some of the present activities are:

The Brazilian Commission for Artificial Satellites, which includes continuing series of lectures, organization of moonwatch teams in São Paulo and Bauru, and detailed reports to the Radio Amateurs Group of Moscow of the Russian satellites and observations.

The National Committee of the Planet Mars has organized a Brazilian network of amateur observers and has developed a series of 56 drawings of the 1954 and 1956 opposition occasions.

The Scientific Council is devoted to increasing public interest and stimulating the study of astronautics. Lectures are presently being given at most of the leading universities in Brazil.

Weekly public meetings of the interplanetary society include conferences, films, and public discussions of astronautics. Over 140 meetings had been held as of the first week in 1958.

BULGARIA

The Bulgarian Astronautic Federation was founded in December 1957, and has approximately 150 members in Sofia. The president is Professor Nikola Bonev, corresponding member of the Bulgarian Academy of Science and Director of the Astronautic Observatory in Bulgaria. He is a well known scientist and author of a number of books concerning the study of the surface of the moon. The general secretary of the Federation is Ing. Georgy Asparuhov, Chief Engineer of the Bulgarian Civil Air Transport, who was one of the founders of the Federation. He is the author of many articles and monographs on the development of rocket technique and has done much to popularize astronautics in Bulgaria. Others prominent in this Federation are Todor Gabrovski, Legal Adviser of the Bulgarian Civil Aviation Authority and one of the most prominent organizers of the Federation; Major General Kiril Kirilov, General Manager of the Bulgarian Civil Air Transport. Delegates from the Bulgarian Federation attended the IXth IAF Congress at Amsterdam in August 1958.

CANADA

There are two Canadian Astronautical Societies.

One Society was inaugurated at McGill University, Montreal, on April 18, 1958. Dr. David L. Thomson, Dean of the Faculty of Graduate Studies and Research at McGill, presided at the inaugural meeting. Dr. E. Pepin, Director, and Mr. H. T. P. Binet, both of The Institute of International Law at McGill University, were very active in organizing this Society. The aims of the Society are to facilitate contacts and interchange of views; to stimulate public interest in space flight, through the medium of books, press, lectures, radio, films, etc.; to secure, through the medium of exchange of publications, collaboration on research, dissemination of technical and other information on space flight, etc.; to promote and stimulate the achievement of space flight; to stimulate work on astronautical and space law subjects by international and national research or other appropriate means. The Council of the Society is actively recruiting members and plans to set up branches when circumstances require. Mr. Binet is secretary of the Society.

The second Canadian Astronautical Society has as its secretary Mr. A. E. Maine of the De Havilland Aircraft of Canada, Ltd., Downsview, Ontario. This group began as a club of engineers and physicists in Toronto who were interested in theoretical and experimental work in the field of astronautics. So much enthusiasm was shown by individuals representing many different professions that an astronautical society was formed in early 1958. The membership is divided into five working sections: (1) propulsion and rocket design; (2) electronic design; (3) astronomic; (4) analysis; (5) vehicle recovery. The primary objective of the Society is to investigate and promote the advancement of all branches of scientific study comprising the field of astronautics, including such areas as propulsion and space travel; flight dynamics and structural design; instrumentation and automatic control; communications and telemetry; navigation and geodetics; astronomy and astrophysics; space medicine and psychology; space law.

REPUBLIC OF CHINA

The Astronautical Society of the Republic of China, Taichung, Taiwan, China, was organized in May 1958, with an initial membership of 38, which will soon be increased. Lynn Chu, Director, Air Technical Bureau, is the chairman of the Society, which includes many eminent scientists. Among the original members are Hsi-Mou Li, Chairman, Scientific Education Committee, Ministry of Education; K. H. Lih, Director, Institute of Ordnance Research; Chih-Bing Ling, Director, Aeronautical Research Laboratory; Yun-Kuei Tai, Head, Department of Physics, National Taiwan University; Chang-Tso Chien, President, Chinese Institute of Engineers; Fu-En I, Major General, Chinese Air Force; Wei-Chou Yuan, Dean, College of Science, National Taiwan University. Mr. Ling attended the IXth IAF Congress at Amsterdam in August 1958 as an observer for the Astronautical Society of the Republic of China.

CZECHOSLOVAKIA

Professor R. Pesek of the Technical University, Prague, was delegated by the Czechoslovak Academy of Sciences to attend the IXth Annual Congress of the IAF at Amsterdam in August 1958. The Academy of Sciences created an astronautical commission within the Academy, which was admitted to membership in the IAF at that Congress. Many renowned scientists from the Technical University and the Astronomical Observatory at

Ondrejov (near Prague) are among the charter members of this group, and include Dr. Frantisek Link, Dr. Vladimir Guth, Jan J. Bukovsky, Dr. Emil Buchar, and Dr. Jaromar Budejicky.

DENMARK

Leo Hansen, a founder of the Dansk Interplanetarisk Selskab, and on several occasions president of that Society, is one of the "immortals" who attended the 1950 Paris founding meeting of the IAF. In honor of Hansen, in 1957, the Hansen Trophy was created, and this trophy was awarded for the first time in 1958 to Mr. Holger Nielsen for his remarkable optical satellite tracking apparatus. A co-founder is E. Buch-Andersen, who was president of the Danish Society when the VIth Annual Congress of the IAF was held in Copenhagen in 1955. Although not remarkably large in number of persons, the Society is high in quality and has sponsored many lecture series in learned institutions in Denmark.

The loyal and hard working group who unselfishly give of their time to the cause of astronautics in Denmark also includes M. F. Petersen, secretary of the Society; Dr. E. O. Errebo-Knudsen, a prominent aero-medical expert; and Borge Michelsen, one of the most competent and best known science writers in Europe. The latter did extensive work in disseminating scientific methods for UNESCO.

EGYPT

Through the initiative and cooperation of Dr. Hassan Marei, Under Secretary of the Ministry of War for Aviation Affairs, and Mr. Rolf Engel, then Technical Manager of the Compagnie des Engins à Réaction pour Vol Accéléré, the Egyptian Astronautical Society was formed in Egypt in September 1953, and approved by the Council of Ministers. The EAS cooperates closely with various universities, engineering and scientific societies. It publishes a Bulletin, and holds monthly public lectures on astronautical and rocket subjects. The Egyptian Society was represented at the Vth and VIth IAF Congresses.

GREECE

The Hellenic Astronautical Society was formed in February 1958, with headquarters in Athens. At a meeting of the General Assembly on February 20, 1958, a Council of Administration was elected. The president of the Society is Stavros Plakidis, Professor of Astronomy at the National University of Athens and Director of the National Observatory in Athens; the vice president is Constantine Exarchakos, Major-General of the Air Forces; and the secretary general is Elie Petropoulos, County Engineer in the Ministry of Communication and Public Works. This society is a member of the IAF.

HUNGARY

A new Astronautical Division of the Hungarian Astronautical Society was organized in May 1958, with an initial membership of approximately 25. Mr. Erno Nagy, one of the leaders of the Division and a fellow of the British Interplanetary Society, attended the Amsterdam Congress of the IAF representing the new society.

IRAN

A group of technicians from the Engineering Club of Tehran and members of the faculty of the Tehran University have formed an Iranian Astronautical Society. Dr. H. K. Afshar, Director of the Tehran University Geophysical Observatory and Secretary of the Iranian IGY Committee was designated by the Chancellor of the University, Dr. A. Farhad, to represent Iran at the IXth Congress of the IAF at Amsterdam in August 1958.

IRELAND

A number of astronomers from Armagh Observatory, Northern Ireland, scientists and professors from Ireland's leading universities have joined in an informal group. Dr. E. J. Öpik of the Observatory is one of the most active members of this group.

ISRAEL

Physicists and other scientists of the Hebrew University in Jerusalem, the Technion and other institutions of learning and research in Israel have formed an Astronautical Society. Professor A. H. Fraenkel, head of the Department of Mathematics of the Hebrew University, attended the IXth IAF Congress in Amsterdam in August 1958 as a semi-official observer on behalf of Israel.

ITALY

The Associazione Italiana Razzi was founded June 7, 1951, by the world-famous physicist General G. A. Crocco, and by Professors G. P. Casiraghi, A. Eula, and Captain Glauco Partel. The new Society was sponsored by the older Italian Aerotechnical Society.

Many scientists, associated with the AIR, have attended every IAF Congress since London [September 1951]. In 1956 the AIR organized in Rome the VIIth Annual Congress of the IAF. Meetings at this Congress were held in the magnificent Palazzo dei Congressi. One of the highlights of the Congress was the very efficient simultaneous translating equipment which carried the Italian, French, English and German languages.

The Delegates to this Congress were addressed by Pope Pius XII on a memorable visit to Castel Gandolfo arranged by General Crocco, who includes among his many honors membership in the Pontifical Academy of Sciences. (See Chapter 10.)

The Italian Society has sponsored a multilingual technical dictionary of rocket and astronautic terms and also a most exhaustive bibliography of rocket and astronautical literature. Members of the Society address learned organizations, publish numerous papers and reviews and lecture at the University of Rome.

JAPAN

Through the initiative of the IAF, Japan was asked to form an astronautical society in 1952, which would in turn enter the Federation. Little interest in the proposals of the IAF was exhibited by the Japanese Science Council. The next year, however, a society was founded under the direction of Mitsuo Harada, an author of astronautical literature and a long time proponent of space flight. He obtained the close cooperation of aeronautical experts, medical scientists and astronomers, many of whom make up the society's list of advisors.

The application of the Japan Astronautical Society for membership in the IAF was tentatively accepted in 1954, pending the receipt of certain documents translated into one of the official languages of the Federation. Formal approval of the Japanese Society was granted in 1955. At the present time the Society is engaged largely in the study and diffusion of astronautics, and publishes a bulletin. The Japanese believe that the study and application of astronautical knowledge will elevate the spirit of tolerance in the world, thereby helping to insure peace. The JAS now numbers 500 members. Recently it participated in a large Exhibition of Space Travel which lasted more than two months.

In addition to Dr. Harada, the following are active workers: Dr. Hidemasa Kimura, Dr. Ittsusei Yamamoto, Dr. Takashi Hayashi, Musei Tokugawa, Prof. T. Asada, Prof. N. Nishiwaki, Prof. I. Shinra, S. Matsukata, Prof. E. Takeda. In 1958 the Japanese Rocket Society was organized under the leadership of Dr. H. Itokawa, and was granted membership in the IAF.

NETHERLANDS

The Dutch Society for Space Travel (Nederlandsche Vereniging voor Ruimtevaart) was formed in December 1951 as a part of the Royal Dutch Aero Society. Membership is open also to members of the Dutch Society of Meteorology and Astronomy. The first publication of the organization, a bi-monthly called the *NVR—berichten,* has now been supplemented by a column in the semimonthly *AVIS Fliegwereld* (journal of the Royal Dutch Aero Club) called "Rockets and Space Flight" written by J. Geertsma. Original membership was around 100, but has grown since to over 200. Major activities of the organization are lecturing and promoting the advance of astronautics, and sponsoring advanced technical discussions by restricted groups of scientists within the Society. The NVR was host to the IAF in 1958. This Society has had a distinguished career under the leadership of Dr. J. M. J. Kooy.

NORWAY

The Norwegian Astronautical Society, a voting member of the IAF, was formed on August 7, 1951. Co-founders of the society, whose purpose was to further public interest in rockets and space flight in Norway, were Erik Bergaust, Klaus Bergersen, H. Bloch-Hoell, Gunnar Oxaal, Frank Scheer, and Thorstein Thelle. Today, regular meetings are held for lectures and technical discussions relating to rockets and space flight, and a mimeographed bulletin gives news of the society and semi-technical news on matters scientifically related to space flight.

POLAND

Polskie Towarzystwo Astronautyczne was founded in 1953, and its membership is affiliated with the Polish Academy of Sciences. The affairs of the Society are managed by Professor K. Zarankiewicz and by Olgierd S. Wolczek—both devoted scientists with deep knowledge of the problems of space flight. The Society has well in excess of 100 members. Dr. Wladyslaw Geisler recently wrote a book entitled, *Earth's Artificial Satellites,* one of the most competent works on the subject. Delegates from the PTA have been present at several Congresses, including Rome, Barcelona and Amsterdam, and they have delivered highly commendable lectures.

Professors Jerzy H. Teisseyre, Z. Paczkowski, H. Muster, F. Misztel, M. Lunc and many others have earned the high respect of the astronautics community throughout the world by their competence in the field.

PORTUGAL

In Lisbon there is considerable enthusiasm among the professors of the Technical University and their colleagues. A. Varela Cid, Director of the Center for the Study of Aeronautics, Instituto Superior Tecnico, and Professor of Aeronautical Engineering, has been very active in organizing a Portuguese Society for the study of rocket propulsion and guidance, as well as aeronautical research.

SOUTH AFRICA

The South African Interplanetary Society (SAIS) was founded by two engineers of Johannesburg, A. W. Andersen and Perry Carlson. The first president was A. E. H. Bleksley, professor of applied mathematics, University of the Witwaterstrand. Professor Bleksley set forth the functions of the SAIS at the inaugural public meeting in May 1953. He stated two functions: "To perform an educational function and to undertake research." The first function involves public lectures and publicity of a conservative nature. Membership qualification of the Society is simply to have a serious interest in astronautics. Technical or professional qualifications are required of Fellow members. Research by the SAIS has been largely academic. A Technical Advisory Committee coordinates such study and performs an advisory function on the various programs.

The SAIS maintains a library at Johannesburg and publishes a quarterly journal containing original articles, pertinent news of the Society, its activities and items of significance to astronautics. The SAIS has been a member of the International Astronautical Federation since 1953. Its membership has just passed the 100 mark.

SPAIN

The Spanish Astronautical Group ("Agripacion Astronautica Española") as it exists today is the result of a merger in 1954 with the older Spanish Astronautical Society (AEA). The present honorary president, Señor Mur, has long been a figure in astronautical activities in the country. In February 1949, with the assistance of Quijano, Rogla and Daza, he formed an organization committee for the Spanish Astronautical Society. He attended the First International Astronautical Congress in Paris in 1950 and became the Spanish member of an interim board until the International Astronautical Federation, approved at that Congress, could be founded.

The Society was officially registered in 1952, with Mur as president and Rogla as secretary. Members numbered 54, most of them with high academic degrees and positions. Meetings, lectures, and radio broadcasts were held in Madrid, but activity waned. In the following two years, influence in the movement passed into the hands of the Astronautical Commission of the "Astronomical Society of Spain and America," with headquarters in Barcelona. The Commission sent observers to the 1953 congress.

In 1954, through the efforts of Marial and Vila Montana, the Commission was admitted to membership in the International Astronautical Federation, by which time it had taken the definite name of "Agrupacion Astronautica Española" (Spanish Astronautical Group) still associated with the parent astronomical society. The journal *Astronautica* has been published quarterly since 1954.

SWEDEN

The Swedish Interplanetary Society, formerly called the Svenska Sallskapet for Rymdforskning (Swedish Society for Space Research), was founded in October 1956 by Ake Hjertstrand, Claes-Otto Sparre, Gunnar Deijenberg and Gilbert Larsson. The original membership of 60 persons dwindled to less than 30 after the first flush of space travel had subsided, but recent events have enlarged this total to more than 150. The membership is now divided into three classes: fellow, member, and junior member. Activities are divided according to fields of interest: Astronomy, flight trajectories, and ballistics; Vehicles and equipment; Propulsion; Navigation, guidance and electronics; Space medicine; and general astronautical concepts. As with other national units, activities embrace lectures, participation in broadcast programs, television, preparation of articles, etc., and result in eight formal and several other meetings a year. At present, the main SIS body is in Stockholm, but other branches are provided for in the by-laws and are expected to be formed in other cities. In 1958 the Society commenced publication of an excellent journal.

SWITZERLAND

Professor Joseph A. Stemmer, President of the Schweizerische Astronautische Arbeitsgemeinschaft (SAA), is not only the perennial Secretary of the IAF, but he also is one of the "immortals" who attended the 1950 IAF founding meeting in Paris, and he has attended every Congress since that time. The SAA, which was founded in 1951 by Professor Stemmer, was host to the IAF at the IVth Congress in 1953 at Zurich. This Congress was characterized by the great efficiency of its secretariat, and by the excellence of the papers delivered, as well as the very fine program of entertainment.

The Society publishes a quarterly Bulletin, which first appeared in 1952.

The scientific emphasis of the Society has been placed on biological studies above 100,000 feet, multistage rocket studies, mathematical investigation of constantly accelerating flight, temperature conditions of a body in space and test stand experiments with liquid rocket motors. Many of Switzerland's leading scientists are associated with the Astronautical Working Group.

TURKEY

The Astronautic Committee of the Turkish Astronomical Society was organized in March 1958, with an initial membership of 32. The general secretary is Saadettin Topuzoglu. The Turkish Astronomical Society has been very active in the field of astronomy and astronautics, holding public and scientific conferences; issuing a bulletin entitled "The Sky" which deals with astronautical progress; writing scientific articles for newspapers; giving scientific talks on the radio; and so on. Professors from the Universities of Istanbul and Ankara, and the Technical University in Istanbul, are among the members of the Society. General Fuat Ulug, Chief of the Scientific Consultation and Development Council of The Ministry of National Defense, and many of his colleagues in the Ministry, are also members.

Representatives of the Astronautic Committee attended the IXth IAF Congress at Amsterdam in August 1958.

YUGOSLAVIA

The founding of the Astronautical Society of the Aeronautical Union of Yugoslavia was on May 10, 1953, when some thirty interested engineers in Belgrade were assembled. They elected the first Board. The founders were Ing. Kosta Sivcev, first president of the Society, Lt. Col. Mihailo Velimirovic, and Ing. Vladislav Matovic, secretary.

The Society is working in the frame of the Aeronautical Union of Yugoslavia, from which it is getting the necessary organizational and financial support, especially needed for the edition of the quarterly *Vasiona* (Space).

The publication of *Vasiona* started in the summer of 1953 and has been published regularly since.

The membership of the Society has raised from about 50 in the first year to above 150, mostly university degree members from Belgrade. It cooperates with the astronautical section of the Croatian Society for the Promotion of Natural Science in Zagreb, which asked recently to unite with the Society.

Until today the principal activities of the Society have been public lectures, film performances, and expositions both in Belgrade and other towns of the country. Because of lack of sufficient financial means, there is, except for theoretical work, no experimentation within the Society. However, all members are well known through their articles in the press, journals, periodicals and as translators of books on astronautics.

Appendix 1

CONSIDERATIONS ON THE RESULTS OF INDEFINITE DECREASE IN WEIGHT OF ENGINES

Written in 1912 by Robert Esnault-Pelterie and published in the March 1913 issue of *Journal de Physique*, Paris

The ideas which will be developed here in this paper have been suggested to the author by the results that have already been achieved by light engines. He has been progressively led to ask himself what could possibly result from a further decrease in weight. For instance, if the weight per horse-power could be decreased almost entirely, what possibilities would be given to man? Would this progress only be limited to greater refinements in flying or would it open new horizons? And what would be these horizons?

Innumerable authors have thought of man travelling from planet to planet as a subject for fiction. Everyone realizing without too much thought and effort the impossibility of such a dream, it therefore seems that no one has ever thought to seek the physical requirements necessary for the realization of this dream and what would be the order of magnitude of the means one had to introduce.

This is the only aim of the present study which is, it must be stressed, only a series of thoughts based on mathematical derivations.

I

The first difficulty that strikes our mind is the fact that between planets there is no atmosphere, and therefore even an airplane could not find the slightest support for flight.

Physiological difficulties will be examined later on. Let us just concentrate on our knowledge of Mechanics. If this knowledge will lead us to a realization of an engine, which would need no support for flight, it would be able to propel a body. As strange as it may seem to someone that hasn't thought about it, our knowledge gives us the answer. This engine has existed for quite a time: it is the Rocket. (The gun imagined by Jules Verne would crush the travellers as they departed and cannot qualify as an engine capable of propelling a vehicle.)

It is often said that a rocket is propelled by a jet stream "through the air." The first part of this expression is correct, but not the second. A rocket would move just as well, if not better, in vacuum than in air.

Let us take a more striking example. Let us assume that a machine gun is fixed on a car capable of sliding without friction on tracks parallel to the gun. At every shot, the machine gun will move backwards according to a well established law in Mechanics.

The respective momenta gained by the car plus machine gun and by the projectile are equal in magnitude and opposite in sign. Air resistance only enters into the phenomenon which decreases the resulting velocities.

In the rocket, the machine gun projectile is replaced by the combustion gases which are emitted continuously.

Let M_0 be the total initial mass of the rocket, M its mass at time t and dm the element of mass of fluid which flows during the element of time dt considered.

Let us first assume that the fluid emission is done with a constant velocity v with respect to the body and a constant decrease in mass per unit time μ. Let V be the body's velocity, F the propelling force and its acceleration at time t.

The calculation shows that the phenomenon is described by the equations

$$MdV = vdm = \mu vdt \tag{1}$$

We will notice that if the whole body would be completely of consumable explosive (purely theoritically speaking, which has its importance) it would completely be used up after a time

$$T = \frac{M_0}{\mu} \tag{2}$$

The introduction of this time limit in the formula defining V as a function of t yields the equation

$$(T - t)dV = vdt$$

thus
$$V = v \log \frac{T - t}{T} \tag{3}$$

which gives for $t = T$

$$V = -\infty \text{ (assuming } v > 0)$$

This is no surprise for us, since the propulsion has remained constant as long as the mass was decreasing, due to the emission of the propelling gas until it vanished completely. The acceleration should therefore have increased and approached infinity.

The equation relating the displacement x as a function of t is

$$x = -v\left\{T\left[\left(\frac{T-t}{T}\right)\log\frac{T-t}{T}\right] + t\right\} \tag{4}$$

and the corresponding distance travelled after complete consumption would be

$$X_T = -vT$$

Aside from all external considerations, we have just seen that propulsion in vacuum is not an impossibility. However, it is not sufficient to move the body, it must be guided.

In the present case, there are no difficulties *in theory*. To alter the vehicle's direction, one need only incline the propulsor in such a way that the direction of the force it develops would be at an angle with the trajectory. If the displacement of the propulsor was not sufficient to obtain rotation in all directions, one or two smaller auxiliary propulsors would be enough to obtain complete maneuverability.

II

To remove a heavy body from the attraction of a planet, one has to spend energy.

Let us consider a mass M at a distance x from the center of a planet whose radius is R. Let γ be the acceleration of gravity at the surface of this planet. To move the body away a distance dx, it will be necessary to do an element of work

$$dZ = M\gamma \frac{R^2}{x^2} dx$$

which gives

$$Z = M\gamma R \left(1 - \frac{R}{x}\right)$$

We can readily see that to move a given mass to infinity the necessary work to be done would be finite and given by

$$Z = M\gamma R$$

Or if we let P be the weight of the body at the surface of the planet, then

$$Z = PR$$

We also see that if we consider the weight of the body as the result of the principle of universal attraction applied to body and planet, we can write after letting U denote the planet's mass

$$P = k\frac{MU}{R^2}$$

This gives for expressing the work necessary for removal of the body to infinity

$$Z = k\frac{MU}{R}$$

Therefore, if we give initially to a body on the surface of a planet a sufficient velocity to remove from the planet, this body would increase its distance indefinitely.

For the earth, the minimum velocity would be 11,280 m/s, i.e., a projectile launched from the earth with a velocity larger than 11,280 m/s (not considering air resistance) would never fall back.

This critical velocity is exactly the same as that which a body would acquire falling toward the earth from infinity and having no initial velocity with respect to the planet.

The motion of such a body would be given by the equation

$$V^2 = 2g\frac{R^2}{x}$$

We see that for $X = R$

1°)
$$V_R = -\sqrt{2gR}$$

2°)
$$\tfrac{1}{2}mV^2 = PR$$

and this velocity limit V_R for the earth is also 11,280 m/s.

It was said before, that to remove to infinity a body from a planet, P being the weight at the surface and R the radius of the planet, the work to be done will be

$$Z = PR$$

For a body weighing 1 kg on the earth, this work would be

$$Z = 6,371,103 \text{ kgm equivalent to } 14,940 \text{ cal}$$

Let us recall that 1 kg of hydrogen-oxygen mixture with appropriate fractions contains 3860 cal for 1 kg; 1 kg of a powder containing gun-cotton and potassium chlorate is equivalent to 1420 cal per kg. We can see that the hydrogen-oxygen mixture contains slightly more than a fourth of what would be necessary to escape from the earth. But 1 kg of radium, liberating during its entire life 2.9×10^9 cal, would have 194,000 times more energy than needed. We will not talk here about the efficiency of a jet engine.

If we consider a body which moves away from a planet according to any accelerated motion, we can see that at the time when its velocity will be larger than the one it would have at the same point moving in the opposite direction, falling from infinity without any initial velocity, it would be useless to give it more energy to make it go farther. Its kinetic energy would be sufficient for it to move indefinitely.

The motion of a body subject to a constant force F larger than its weight, directed vertically upwards and away from the planet would be represented by the equation

$$v = \sqrt{2Ax + \frac{2gR^2}{x} - 2R(A + g)}$$

The body would acquire a sufficient velocity to permit the stoppage of propulsion at a distance from the center of the planet equal to

$$x = R\left(1 + \frac{g}{A}\right) \quad \text{where } A = \frac{F}{M}$$

We can see that if a body could move away from the earth with an upward propelling force exactly equal in magnitude to its weight, i.e., if $A = g$, it would reach that critical speed at a distance from the center of the earth equal to twice the earth's radius at an altitude equal to the earth's radius.

This remark calls our attention to the fact that a body could perfectly well move away from a planet using a propelling force smaller than its weight. If the planet has an atmosphere, the body could in fact function first as an airplane, rising gradually and increasing its velocity as this atmosphere became rarer and rarer, until it reached the critical velocity corresponding to the given altitude.

III

Let us consider what would be the required energies if we wanted, by this method, to transport a body from the earth to the moon and back.

Let us consider that the operation will take place in three phases:

1°) The body is accelerated until it reaches the critical velocity of liberation
2°) The motor is stopped, and the body keeps moving due to its acquired velocity
3°) At the desired point, the body is turned upside-down and the motor that has been re-started diminishes the velocity until it becomes zero at the surface of the moon.

First Phase

We apply to the body a force

$$F = \tfrac{11}{10}P, \quad \text{therefore } A = \tfrac{11}{10}g$$

which seems acceptable assuming that the vehicle would carry live beings.

The critical distance is then

$$x = \tfrac{21}{11} \cdot R$$

corresponding to an altitude of 5,780,000 m above the surface.

The velocity at that instant would be

$$V = 8180 \text{ m/sec}$$

The time necessary to reach that point would be approximately

$$t = 24 \text{ min } 9 \text{ sec}$$

Second Phase

The body continues on its path due to its inertia; it is constantly attracted by the opposite gravitational forces of the earth and its satellite.

Let P be the weight of the body at the earth's surface, P_t its weight at the moon's surface and ρ the radius of the moon, $D = x + y$ the distance between the two planets; the calculation gives

$$v = \sqrt{2\left(g\frac{R^2}{x} + 0.165 \cdot g\frac{\rho^2}{y} + 0.82 \times 10^6\right)}$$

At the point where the respective gravitational forces of the earth and moon cancel each other, the velocity would be

$$v = 2030 \text{ m/sec}$$

It is the lowest velocity.

At the moon's surface it would become approximately

$$v = 3060 \text{ m/sec}$$

The velocity of the body falling freely from infinity to the moon would be

$$v_\infty = 2370 \text{ m/sec}$$

The time used to go through the second phase can be calculated approximately by neglecting the moon's action which is entirely negligible during the total journey.

It would be the same time as that taken by the body during a free fall from the moon to the point where we had stopped the engine:

$$t = 48 \text{ hr } 30 \text{ min}$$

Third Phase

One must now decrease the speed by turning the body upside-down as said before, and by re-starting the motor.

What will be the law of this slowing down?

We would establish it in the same manner as we did for the earth; but the moon's attraction being much smaller, and as we do not at this stage seek a great precision, we will deduct from the acceleration due to the propulsor, half the acceleration due to the moon, and we will assume the motion uniformly slowed down under the action of this fictitious acceleration. We find that the body has to be turned upside-down at a distance from the moon's surface equal to

$$d = 250,000 \text{ m approximately}$$

This point is so close to the moon, and the present calculations not being rigorous, the time necessary to reach the surface could be mistaken for the time necessary to reach the moon itself.

The time of the slowing down will be

$$t = 226 \text{ sec} = 3 \text{ min } 46 \text{ sec}$$

The total time for the whole process is approximately then:

First phase	0 hr 24 min 9 sec
Second phase	48 hr 30 min
Third phase	0 hr 3 min 46 sec

48 hr 58 min approximately

The return trip could be done by reversing the process and in the same time.

It must be pointed out that, by this means, the propulsor is used only 28 min going and the same time coming back unless the earth's atmosphere is used for the slowing down process, in which case the 28 min used for the departure, and the time necessary to orient the body properly, would suffice.

We will now consider the power actually needed to realize these minimum conditions and the resulting efficiency output of the motor with respect to the theoretical work given.

If we consider a 1000 kg vehicle out of which 300 kg are consumable; and if the engine has to work 27 min + 3.5 min and to have a sufficient flow margin 35 min

= 2100 sec, the rate will have to be

$$\mu = \frac{300}{2100} = 0.143 \text{ kg/sec}$$

and the fluid's expulsion velocity

$$v = 65,300 \text{ m/sec}$$

Therefore, by providing per kilogram of fuel

$$T = 217.2 \times 10^6 \text{ kgm} \quad \text{or} \quad 512 \times 10^3 \text{ cal}$$

one sees that the mixture $H^2 + O$ would contain 133 times too little energy and the most powerful explosives 360 times too little.

On the other hand, 1 kg of radium would contain 5.670 times too much.

The power of the motor necessary for our 1000 kg vehicle would be

$$\frac{300 \times 217.2 \times 10^6}{2100 \times 75} = 414,000 \text{ HP}$$

We could also see that the efficiency of the jet engine is in our particular case quite bad. Since to remove a mass of 1 kg from the earth to ∞, we have to apply to it 6,371,103 kgm and we have spent 217.2×10^6, so that the efficiency is

$$\rho = 0.0293$$

Moreover, to give a gas an ejection speed of 65,300 m/sec in vacuum, we would have to reach the fantastic temperature of 2.525×10^6 degrees.

In air, it would be even worse, since added to this temperature one would need a pressure of about the same magnitude.

IV

As an indication, we could assume the body moving to infinity, and also that we have kept the motor working even after the critical speed is reached, so that it eventually acquires and conserves a speed near to 10 km/sec. The times necessary to reach the closest planets as they attain their conjunction with the Earth are respectively:

For Venus   47 days 20 hr

For Mars   90 days 15 hr

These figures are merely mentioned for curiosity and we must also notice that the amount of work to cover this distance would not be much larger than the minimum necessary to remove the body from the earth. In fact, once the vehicle has reached a sufficient distance, it would keep on going due to its inertia without being slowed down by the earth's attraction which has become quite weak.

In other words, the difficulty would be to overcome the earth's attraction; but if some day this difficulty would be overcome, it would hardly be more difficult to reach a very distant planet than a close one. Subject, of course, to a cramped and hermetically closed vehicle being inhabitable for a sufficient amount of time and to another difficulty that we will consider later on.

V

In all the preceding sections we have only considered the theoretical possibility for a body with special properties to travel between the earth and the moon. This is a problem of pure mechanics which does not really answer the question of whether man will be or will never be able to leave his world to explore others.

The complete study of the question will lead to the study of the physiological conditions that must be fulfilled so that life will be possible under such conditions.

The progress made in submarines can already make us consider as quite feasible in the future the regeneration of an atmosphere which has been confined for some hundred hours.

The question of temperature deserves being particularly considered. It is often said that the interplanetary spaces have an almost absolute zero temperature. The author believes it is false.

The concept of temperature is only related to material bodies and therefore a vacuum cannot have any.

If the amount of heat absorbed per unit time by our vehicle is less than the quantity of heat that it radiates, its temperature will decrease. If the amount of heat received and absorbed is greater than the amount that is radiated, the temperature will increase.

It would therefore be possible to construct a vehicle in such a way that one half of its surface would be of a polished metal and the inside insulated. The other half of the surface, for example, would be covered of copper oxide to give a black surface.

If the polished face would face the sun, the temperature would decrease. In the opposite position, the temperature would increase.

All the difficulties that we have just considered do not seem to be theoretically impossible. But a new difficulty will arise which although a mechanical solution offers itself, will nevertheless complicate further the problem.

In fact, in the calculations related to the vehicle's journey from the earth to the moon, we have considered that we were applying an acceleration

$$A = \tfrac{11}{10}g$$

and this up to a distance of 5780 km from the earth's surface. During all this phase of the voyage, the travellers would therefore have the impression of weighing $1\tfrac{1}{10}$ of their weight.

One may hope that as unpleasant as this sensation may be it will not cause any disturbance to a human organism. But what is most alarming is what will happen at the instant of sudden stoppage of propulsion. At this moment, the traveller would suddenly cease to have any weight and he would have the sensation that both he and his vehicle were falling in a void.

If the human organism cannot go through such vicissitudes, we would have to replace the absence of a gravitational field by creating constant artificial acceleration produced by the motor. If this acceleration is made equal to gravity, the traveller will constantly feel he is weighing his normal weight, without any consideration of the fact that he may or may not be in the gravitational field of a planet.

It is obvious that this kind of a process would introduce a very important difficulty with regard to the amount of energy which would become necessary, and would bring us far away from the conditions of realization which were studied previously and which were already quite extreme.

If we use the formula representing the law of motion of a body acted on by a constant force due to the earth and if we assume that until we have reached the maximum velocity between earth and moon, the acceleration used is equal to $1\frac{1}{10}$ g, then the other maneuvres will be done with an acceleration equal to gravity. The moon's influence can be neglected, it being so small. It is found that the vehicle has to be reversed at a distance from the center of the earth equal to 29.5 times the earth's radius.

The speed at this instant of time would be 61,700 m/sec, then the reversed vehicle would be slowed down by a force equal to its weight on the earth.

The time used to reach the moon would be

$$t = 3 \text{ hr } 5 \text{ min}$$

But in this new case, the work to be furnished, using the assumption of a 1000 kg vehicle of which 300 kg are consumable, would reach 67.2×10^6 cal/kg of fuel, i.e., 131 times more than in the first case.

Dynamite would be 47,300 times too weak, but radium would still be 433 times too powerful.

As to the necessary power, it would be

$$\frac{857 \times 10^{10}}{24,000 \times 75} = 4.76 \times 10^6 \text{ HP}$$

If we now assume that this method of constant propulsion is used for voyages to the closest planets and investigate what the times and velocities would be, we find for the maximum velocity:

For Venus	643 km/sec
For Mars	883 km/sec

and the corresponding times:

For Venus	35 hr 4 min
For Mars	49 hr 20 min

VI

The maximum velocities we have just considered are evidently fantastic. However, there exists at least one celestial body which reaches such velocities: Halley's comet.

Only the forces and energies which seem to be contained by molecules could produce concentrations of power and work similar to those we just considered.

If we suppose for a moment that we have available 400 kg of radium in our 1000 kg vehicle and that we knew how to extract from it the energy within a suitable time, we should see that these 400 kg of radium would be more than enough to reach Venus and come back (with a constant acceleration), so that such a formidable reservoir would be just enough for man to visit his closest planets.

Appendix 2

INTERNATIONAL ASTRONAUTICAL FEDERATION

The International Astronautical Federation proposes the C.C.I.R. study astronautical communications services. On behalf of the Federation, Mr. Andrew G. Haley has discussed the use of frequencies by space-circling vehicles as well as the future of the service, and is available to expand on the needs of this new service as well as the problems involved.

At the twelve-day meeting of the C.C.I.R. Study Group XI in Moscow it was decided that the questions, problems, and study proposals which were submitted by the author to the Plenary Session could better be acted upon by Study Groups V and VI, and the Director of the C.C.I.R. proposed the following programme, which, of course, must be studied by the C.C.I.R.:

"*considering*

a) the rapid development of rockets in general and of artificial satellites in particular;
b) that transmission of radio signals between the earth and extraterrestrial positions in space is now an established fact;
c) the use of satellites as measuring and observation stations and possibly as relay stations;
d) that extraterrestrial objects may well be consecutively above different countries of the world, thus necessitating international collaboration;
e) that radiocommunication between extraterrestrial objects and the earth will be of utmost importance;

"*decides* that the following questions should be studied:

1. what frequencies are specially suitable for penetration of the layers of the earth's atmosphere;
2. what are the influences on these frequencies of the hour of the day, the season, the geographical location and solar activity;
3. what deviations in propagation direction can be expected by the penetration of the ionosphere;

4. what, if any, will be the differences in propagation between in-going and out-going signals relative to the earth;

5. are special phenomena to be expected that do not occur in transmission between two points on earth;

6. what is the possible influence of the troposphere on wave propagation to and from extraterrestrial objects?"

In addition to the foregoing, the United States Preparatory Committee—International Radio Conference, which is considering the programme of C.C.I.R. Study Group VI in anticipation of the IXth Plenary Assembly of the C.C.I.R. to be held in Los Angles in April 1959, has circulated a proposal based upon findings that "observation of radio emissions of the first earth satellite have already yielded valuable information about the ionosphere, as well as about problems of space travel," and the Committee recommends that "clear channels be set aside for the use of satellite and space ship emissions." These observations and recommendations were timely, as they are available for consideration by C.C.I.R. Study Group VI in its Geneva meeting during August 1958. The proposals for the service as foreseen for the present are reproduced in the attached paper (see Annex).

It is proposed the C.C.I.R. study and modify or confirm these needs for the astronautical services and invite the I.F.R.B. to make the appropriate frequency allocation proposal for the consideration of the Administrative Radio Conference convening in August 1959.

ANNEX

I. PROPOSALS TO SATISFY THE FREQUENCY REQUIREMENTS FOR ASTRONAUTICAL SERVICES

In order to assemble as much data as are currently available on the frequency allocation needs of astronautical radio services, the Counsel for the American Rocket Society (Andrew G. Haley) has availed himself of the advice of an informal and entirely unofficial panel of renowned scientists.

Tentative proposals for frequency allocations were accepted by Counsel on the basis of information finally sifted at the May 13, 1958 meeting. These proposals are set out herein. Generally, the Panel has suggested that an immediate need exists for frequency allocations for the astronautical radio services in the areas of 20, 40, 100, 150, 300, 450, 1000, 4500, 10,000, 20,000 and 35,000 Mc/s. The requirements can be substantiated as desired.

a) *20 Mc/s and 40 Mc/s areas*

With respect to the 20 and 40 Mc/s areas of the spectrum, Dr. Richard W. Porter [1] set forth the thinking of the Panel as follows:

Experience gained from the observation of transmissions from the Russian Sputniks on the frequencies around 20 and 40 Mc/s has shown a definite need

[1] Consultant to the General Electric Company and Chairman, Technical Panel on Earth Satellite Programme of the U. S. Committee for the Geophysical Year.

for continuous recording in connection with ionospheric experiments. It is not necessary to set aside large numbers of frequencies in these ranges, but a definite need exists for the use of one and maybe two frequencies in both the 20 and 40 Mc/s areas of the spectrum for experimentation involving the effect of the ionosphere on radio propagation from satellites to earth.

Counsel suggests the frequencies 20.01 and 37.00 Mc/s. Regarding these two frequencies, Counsel agrees that any other specific frequencies in the same area would be equally satisfactory. Depending, therefore, on the needs of other users of the frequencies, a slight change could be made in this part of the proposal, if necessary.

b) *100 Mc/s area*

Considerable experience has been obtained by the United States from transmissions in the 100 Mc/s region. John P. Hagen,[2] John T. Mengel,[3] and J. Carl Seddon [4] on behalf of the Panel have pointed out that the United States now utilizes the frequencies 108 and 108.03 Mc/s on a temporary, non-interference basis. These frequencies are particularly suitable for transmissions from the earth encircling satellites which have been placed in orbit and which will be projected into orbit in the future. Satisfactory hardware has been developed for utilization in these frequencies. Hagen, Mengel and Seddon point out that at this time omnidirectional transmissions from earth encircling satellites are essential because such satellites cannot accomodate heavy equipment and power supply for directional or microwave transmission in higher frequency ranges. Hagen, Mengel, and Seddon further point out that there will be a need for use of the 100 Mc/s region for communications of the following varieties:

> Satellites to positions in space (the term "positions in space" means a natural position, such as the moon, or other than a man-made position).
> Space vehicle to position in space.
> Satellite to satellite.
> Satellite to space vehicle.
> Space vehicle to space vehicle.
> Tracking and guidance.

The Panel suggests, therefore, the allocation of the frequency band 107–108 Mc/s for the foregoing purposes.

This allocation would cause slight loss of spectrum space to mobile and FM broadcasting services. However, we actually are suggesting a minimum use of spectrum space. Studies of all the frequencies in this area of the spectrum show more extreme crowding conditions, and our judgment inevitably leads to suggesting the frequencies indicated, namely, between 107–108 Mc/s, inclusive.

The request for 1 Mc/s of spectrum space in this region is not unreasonable when it is considered that within the next year radio transmitters in some 40 or 50 earth encircling satellites will be sending data to earth. Mengel and Seddon estimate that up to 50 satellites will be operating within one year. Mengel reports that tracking

[2] Superintendent, Atmosphere and Astrophysics Division, U. S. Naval Research Laboratory.
[3] Chief, Tracking Branch, U. S. Naval Research Laboratory.
[4] Section Head, Ionosphere Research, U. S. Naval Research Laboratory.

that number of satellites becomes an impossible problem if additional spectrum space is not allocated immediately. Mengel also observes that it would be unwise to allocate numerous single frequencies throughout the spectrum for transmissions of this character, and he urges that the various frequencies allocated for these purposes be concentrated in a single continuous band of the spectrum.

c) *150 Mc/s*

Hagen, Mengel and Seddon also point out that so-called "command frequencies" are required for transmission from earth to present satellites, and such frequencies will certainly be necessary for future operations. The Panel suggests that the frequency band 148.0–150.8 Mc/s be allocated for command frequency usage in the astronautical radio services. Here again the Panel encounters a need to displace some present users. But the Panel believes that earth-to-satellite control or "command" is so vital as to merit such treatment. Seddon points out that at present we have satellites in service whose transmissions may well go on for 200 years. A means of "commanding" these satellites must be on hand, and the Panel finds the 148–150.8 Mc/s band best suited for this function.

d) *300 and 450 Mc/s areas*

The Commander, Army Ballistic Missile Agency, Redstone Arsenal, Alabama, has informally advised Counsel (on behalf of Panel members von Braun and Saunders) that that Agency agrees with the general proposals of the Panel. In addition, the Army Ballistic Missile Agency advises that "frequency bands in the following frequency ranges are considered essential":

    * * *

"(B) 200–300 Mc/s for MSL telemetry MSL and Satellite TV.
"(C) 450–500 * * * MSL tracking and space communications."

Counsel adopts this proposal and urges the allocation of a band between 320 and 328.6 Mc/s for the former purpose and a band between 450 and 455 Mc/s for the latter purpose. These proposals require a certain amount of displacement of existing services, and the Panel emphasizes that experience may permit of reduction of the bandwidth now requested. For instance, a narrower band for television operation may be evolved from future work in the field.

e) *1000 and 4500 Mc/s area*

Frequencies in the order of 1000 Mc/s will be highly essential for space communications needs. Dr. John R. Pierce [5] reported to Counsel that his best estimate "for ground to satellite communications is somewhere between 1000 and 6000 Mc/s." Furthermore, Dr. Pierce states that "as many and as broad as possible channels (20 Mc/s and more) should be acquired within these limits." The Panel has suggested that a need exists for frequencies in the 1000 Mc/s range for communications between earth and space vehicles and between earth and positions in space.

Considering the present congestion in the 1000 Mc/s range and the magnitude of the operations proposed to be conducted, Counsel takes the position that the fre-

---

[5] Director of Research, Electrical Communications, Bell Telephone Laboratories, Incorporated.

quency band 890–942 Mc/s should be allocated for use by astronautical radio services. The astronautical radio services might well share a part of this frequency band with industrial, scientific and medical radio services presently authorized. It is contemplated, however, that eventually the astronautical radio services would require exclusive use of all of this band.

A band at least 20 Mc/s wide in the 4400 to 4500 Mc/s region will be needed, according to Pierce, Hagen, Mengel and Seddon. Frequencies in this band would be used in conjunction with the operations in the 890–942 Mc/s band. The 4400 to 4500 Mc/s band is not as congested as lower bands, but some displacement may occur. The Panel believes that room for some of the displaced services might be found in higher parts of the spectrum, which are presently not utilized or allocated.

f) *10,000 Mc/s area*

Dr. Porter reported to Counsel that there is a substantial need for accurate positioning measurements of space vehicles and positions in space. Dr. Porter believes that frequencies in the order of 10,000 Mc/s are well suited for precision tracking. Accordingly, the Panel suggests that frequencies in the approximate range of 10,000 to 10,100 Mc/s be allocated to the astronautical radio services. Displacement in this area should be a less critical problem than in lower parts of the spectrum. At present, a 500 Mc/s band is set aside for amateurs. The Society's proposal is to reallocate only 20% thereof to astronautical radio services.

g) *15,000 to 40,000 Mc/s area*

The members of the Panel agree that the use of frequencies in the 15,000 to 40,000 Mc/s portion of the spectrum by astronautical radio services will become a reality at an early date. Dr. Pierce stated to Counsel, for example, "for communication outside the earth atmosphere frequency bands beyond 20,000 Mc/s and up to 100,000 Mc/s will be most useful." Counsel agrees with this view and takes the position that the frequencies in this range will be required for astronautical radio services of the following types:

> Between earth and positions in space.
> Between space vehicles and positions in space.
> Between two or more positions in space.
> Between two or more space vehicles.

After reviewing the present frequency allocations the Panel suggests the exclusive allocation of the frequency bands 17,500–20,000 Mc/s and 36,000–38,000 Mc/s to the astronautical radio services.

No displacement would occur if this proposal were implemented. The areas specified are not now allocated for *any* service.

II. BANDWIDTHS

As is indicated in the above discussion of various frequencies, in most instances the Panel has informally suggested a specific bandwidth for each allocation. The Panel considered at length minimum bandwidths which could be temporarily utilized in the event that the allocation at this time of the entire band requested proved to be unfeasible. As a general proposition the Panel decided that with one or two exceptions the bandwidths should be at least 1% of the frequency range, e.g., a bandwidth of 1 Mc/s at 100 Mc/s, 10 Mc/s at 1000 Mc/s, and so on. The computation of bandwidth under this formula represents a *minimum* amount of spectrum space, and it should be emphasized that Counsel urges very strongly the allocation of greater amounts of spectrum space wherever possible.

III. SUMMARY AND CONCLUSION

The presently known frequency requirements of the astronautical radio services are tabulated below. These frequency requirements were carefully considered over the last six months, on the basis of theory, and experience in observing orbits of satellites, and the list was prepared on May 13, 1958. These proposals are by no means final, as developments in the astronautical sciences will require changes in the future as space flight develops. Likewise, the terminology used in the proposed allocations will change. Already, in the few months since the Society proposed new definitions for services, changes have taken place. Thus, new terms will be used herein for descriptive purposes. Those terms will be defined in future documents to be filed by the Society with the Federal Communications Commission and the International Organizations concerned on appropriate occasions.

Frequency Band kc/s	Allocation to Services (World-Wide)	Footnotes
20,010	Astronautical Mobile (Ionospheric propagation)	

Frequency Band Mc/s	Allocation to Services	Footnotes
37.00	Astronautical Mobile (Ionospheric propagation)	
107.0–108.0	Astronautical Mobile Astronautical Radiolocation (Tracking)	
148.0–150.8	Astronautical Radionavigation (Command)	
320–328.6	Astronautical Mobile (Telemetry and Television)	
450–455	Astronautical Mobile Astronautical Radiolocation (Tracking)	
890–942	Astronautical Mobile	The frequency 915 Mc/s is designated for industrial, scientific and medical purposes. Emissions must be confined within the limits of $+25$ Mc/s of that frequency. Radio-communication services operating within those limits must accept any harmful interference that may be experienced from the operation of industrial, scientific and medical equipment.
4,380–4,400	Astronautical Mobile	
10,000–10,100	Astronautical Mobile Astronautical Radiolocation	
17,500–20,000	Astronautical Mobile Astronautical Radiolocation	
36,000–38,000	Astronautical Mobile Astronautical Radiolocation	

General Index

Index to Illustrations

In addition to names of persons and rockets or missiles, this index includes all important references to related subject matter appearing in the illustrations of this book. Consult also General Index.